HISTORY OF THE

CANADIAN

MEDICAL

ASSOCIATION

INTEGRITATE ET MISERICORDIA

1954–94

Canadian
Medical
Association

Association
médicale
canadienne

Canadian Cataloguing in Publication Data

Bennett, John Sutton, 1920-
    History of the Canadian Medical Association,
1954-94

Includes index.
ISBN 0-920169-83-X

    1. Canadian Medical Association — History.
I. Canadian Medical Association. II. Title.

R15.C3B45 1996   610.69'52'06071   C96-900466-4

Published by the Canadian Medical Association

Ordering information and additional copies are available from:

Membership Services
Canadian Medical Association
1867 Alta Vista Drive
Ottawa ON KIG 3Y6

Tel: 800 663-7336 or
         613 731-8610, ext. 2307
Fax: 613 731-9013
E-mail: **hewsom@cma.ca**

I keep six honest serving-men

They taught me all I know;

Their names are What and Why and When

And How and Where and Who.

Rudyard Kipling (1865–1936)

CONTENTS

JOHN SUTTON BENNETT

OStJ, AEM, MB BS(Lond), MRCS(Eng), LRCP(Lond),
LMSSA(Lond), FRCSC, FACOG, FASAS

THE AUTHOR was born in Pembrokeshire, Wales, and received his early education at Haverfordwest Grammar School. On the outbreak of the Second World War in 1939 he joined the Royal Air Force. After obtaining his "wings," he flew Hurricanes and Spitfires in squadrons of Fighter Command. At the end of the war in Europe he was one of the first pilots to qualify on Meteor jet aircraft.

He obtained his medical degree at St. Mary's Hospital Medical School, University of London, and received postgraduate training in obstetrics and gynecology. He immigrated to Newfoundland in the 1950s and practised in St. John's for several years before moving to Kelowna, BC. He participated actively in the affairs of the British Columbia Medical Association, serving on a number of its committees. When the Canadian Medical Association (CMA) moved from Toronto to Ottawa in 1969, he joined the Association as an assistant secretary. In 1979, he became secretary of the New Brunswick Medical Society, a post he occupied until his return to the CMA in 1983. In 1986, he was appointed the CMA's first associate secretary general. In 1991, he retired but retained his involvement with the CMA by becoming the assistant honorary secretary of the Commonwealth Medical Association.

John Bennett has had many interests outside medicine. As a Welshman, it was a given that he could sing, and this he did, with male voice choirs. In his schooldays he had taken part in stage plays and became "hooked" on the stage; in the 1960s, he acted in, produced and directed plays and musicals. This involvement led him into the Dominion Drama Festival (DDF), both on and off stage. During this time he won a DDF best actor award and later became vice-president of Theatre Canada, the DDF's successor. The 1980s saw him still treading the boards in Gilbert and Sullivan operas.

Soccer has been one of his loves, and he has been a referee for over 30 years. Since the early 1980s he has been a team physician for the Canadian Soccer Association, travelling to many countries with national teams. A believer in physical fitness, he enjoys running and has completed numerous marathons. He has been a member of the medical staffs at the Canada Summer and Winter games and at other national and provincial competitive sporting events. He is an experienced off-shore sailor and has delivered yachts from Canada to the United States and from the Caribbean to Europe. In his spare time he enjoys woodworking and has a ready market for his carved Victorian-style rocking horses.

In 1948, he married Robina Davies. They have two children, Karen and Mark, and two grandchildren, Allison and Matthew.

Preface and acknowledgements

The first two volumes of the *History of the Canadian Medical Association* covered the period from 1867 to the late 1950s. Volume III covers the period from the mid-1950s up to the end of 1994. In some of the chapters, readers will note that events preceding the 1950s have been described; this was done so as to give a historical lead-in to the narrative and to set the stage for understanding the outcome of deliberations and decisions.

The sources of information for this volume have been numerous. They have been found in many places and in the memories of those who were involved in the affairs of organized medicine throughout the 40 years covered in this volume. The minutes of meetings of the Executive Committee, the Board of Directors, committees and councils, and the proceedings of general councils, provided a wealth of information far in excess of what could be expressed within one volume. It was necessary to zero in on specific areas and highlight some of the Association's activities as examples of what has been achieved.

One of the difficulties experienced by those who write history books is the absence of archival material of value, and this problem was encountered in the writing of this volume. Not everything retained is of archival value, and it needs expertise to decide what to keep and what to discard. For a number of reasons, the Association's archives have not had a high priority, and it is only in recent years that this shortcoming has been corrected. It is hoped that, when Volume IV comes to be written, the author will have material that has been carefully selected, catalogued and made readily accessible.

In going through the many files, boxes and books, I was struck by records of events that, although reporting conversations and actions that had happened years before, bore an amazing similarity to today's activities. The oft-repeated aphorism "It's déjà-vu all over again" certainly held true and led me to realize how right Samuel Taylor Coleridge was when he wrote, "If men could learn from history, what lessons it might teach us. But passion and party blind our eyes, and the light which experience gives is a lantern on the stern, which shines only on the waves behind us."

There are many people to thank for assistance in writing this book. Gratefully acknowledged are the many contributions to the writing of the history made by Council coordinators — Dr. Normand P. DaSylva, Ms. Alexandra Harrison, Mr. Orvill Adams, Mr. William Tholl, Dr. David Walters and Ms. Fleur-Ange Lefebvre. The writing and recollections of the late Mr. Douglas A. Geekie were of inestimable value to me. Dr. Reginald D. Atkinson's records on the building of CMA House in Ottawa were most helpful as were documents provided by Mr. Ron Bannerman on the subject of MD Management Ltd. Mr. Bob Wright provided the background information on Lancet Insurance Agency. Ms. Michelle McCart, CMA librarian, was always on hand to find documents, which made my task easier. Mrs. Deborah Scott-Douglas, the recently appointed manager of Information Services; Mr. Joe Chouinard, director of CMA Corporate Affairs; Dr. John Williams, director; Ms. Carole Lucock and Ms. Judith Bedford-Jones, associate directors, Department of Ethics and Legal Affairs; Mr. Lucian Blair, director of the Department of Public Affairs; Mr. Torindo Panetta, director of Finance and Operations; and Mrs. Christine Pollock, Mrs. Deborah Rupert and Mr. Raymond Rocan from Special Projects, Department of Publications, all of whom provided helpful assistance. Mrs. Colette Copeland, Toronto, and Mrs. Gillian Pancirov, Specialty Journals, Department of Publications, carried out the copy editing and proofreading. Special mention must be made of Mrs. Rita Sherman who not only printed each and every draft, but who also patiently explained the mysteries of word processing to me and tolerated my early inabilities to gain computer literacy.

The support of the Archives Committee — Drs. Peter J. Banks, Lloyd C. Grisdale, Athol Roberts, Bette Stephenson and Lorraine Trempe — was valuable, as was the kindness of the CMA Secretary General, Dr. Léo-Paul Landry, in providing space in CMA House for me to carry out the research and do much of the writing. The grant from the Canadian Medical Foundation, which helped to make possible the publication of Volume III, is acknowledged with gratitude.

Ottawa, June 1995

INTRODUCTION

THE CANADIAN MEDICAL ASSOCIATION (CMA) came into being on Oct. 9, 1867, just over 3 months after the proclamation of the Canadian confederation. One hundred and sixty-four physicians met in Quebec City, and out of that meeting came the organization widely recognized as the voice of organized medicine in Canada. Its first president was Sir Charles Tupper who, in 1896, served as prime minister of Canada.

The CMA is a voluntary organization representing 46 000 physicians. The provincial and territorial medical associations are autonomous within their own jurisdictions but form a federation at the national level, where the CMA acts as the focus point in handling matters that have a commonality and that can be handled better at a central level. The provincial/territorial medical associations are called divisions of the CMA. Physicians become members of the CMA through their provincial/territorial medical associations. Membership dues are collected by those associations, each of which has the right to set its own fees but undertakes to collect the CMA dues on behalf of the CMA. These dues are standard across the country, whereas those of the provincial/territorial medical associations vary.

On behalf of its members, the CMA is:

- a provider of leadership for physicians and a promoter of the highest standards of health and health care for Canadians;
- the voice of Canadian medicine, representing Canadian physicians on health and health-related policy issues;
- the voice of Canadian medicine in the international health sphere;
- a physician advocate and promoter of the role, status and image of medicine as a profession and of physicians as professionals;
- a consensus builder for physicians and their medical associations;
- a provider of physician membership services;
- a health advocate, developing health promotion and disease/accident policies and strategies;
- an influencer of planning, direction, standards and decision making on health and health-related policy;

- a catalyst for establishing and maintaining high standards of medical training and practice, and a link between practising physicians and the academic medical community;
- an adviser to Canadian physicians on ethical matters;
- a source of expert advice, research and information on health and health policy issues.

Contrary to a belief held by some, the CMA does not license or have any disciplinary powers over physicians. The licensing authority in each of the 12 jurisdictions grants licences to practise medicine and has the authority to discipline those physicians who transgress. The CMA does have the right to withdraw membership from members who are not in good standing in their respective divisions. The CMA neither sets physicians' fees nor enters into negotiations on the question of schedules of benefits for physicians; both of these matters are the prerogatives of the provincial/territorial medical associations in negotiations with their respective paying agencies. Entry into medical school or the conducting of medical research do not fall within the CMA's purview.

Association policy is developed through the work of various departments, and through committees and councils whose members are physicians representing their divisions. The outcome of that work is channelled to the Board of Directors and to the General Council, and it is from those bodies, after appropriate study and review, that pronouncements of policy are made. The General Council is the legislative body and is often described as "the Parliament of Canadian Medicine"; in 1994 its membership was 191. Membership of both the Board of Directors and the General Council is by proportional representation from the divisions, but both bodies have additional input from other bodies, such as the medical specialty organizations known as affiliate societies.

Medical ethics is a very important part of the work of the Association. In the late 1980s, the Department of Ethics and Legal Affairs was established to provide leadership and advice to physicians, other health professionals, policymakers and the general public on the ethical and legal aspects of health and health care. The department coordinates the work of the Committee on Ethics and the Committee on Gender Issues, and works in an advisory and cooperative way with other CMA departments, councils and committees in areas where matters cross departmental boundaries. The *Code of Ethics* is updated on an ongoing basis so as to reflect changes occurring in the practice of medicine and in society. On the international scene, the CMA's views and activities in medical ethics contribute to the work of organizations such as the World Medical Association and the Commonwealth Medical Association.

Medical education in all its facets has a high priority in the Association through the Department of Medical Education and the Council on Medical Education. On the accepted premise that medical education is a continuum throughout the whole of the physician's life, beginning at the undergraduate level and being maintained to the end of the physician's career, the CMA keeps close contact with all groups involved in that field, e.g., medical schools, specialty colleges and licensing authorities. Because physicians are part of the health care team that includes a number of other health care professionals, the CMA cooperates with nearly 40 other national organizations to accredit educational programs in 10 health sciences including, inter alia, medical laboratory technologies, medical radiation and ultrasound technologies, respiratory therapy and emergency medical technology. It is the CMA that provides the administrative centre for this cooperative accreditation process, which acts to ensure that the educational programs being provided by the educational institutions prepare competent technologists to assist physicians in the provision of high-quality health care.

Professional development for physicians is also given a high priority by the Association. The Physician Manager Institute program provides a series of management courses designed to prepare the physician for managerial roles in departments and programs. Quality management is a new approach in health care, and the CMA is developing programs to help physicians become more knowledgeable in the theory of quality management and more skilled in integrating traditional quality assurance, risk management and utilization management activities within the philosophy of continuous quality improvement.

The Department of Health Care and Promotion and its council have as their mandate matters related to health promotion and public health, quality of care, health facilities and medical practice. Both bodies have made significant contributions to health care. Some of these contributions are: researching and developing policy on the physician's role in primary health care; development of policies in the matter of tobacco products and health; a successful bicycle helmet campaign that in 1991 and 1992 resulted in the sale of over 80 000 helmets; development of policies on the fetal alcohol syndrome and drug testing in the workplace; statements on human immunodeficiency virus (HIV) and acquired immunodeficiency syndrome (AIDS). The department has also produced a number of important publications, an example of which is *Quality of Care: Issues and Challenges in the '90s.*

The mandate of the Department of Health Policy and Economics and its council is the collection, production, analysis and dissemination of information relating to the organizing, financing and operation of the Canadian health care system. The department acts as a clearing house of information and expert analysis for the divisions on the development and implementation of health policy and economics. Support is given to the divisions on the subject of negotiations with paying agencies through regional and national negotiating workshops, as well as providing expertise when requested. Health policy research is carried out on the many aspects of health care financing and medical manpower strategies, regionalization and physician remuneration. This work is valuable in contributing to representations made to governments and others.

The Department of Public Affairs has the responsibility of providing the media and the laity with details of Association policies and news releases on matters of concern to the Association in health care. Political action falls under this department, and a committee, called the Political Action Committee, operates under its aegis. Representatives from the CMA divisions form the membership of the committee whose responsibility is to study matters involving health care, particularly where governmental decisions have impinged adversely on physicians and the provision of quality health care. The move of the CMA headquarters to Ottawa in 1969 allowed the Association to establish, in general, a good working relationship with federal ministers, senior officials and ministerial political staffs. The Association's frequent appearances before various committees of the House of Commons and the Senate require action on the part of the department, inasmuch as the making of arrangements and documentation preparation in approved format, as well as intensive preparation of spokespersons, are among its many responsibilities. The funding of health care is of major concern, not only to the profession but also to the public in general, and through political action, the Association lobbies the federal government to ensure that it maintains funding sufficient to provide the quality of health care that Canadians have come to expect.

Through the CMA's Department of Membership Services, CMA members benefit from a wide range of professional, financial and personal benefits, including comprehensive financial and practice management planning and investment advice. MD Management Ltd. provides many financial products geared to physicians and their dependents.

The Department of Publications has come a long way from the days when there was one publication, the *Canadian Medical Association Journal*, its 1954 flagship. In 1994 there were five mainstream journals. The department's mandate is to provide contact with and among physicians on scientific, professional and personal interest issues; to publish educational consumer books; and to increase the number and type of publications to assist CMA departments, affiliated societies and associations produce professional publications in a cost-effective manner. The publication of the journals and newsletters is financed from the sale of advertising to pharmaceutical and consumer companies and the sale of classified advertising to physicians and health care institutions. Collaboration is also entered into with other publishing houses to produce authoritative medical reference books for both home use and the medical profession at large, as well as books directed specifically to the professional.

Since 1867, the CMA has survived a number of vicissitudes and grown in strength. Its staff has gone from one part-time volunteer to over 250 salaried personnel, and its headquarters has grown from a one-room office to a spacious multistorey building in the nation's capital. In 1995, the Association gives every indication that it intends to build on its successes, learn from its failures and continue to live up to its motto, *Integritate et Misericordia,* and its mission statement, "To provide leadership for physicians and to promote the highest standard of health and health care for Canadians."

CMA House, Toronto, 1956.

Chapter I

CMA HOUSE

THROUGHOUT THE EARLY YEARS of the 20th century there were numerous calls from the membership of the Canadian Medical Association (CMA) for the formalization of the Association's administrative operations. In 1912, the CMA's Finance Committee recommended a greater degree of centralization of the Association's operations. Nine years later an understanding was reached whereby the CMA would operate from two locations, Toronto and Montreal. The general secretary was to be in Toronto, whereas the honorary treasurer and the editorial staff were to operate from Montreal. The Association's journal was to be printed in Toronto.

Over the next 30 years there were many discussions on the matter of unifying the operations under one roof. Both Ottawa and Toronto were considered as possible sites for the Association's head office, but the former was discounted because it was strongly argued that locating in Ottawa would mean difficulties for the journal in that the printing would still be done in another location, i.e., Toronto. Another factor militating against the location in the nation's capital was the perceived lack of a large medical library.

In Toronto, the CMA was located in a house at 184 College St. owned by the University of Toronto, which provided the space rent free. The offices in Montreal were located in the McGill Medical Building. In 1945, the Toronto office was relocated in rented space at 135 St. Clair Avenue W. Nine years later it was moved to 244 St. George Street. The Association occupied the second and third floors of a building purchased and renovated as an office building by the Ontario Medical Association.

In spite of the moves to accommodate the increased work load and staff, the Executive was concerned that the operations of the Association were still somewhat fragmented. In 1952, a special committee was established to study ways and means whereby consolidation could be achieved. In 1953, the General Council approved that the committee be enlarged in order to consider the feasibility of a permanent home for the CMA. After a number of meetings and a review of the possibilities, the committee recommended to the Executive Committee:

- *That all the national activities of the Association be consolidated under one roof.*
- *That the above-mentioned activities so consolidated be in Toronto.*

These recommendations were presented to the General Council in 1954. There were several hours of debate as the members of General Council wrestled with the pros and cons of the subject in an atmosphere described as "very emotional at times." Dr. T. Clarence Routley, the general secretary since 1923 who would be retiring in 1954, becoming the president of the CMA and the BMA in 1955–56, said:

> *If this transition does not occur, I would not feel that the CMA will fail. However, you will have a new General Secretary and a new Editor shortly, and I would think that Dr. Kelly and Dr. Gilder would be more apt to reflect that unity in the Journal if they were located close to one another.*
>
> *From the time of its inception in 1867 until 1923, the CMA had its offices in Montreal, in McGill. When I became General Secretary in 1923, the Dean of Medicine at McGill, Dr. C.F. Martin, asked me what I thought of moving to Montreal. I told him that I had taken over a post at the Ontario Medical Association (OMA) and that I had not finished my work there. I said that I could not go to Montreal and I thought that the office would have to move to Toronto, because Ontario would one day have a large concentration of doctors.*
>
> *I went to the University of Toronto and asked them if they would do the same thing for us as McGill was doing, in providing office space, and until the end of World War II we had offices for a rental of one dollar per annum.*
>
> *I have given my life to the CMA and the doctors of Canada. I would be very sad to see anything happen to what I have helped to build up. It has been my hope that in viewing this in its entirety, there would be no feeling that [in] putting the executive staff together anything would be given up, no matter where that staff might be placed. I hope that whatever your decision may be, it will be unanimous. We need balance in this country of ours.*

Following debate, the first recommendation was approved 61 votes to 32. The General Council then involved itself in procedural manoeuvring and eventually moved to a Committee of the Whole. When it came to the vote, the second recommendation was approved 60 votes to 31. A further recommendation, directing the Executive Committee to set up the machinery for site exploration, was approved.

By mid-October temporary quarters had been found at 176 St. George St., Toronto, and the editorial department moved from Montreal. In its search for a permanent home for the Association, the Executive Committee had been offered, by the University of Toronto, 1.4 acres on Bayview Avenue at $1 per annum over a 50-year lease. Another site considered was 150 St. George Street, owned and occupied by the China Inland Mission.

After careful deliberation the Executive Committee declined the university's offer, basing its decision on the remoteness of the property, its distance from a medical library, certain building restrictions, which may have been difficult to overcome, and the fact that the property could only be leased and not purchased with title going to the Association. The CMA expressed its gratitude to the University of Toronto for the generous offer.

An option to purchase was taken out on the property at 150 St. George Street, and shortly thereafter it was purchased by the CMA for $140 000. There were substantial buildings on the site, which had a 125-foot frontage and a depth of 190 feet back to a laneway. The site was in the centre of Toronto's medical services, close to hospitals, the Medical Arts Building and the library of the Toronto Academy of Medicine. Occupancy was planned for September 1955 after necessary renovations had been completed.

The 1955 General Council meeting approved the following:

> *Whereas for many years the editorial and financial offices of the Canadian Medical Association have been situated in accommodation provided through the courtesy of McGill University, without cost to the Association; and whereas the Principal and his associates have been extremely cooperative throughout the years of occupancy, be it resolved that the General Council of the Canadian Medical Association record its appreciation of the many benefits received at the hands of McGill University throughout those years.*

Some General Council members were concerned that moving the editorial offices from Montreal to Toronto would cause a decrease in CMA membership among doctors from the Province of Quebec. After discussion, however, the feelings of concern were assuaged by statements from Quebec members who thought it unlikely that such a loss would occur.

In the summer of 1955, the CMA was busy with plans and contracts for the renovations at 150 St. George Street. Work began on Sept. 1, and the general secretariat and editorial staffs moved in on Nov. 21. Office space was made available for the Canadian Commission on Hospital Accreditation and the Trans-Canada Medical Plans.

Opening of new headquarters of CMA at 150 St. George Street, Toronto,
on Saturday, Mar. 17, 1956.
From L–R: Clarence Routley, President of the CMA and the BMA, and Health Minister Paul
Martin.

Official opening of the addition to CMA House at 150 St. George Street, Toronto
on Apr. 24, 1960.
From L–R: Hon. Matthew B. Dymond, Ontario Minister of Health; Dr. E. Kirk Lyon, Deputy
to the President of the CMA; Hon. J. Waldo Monteith, Minister of National Health and Welfare, who officially opened the new addition; Rt. Rev. F.H. Wilkinson, Bishop of Toronto.

On Mar. 17, 1956, the opening ceremony was held in the presence of many distinguished people, including all living past presidents of the Association, the Right Reverend F.H. Wilkinson, bishop of Toronto, and the Hon. Paul Martin, minister of national health and welfare.

By 1958, it became apparent that the activities of the secretariat had increased to a level where they were further restricted by the size of the building. An architectural firm was engaged to examine how more working space might be created in order to solve the problem. The architect's recommendation was for a two-storey addition plus a basement along the front of the property, adding 8700 square feet of usable floor space and costing about $200 000. After meeting a number of city bylaw requirements, construction of the addition began in May 1959, and the new quarters were ready for occupation in January 1960. The general secretariat occupied the ground floor and part of the basement; the staff of the *Canadian Medical Association Journal* and the *Canadian Journal of Surgery* took over the second floor, and two new tenants — the College of General Practice of Canada and the Ontario Division of the Canadian Mental Health Association — were provided with office space. The "new" CMA House was opened by the minister of national health and welfare, the Hon. J.W. Monteith, on Apr. 24, 1960.

The Association continued to grow and so did its work load. In its report to General Council in 1963, the Executive Committee stated: "That this Executive Committee reaffirm its decision that the CMA office should be maintained for the foreseeable future in Toronto, and that plans now be investigated and, if possible, developed for the further extension of our facilities and property at their present location on St. George Street." By 1964, the need for additional space was estimated to be 10% each year if the current growth continued along the same lines as in the past 5 years. The Executive Committee's House Committee was directed to undertake a study of the immediate and foreseeable needs in terms of building space. Studies were undertaken on the re-zoning laws in the immediate area of CMA House, plus finding out the possibility of purchasing other property or properties in the area. Another factor taken into consideration was how the University of Toronto's expansion plans might affect the area.

At its meeting in Edmonton on June 10 and 11, 1966, the Executive Committee directed the House Committee to explore with architects the possibility of building a new CMA House on the site presently occupied by the Association. Proposed was consideration of a seven-storey building with provision made for the addition of five more stories as required. Phase one would provide an additional 25 000 square feet of usable space with provision for underground parking and cost about $1.6 million, based on $67 per square foot. The Executive

CMA House, on St. George Street, Toronto, 1960.

Committee authorized the architects to proceed with drawing-up detailed plans required by the various municipal and provincial committees and boards so that the zoning and building regulations requirements could be met.

The 1965 General Council was told that the erection of the 12-storey building was designated as a tangible project for the coming-of-age of the Association and a worthy addition in time to be included in the celebration of the Association's centenary in 1967. A number of non-profit organizations expressed interest in occupying space that was in excess of CMA requirements in the new building. The architects had recommended against the building of the seven-storey building, basing their decision on the costs involved.

After investigation by the House Committee the General Council in Edmonton in 1966 was told that the costs involved in such an undertaking militated against proceeding with the concept. When the plans for the proposed 12-storey building had been put out to tender, the lowest bid was $1 978 000, nearly $500 000 above the estimated cost. Four options were considered by the House Committee, but two of these were dropped after investigations revealed that a reduction in building costs could lead to a second-class building and that rents on a lease-back arrangement would be too high for a voluntary organization. Two further ideas were put forward by the staff members of the House Committee, viz., that either a joint building program with the OMA and the Toronto Academy of Medicine be considered or another property that would lend itself to a more economical building program be purchased. Delegates from the Alberta Division had raised the question at General Council of locating CMA House in Ottawa and proposed that the membership of the CMA should be asked to become more actively involved in the matter, either through a voluntary contribution to a building fund or through a bond issue at 6%.

At a joint meeting of the house and building committees of the CMA, OMA and the academy on Sept. 15, 1966, it was suggested that consideration be given to a feasibility study of a joint building program, at a cost not to exceed a budgeted amount of $2000, shared equally by the three organizations. The CMA House Committee recommended to the Executive Committee that the CMA share in such a study to determine the feasibility of

- alternative joint ownership arrangements,
- the ability of the three organizations to pay for the amount of space required and
- an architecturally acceptable building.

A member of the Executive Committee suggested that consideration be given also to the acquisition of land within four or five blocks of the present building and the erection thereon of a new building. Dr. Douglas G. Cameron of Montreal suggested that the feasibility study might be extended to include the possibility of building new CMA headquarters in Ottawa. This suggestion was debated at some length after Dr. Robert O. Jones, immediate past president of the Association, pointed out that the matter had been fully considered the previous year but the majority of the divisions had indicated Toronto as their choice for the location of CMA headquarters. After further discussion, it was approved: "That a feasibility study of a joint building programme by the CMA, the OMA and the Toronto Academy of Medicine be undertaken, at a cost not to exceed $2000, to be shared equally by the three organizations; that the proposed study be extended to include other properties in the Toronto area and Ottawa; and that a report be submitted to the next meeting of the Executive Committee."

The House Committee met on Nov. 28, 1966, and reviewed the feasibility study findings. There was no disagreement between the three parties on the architectural design of a projected joint building, but the CMA and OMA had some reservations about the ability of the academy to meet its financial commitments on an ongoing basis. The majority of academy members were agreeable both to joint ownership and an increase in their fees to meet the academy's financial commitments. The tripartite body had been offered a cost-free engineering survey by Mr. Gairdner of the Gairdner Foundation, and it was anticipated that such a survey would answer many of the questions raised in the feasibility study.

Investigation of the area around CMA House revealed three potential building sites nearby; there were two more sites on the outskirts of Toronto and one in downtown Ottawa. The Executive Committee and House Committee were aware that the Nova Scotia Medical Society, at its 1966 annual meeting, had passed a motion to drop the proposal for a tripartite building and that the CMA consider further the question of locating CMA House in Ottawa. The Quebec Medical Association was of the opinion that the CMA should be based in Ottawa.

When the House Committee met on Dec. 8, 1966, it proposed that the divisions be canvassed as to whether or not the CMA headquarters should be located in Toronto or Ottawa and, if in Toronto, whether it should be a joint venture building program with the OMA and the academy. After discussion at its meeting on Dec. 9, the Executive Committee approved the polling of the divisions. At the same meeting, a Building Committee, chaired by Dr. Reginald D. Atkinson, chairman of the Executive Committee, and separate from the House Committee, was also approved.

At its meeting on Mar. 3 and 4, 1967, the Executive Committee was given the results of the questionnaire sent to the divisions. Seven divisions indicated their preference for the CMA headquarters to be located in Toronto, and two named Ottawa as their choice. The OMA did not participate because it was perceived to have a conflict of interest but, subsequently, and perhaps not surprisingly, it did cast its vote in favour of Toronto. On the question of a joint building program with the OMA and the academy, seven divisions voted against it; two of the seven were ambivalent on the matter.

Dr. Atkinson reported that the responses from the divisions clearly indicated that the CMA should be located in Toronto and that the Association should "go it alone" in a building program. It was the opinion of the Building Committee that efforts be directed to obtaining a suitable property near the existing CMA House.

A motion by Dr. Douglas G. Cameron, seconded by Dr. J.M. Lessard of Quebec, "that the whole question of CMA headquarters not be decided until every member of the Association had been polled and provided with a clear statement of the pro's and con's of remaining in Toronto or moving to Ottawa," was defeated. Dr. R. Kenneth Thomson, president of the CMA, pointed out that this matter had been before both the Executive Committee and General Council on a number of occasions, and that in both fora it had never been felt necessary or desirable to conduct such a vote. This point of view was reinforced by Dr. Atkinson, who stated that, in his opinion, the Executive Committee had been given a mandate to proceed on the strength of the wishes of the divisions and also from the recommendation of the Executive Committee to the General Council in 1963.

It is recorded in the minutes of that meeting that:

> in considering the possibility of having a CMA office in Ottawa to have a closer liaison with Government Departments and members of the House of Commons and the Senate, the Executive Committee felt that the only people who could properly liaise with Government representatives were senior members of the Secretariat or the Officers of the CMA. It was therefore agreed that the Staffing Committee should consider ways and means of supplementing the CMA staff to provide more frequent liaison with Ottawa from the Toronto office.

Dr. Atkinson suggested a deferral of this matter to the next meeting of the Executive Committee, at which time appropriate recommendations would be obtained from the staff.

By the time of the Executive Committee meeting in April 1967, the Building Committee had explored the possibility of obtaining suitable property for the new CMA House in the centre of Toronto. One site was a vacant lot, used for parking, at Wellesley and Yonge streets. Another site was on Avenue Road near

Bloor Street West, and the third site was in Flemingdon Park on the outskirts of the city. The last property could be bought for $400 000. The vendor, the Olympia-York Development Company, was prepared to sell the land and erect a building for $2 250 000.

The Executive Committee entered into long discussions on the advantages and disadvantages of the three sites. Once again Dr. Cameron expressed his concern that although the Building Committee had been directed to explore suitable building sites in Ottawa, in his opinion no definite figures of comparison in costs of square footage between Toronto and Ottawa had been submitted for consideration. A staff response was that there appeared to be little difference in the costs of square footage between the two cities. Dr. Cameron's concerns were echoed by Dr. N.J. Belliveau of Montreal who seconded a recommendation, made by Dr. Cameron, that the final decision on location be deferred until June after a much more complete investigation of the sites and estimated costs in the two cities had been carried out. The Executive Committee did not approve the recommendation.

The Executive Committee then went on to give permission to the Building Committee to proceed with a design of a suitable building on the Flemingdon Park site, with the proviso that the CMA was not committed to the designs. Drs. Cameron and Belliveau, along with Dr. Alvin R. Mercer from St. John's, voted against the motion. It was further agreed that the final decision would not be made until the meeting of the Executive Committee in Quebec City on June 8, 1967, the day before the opening of General Council. At the meeting of the Executive Committee preliminary plans of the building and estimates of costs would be presented. The recommendation of the Building Committee that the costs of the proposed building program be covered by a liquidation of the Association's reserves, plus the proceeds from the sale of the property on St. George Street and a mortgage from an outside agency, was approved by the Executive Committee. Following this, there were discussions on the matter of membership participation, possibly through a bond issue, a matter on which the staff was asked to express recommendations after study.

The membership gathering in Quebec City for the centennial meeting of the Association had been looked forward to by many for numerous reasons, not the least of which was the report of the Executive Committee on the status of the building program. At its June 8 meeting, the Executive Committee was advised that a meeting had been held between the CMA, representatives of the vendor and an architectural firm on the Association's space requirements and other details in connection with costs. A further meeting was held on May 16 at which time preliminary sketches of the Flemingdon Park site were submitted by the architects. These plans indicated space far in excess of that required by the Association. Modifications were requested and on completion of these, firm costs were submitted by the vendor: land and building originally set at $2 264 000 would be reduced to $2 200 000; an additional $50 000 would be spent on landscaping. A model of the property, together with a number of colour transparencies of the site and the proposed building were available for viewing by the committee.

The Executive Committee was told that the Building Committee had also investigated sites in Ottawa. Two were in downtown Ottawa, and two were in the outskirts of the city. One of the latter properties could be purchased for about $150 000, the other for about $200 000. Dr. Atkinson drew the attention of the Executive Committee to the recommendation proposed for submission to General Council the following day, viz., "That the General Council approve the building programme, as recommended by the Executive Committee in its supplementary report," and asked members of the committee for their views.

Dr. Peter J. Banks of Victoria, BC, was of the opinion that the whole matter should be submitted to General Council for full discussion, and particularly on the question of location. Dr. Atkinson responded by pointing out that the opinions of the divisions had been sought and the majority had voted for Toronto. Dr. Cameron stated that the availability of four sites in Ottawa was good reason to again raise the question of the future location of CMA House. A motion, proposed by Dr. D.N.C. McIntyre of Winnipeg and seconded by Dr. Hart Scarrow of Vernon, BC, to the effect that the CMA purchase and develop the Flemingdon Park site was subject to a proposed amendment by Dr. Cameron, seconded by Dr. Banks, viz., "That the question of the location of CMA headquarters be submitted to General Council for consideration and decision." After a long discussion, the motion was approved. Dr. W. James S. Melvin of Kingston, Ont., advised the Executive Committee that when the matter was submitted for consideration by the General Council, the OMA would propose that a decision be deferred until the divisions had had an opportunity to meet in caucus and discuss. The general secretary said that members would vote by ballot, and that each voting member would be provided with two documents outlining the decisions made previously concerning the location of CMA House; this, it was believed, would assist members to make an informed choice.

The centennial meeting of the CMA opened in Quebec City on June 9, 1967, and Dr. Reginald D. Atkinson, chairman of the Building Committee, presented an update on CMA House. The Executive Committee had met the previous day and discussed at length and in detail what had been done and should be done. At the end of the day no firm consensus had been reached and the committee came to General Council with no firm recommendation, other than to ask it for direction. To give everyone an opportunity to be fully conversant with the many aspects of the matter, discussion was postponed until the following day, June 10, and, to allow a free and full discussion, members moved into a Committee of the Whole.

The ensuing debate provided opportunities for numerous opinions, points of view, prejudices and endorsements. Dr. Douglas G. Cameron spoke eloquently on the merits of siting CMA House in Ottawa, stating that there were as many suitable sites in that city as in Toronto; land and construction costs were cheaper in Ottawa; it was the nation's capital and it was certain that the Association in the future would require more dealings with the federal government; that good library facilities were available in Ottawa; that transportation and hotel facilities did not present problems; that Ottawa was a bilingual city; that many other national medical organizations, e.g., the Medical Council of Canada, the Royal College of Physicians and Surgeons of Canada and the Medical Research Council, were located there.

Responding to the points raised by Dr. Cameron, Dr. Atkinson stated that a number of them had not been fully explored by the committee. He agreed that the availability of good-quality library facilities was important and expressed the opinion that, in the final analysis, the major considerations were the growth of the Association, the needs of its members and the needs of the people of Canada.

Dr. Peter Banks said that General Council was being asked to make a historic decision and that in reaching that decision, members should remember that they were doing so as members of the medical profession of Canada and not as members of a particular province. He concurred with the premise that the Association would have to have a closer liaison with the federal government than in the past and that applied also to other national organizations. In his peroration, Dr. Banks stated that Canada was a great country and that a great country needed a great capital city, the centre and location of many great national institutions, of which the CMA should be one. There were some impassioned pleas made on behalf of both cities and, after a full review of all that had transpired, the General Council reconvened and a vote was taken.

LOCATION OF CMA HEADQUARTERS		
In favour of Ottawa	—	111
In favour of Toronto	—	55
Abstention	—	1

The following resolution was then approved: "That the Executive Committee be empowered by the General Council to proceed to develop plans and to build a building in Ottawa, in accordance with the vote of Council."

The Executive Committee reappointed the Building Committee, with Dr. Atkinson as chairman and members Drs. W.L. Leslie, John H. Maloney and James Small.

The president of the CMA, Dr. Normand J. Belliveau, accompanied by Dr. Atkinson, Dr. Arthur F.W. Peart and Mr. Bernard E. Freamo, met in Ottawa with Mayor Don Reid and General F. Clark, chairman of the National Capital Commission (NCC). Subsequent to that meeting, the Building Committee reported to the Executive Committee that, on Sept. 21, its members had inspected various properties in Ottawa suitable for the type of CMA House visualized. Consideration had been given as to where in Ottawa the new building should be located, i.e., in central Ottawa near the parliament buildings or in the outskirts, where both the airport and railway station were located.

In the past, the NCC had provided land for various organizations and was quite prepared to enter into a leasing agreement with the Association for a period of 60 years at a rental of 6.5% of the current land value. Amortization of the building would be over the period of the lease, at the end of which the NCC would have the option to take over the building and the land. Inasmuch as the policies of the NCC are directed by the Government of Canada there was no guarantee that the situation would not change during the period of the lease and a renewal not approved.

The Executive Committee continued to inspect sites and eventually narrowed the choice down to three as being worthy of further consideration. These were:

1. In downtown Ottawa at the corner of Albert Street and Lyon Street — cost $450 000.
2. On Sussex Drive — rental only.
3. On Alta Vista Drive at Smyth Road — NCC land at $25 000 per acre.

After reviewing all three sites again and weighing the advantages and disadvantages, such as buying versus leasing, the Building Committee recommended the purchase of four acres of the NCC property on Alta Vista Drive at a cost not exceeding $100 000. This recommendation received the approval of the Executive Committee, which passed the following resolution: "That the CMA secure the Alta Vista property by the purchase of at least four acres from the NCC; if a purchase cannot be arranged, the Building Committee be authorized to negotiate a lease of the property."

At a meeting of the Executive Committee on Nov. 30 and Dec. 1, Dr. Atkinson read a letter from Mr. E.W. Thrift, general manager of the NCC, advising that the NCC had been given the authority to negotiate the sale of approximately three acres of land at the north-east corner of Alta Vista Drive at Smyth Road, Ottawa, to the CMA for the sum of $75 000, subject to certain conditions. The land was the property of the NCC, but under the National Capital Act the approval of the governor-in-council had to be obtained before the commission could dispose of any real property for consideration in excess of a value of $10 000. The necessary submission to the governor-in-council was prepared by the NCC, requesting authority to sell the land. The Executive Committee authorized the Building Committee to offer $75 000 for the land, subject to conditions set by the NCC.

While the matter was being channelled through the NCC, the Building Committee looked at two options. One was hiring an architect and then going to tender; the other option was a package deal that required approaching reputable builders who would hire the CMA's choice of architect and provide a building to the Association's specifications at a fixed cost. The Executive Committee approved the second option.

In February 1968, Dr. Atkinson told the Executive Committee that the NCC was ready to sell the three acres of land chosen by the CMA for $75 000. The land would be available on June 1, and the sale would be dependent upon the CMA submitting site and architectural plans to the NCC for its approval, and undertaking to bear the cost of providing services for the building. Further conditions were that the CMA would agree to sell the land back to the NCC at its purchase price if, for any reason, it was unable to proceed with the development of the site, and that the CMA would take full responsibility for securing the necessary changes to the zoning bylaw of the City of Ottawa. This offer was accepted by the Executive Committee. The Executive Committee also received a report from Dr. Atkinson on the matter of the package-deal concept, showing that a number of building firms were interested in submitting tenders for the project.

The Building Committee was authorized to inspect buildings in Ottawa and Toronto in order to get ideas on the style and quality of the works of architects and builders. At this time the University of Toronto offered to buy the CMA property at 150 St. George Street, Toronto, for $500 000 and lease it back to the Association at a negotiated rent. If this offer were acceptable, the university hoped to get possession of the old building by July 31, 1968, and the new building by June 30, 1969.

The building visualized for the Ottawa site would be approximately 25 000 square feet, of which 15 000 would accommodate the staff. The Building Committee had suggested that other medical organizations might be approached to see if they had any interest in renting space in the new CMA House. The general secretary, Dr. Peart, was authorized to contact organizations such as the Medical Council of Canada and the Canadian Medical Protective Association to see if they were interested in such an arrangement.

At the March meeting of the Executive Committee, the Building Committee reported that its members, together with some members of the Executive Committee, had met with Mr. H. Whelan of Perini Ltd. and inspected a number of buildings erected by that firm in Toronto. Buildings in Ottawa had also been inspected. After serious consideration, the Building Committee selected Perini Ltd. as contractors and the firm of Webb, Zerafa and Menkes as the architect. Following the selection, preliminary drawings of the proposed building were prepared and these were scrutinized by the Executive Committee.

On Mar. 8, Dr. Peart, Mr. Freamo and Dr. Atkinson met with the architects to go over their thinking and to ensure that they and the Association were on the same wavelength in the matter of design. The preliminary plans shown to the Executive Committee depicted a wing of the building, to be occupied by the secretariat, attached to an executive block by a linkage that would house the offices of the general secretary and the executive secretary, as well a large entrance lobby and reception area. The square footage visualized was about 34 000 and the associated costs of building would be approximately $900 000. Consideration was given to the possibility of further enlargement of the building in the future; costs involved in this were estimated to be about $150 000 to $200 000. The Executive Committee approved the concept, including the 8000 square feet addition that the committee believed could be rented by other medical organizations until such time as it would be required by the Association.

A budget of $900 000 had been set for the building: $75 000 for the land, up to $150 000 for finishing and furnishing, the costs of the additional 8000 square feet, and costs of moving staff and effects from Toronto to Ottawa. The total cost was estimated to be in the region of $1 325 000. After some slight modifications were incorporated, the Executive Committee approved the plans and authorized the Building Committee to enter into negotiations with the builder, Perini Ltd., on the construction costs of CMA House.

The Executive Committee set a target date of July 1968 for construction to begin, with the intention that the CMA would move from Toronto 1 year later and permit the University of Toronto to acquire the whole of the buildings at St. George Street at that time.

The April 1968 meeting of the Executive Committee was attended by Mr. H. Whelan of Perini Ltd., Mr. R. Clarke and Mr. Sato of the architectural firm of Webb, Zerafa and Menkes, Mr. Duncan Green, the consultant architect, and

Dr. Leslie, a member of the Building Committee. At the last meeting of the Executive Committee, the architects had appeared before the NCC and been told that changes would have to be made to the original designs submitted earlier. Those changes were shown on the modified plans. Mr. Whelan pointed out that the changes imposed by the NCC had meant the preliminary budget figure would have to be amended and the new figure was $1 120 000 for 41 500 square feet. It was his intention to get a firm price in the near future and to present it to the Executive Committee in June. After much discussion, the executive approved the new design and plans and authorized the Building Committee to negotiate with Perini Ltd. building costs to be presented to, and considered by, the Executive Committee in June.

A Finishing and Furnishing Fund was established in 1968 to raise $131 000 to be applied to some of the rooms in the new building. The committee, chaired by Dr. Belliveau, with members Drs. Peter J. Banks, Estathios W. Barootes, W.J.S. Melvin, A.F. Jones and C.L. Gosse, was successful in its quest and disbanded in early 1969. The committee was congratulated and thanked by the 1969 General Council. A number of Canadian physicians and their friends had donated paintings and other works of art, and the divisions and affiliate societies had generously supported the committee in its reaching the target figure. Some of the divisions had committed themselves to contributions to the fund over a period of years. CMA Savings Plan donated $25 000 toward the fitting and furnishing of the boardroom. By mid-1970 more than $140 000 had been received from individuals, the divisions and affiliated medical specialty bodies. The RCPSC donated $5000 to the fund. A committee, chaired by Dr. Harvey Agnew of Toronto, assembled a fine art collection for CMA House.

The divisions, their financial commitments and the projects for which they accepted the responsibility of finishing and furnishing, were:

- President's office — Saskatchewan Medical Association — $6000
- Meeting room known as the Atlantic Room — New Brunswick Medical Society, Newfoundland Medical Association, Medical Society of Nova Scotia, Prince Edward Island Medical Society — $10 000
- Lounge — Alberta Medical Association — $9465
- Cafeteria — Manitoba Medical Association — $6336
- Entrance Lobby — Quebec Medical Association — $15 000
- Powell–Argue Meeting Room — The Canadian Medical Protective Association, in honour of Dr. R.W. Powell and Dr. J.F. Argue. Dr. Powell, CMA president in 1899–1900, had been a strong proponent of the formation of an organization for the protection of medical practitioners who might become involved in unjust prosecutions for malpractice, and his appeal led

to the setting up of the Canadian Medical Protective Association in 1901. Dr. Argue served as the secretary-treasurer of that association from 1907 to 1934. — $12 000

◆ The British Columbia Medical Association donated $2500 annually over 5 years for a total of $12 500.

Mr. Whelan met with the Building Committee and submitted a price for the new building and a number of drawings showing changes to the originals, which would increase building costs. Granite slabs would replace the brick facing on the south side of the building and in the foyer and boardroom. The figure submitted for consideration was $1 228 527. The NCC had expressed its opposition to the use of structural steel and this, too, had led to a cost increase, resulting in an additional $41 000. The Building Committee was of the opinion that there were areas where costs might be reduced without affecting the building's appearance or effectiveness, and Mr. Whelan was asked to review the stated price to see if any economies could be effected.

In September 1968, Dr. Atkinson reported that a price of $1 108 736 on a fixed-cost basis had been submitted by the builder, and this price was accepted by the Executive Committee. On Sept. 20, 1968, the ceremonial laying of the cornerstone of CMA House was carried out by His Excellency, the Rt. Hon. Roland Mitchener, governor-general of Canada. That evening the CMA hosted a formal dinner at which His Excellency was presented with honorary membership in the Association. In July of 1968, the first of the CMA staff moved from Toronto to temporary quarters in the auditorium of the National Defence Medical Centre. Staff who had decided to move to the nation's capital arrived in July 1969.

The general secretary's office was located in the basement of St. Timothy's Presbyterian Church on Alta Vista Drive, south of the new CMA House, but the rest of the secretariat staff operated out of the National Defence Medical Centre auditorium located in the Rideau Veterans' Home. Working conditions were less than ideal in the auditorium. Cubicles 6x8 feet with sheets of plywood for dividing walls, constituted the secretariat "offices." The lucky ones had appropriated the stage from which they were able to survey the area normally occupied by an audience. Beneath the floor of the auditorium lay the swimming pool and the gymnasium, but both were out of bounds for CMA staff. It was with some relief that the general secretary and his staff moved into the second floor of an unfinished CMA House in the winter of 1969–70. In the spring of 1970, the ground floor was more or less complete and the tenants — the Canadian Medical Protective Association, the Medical Council of Canada, the Ottawa Academy of Medicine, the Canadian Association of Prosthetists and Orthotists and the

CMA House, Ottawa, 1970.

CMA House, Ottawa, 1971.

Canadian Nurses Association — moved in, occupying about 80% of the space on that floor. There was enough unoccupied space to be taken over by the journal staff and the library when they moved to Ottawa, planned for 1971. There were the usual problems experienced when moving into a new, and in this case, unfinished building; the heating system was, at its best, described as "temperamental." It was not at all unusual to see CMA staff at their desks, carrying out their duties clad in hats, overcoats, scarves and gloves.

Landscaping was costed at $35 000. The plan for the parking lot was revised and the proposed reflecting pool in the foyer was taken off the list. In February 1970, the comptroller, Mr. William Gowling, reported to the CMA Board of Directors that a letter had been received from the NCC, stating that it was considering the sale of a parcel of land on the corner of Alta Vista and Smyth, adjacent to the CMA property and, having given an undertaking that the CMA would have the first refusal when the land was available for sale, it was now making good on its pledge. The Building Committee recommended that the offer by the NCC be followed up and that the CMA should indicate an interest in purchasing the land, if and when it became available. Correspondence and meetings ensued between the CMA and the NCC for clarification of certain conditions of sale. After review of all aspects related to the purchase of the land, the Board of Directors concluded that the CMA had sufficient land for its foreseeable needs and that it would not proceed to purchase the land. In hindsight it may not have been the best decision, and there were many occasions over the next two decades when one heard the words, "We should have bought that land when we had the chance."

A meeting was held on May 21 with representatives of the general contractor. Dr. Atkinson said that he had hoped to accept the building on behalf of the CMA but, because of the unresolved major problems in the heating and cooling systems, he was not in a position to do so. The builder was anxious to receive payment so that the subcontractors could be paid. Discussions on the hold-back sum of $208 000 followed, and it was the position of the CMA that it could not hold back any less than $200 000. In addition to the problems with the mechanical equipment, there were many deficiencies, mostly of a minor nature, requiring the attention of the builder and his subcontractors.

The Building Committee carried out an inspection of CMA House on June 9, 1970, and found that the point had been reached where the building could be declared as "substantially complete." A further examination in mid-July and ongoing discussions with the contractor led to the building being declared "complete" except for a few minor details, and the hold-back was paid to the contractor. The revised contract costs for the building were $1 101 023.

At 15:00 hours on Oct. 2, 1970, CMA House at 1867 Alta Vista Drive, Ottawa, was officially opened by Dr. Duncan Graham, who had been president of the CMA in 1940–41. The Board of Directors publicly thanked the committees, the CMA and all others who had worked long and hard to translate the resolution of General Council in 1967 into the bricks and mortar of 1970. The board's thanks were particularly directed towards Dr. Atkinson and the members of the Building Committee who had been involved in the project since December 1966.

During the FLQ crisis in Quebec in 1970, CMA House became the centre of operations for the Fédération des médecins spécialistes de Québec. The basement was set up like a wartime operations room with long tables on which there were banks of telephones connected to hospitals and other health institutions in Quebec. Each morning the doctors would assemble in the parking lot and be allocated the location of the health facility in Quebec where their services were needed at that time. This ensured that adequate coverage of emergency was not compromised. Because of the threats against CMA staff, the specialists and even CMA House itself, the area around CMA House took on a high-security aspect. Floodlights were installed on the roof and, in the nearby wooded bank of the small stream bordering the property, a group of armed soldiers maintained a 24-hour watch on CMA House and the neighbouring National Defence Medical Centre. With the end of the crisis CMA House returned to normal although the floodlights are still on the roof a quarter of a century later.

By the end of 1983, working conditions at CMA House had deteriorated because of overcrowding, and there were discussions by the Board of Directors and the Executive Committee on the tenancies still in the building. The lease of the Medical Council of Canada was due to expire in 1984, and as the council considered that it was to its advantage to remain in CMA House, discussions between the parties led to a proposal that an addition be built, jointly funded by the Medical Council of Canada and MD Management Ltd. (MDM). After further consideration, the Medical Council of Canada withdrew its offer to cost-share any addition, and MDM purchased a one-third interest in the CMA property. The price was over $1 million, based on an appraisal of building and land as of Sept. 26, 1984, and the transaction gave MDM a 50% stake in CMA House.

A building program was embarked on and the construction of a 20 000 square-foot, two-storey extension began in the south-east corner of CMA House. Joining the two buildings would be a glass-walled covered walkway. Occupancy by MDM was scheduled for May 1, 1986, but numerous delays, in the main due to labour disputes and late deliveries of equipment, moved that date back, and it was only at the time of the General Council in Winnipeg in August that MDM was able to move into its new quarters. Following MDM's move, some repositioning of departments took place in the main building.

In 1989, two decades after moving to Ottawa, the increase in staff had been substantial, due mainly to the operations of MDM. It had been anticipated that the 1986 addition would meet the requirements of the Association for some time to come, but this was not to be the case. If that rate of growth continued it was conceivable that approximately 7000 square feet of new space would be needed each year. In addition to poor working conditions, storage facilities were lacking and the use of corridors and stairwells as storage areas was not accepted by those concerned with fire prevention. One of the meeting rooms had to be converted to working space, and it was thought that some of the departments would have to relocate outside CMA House.

In view of all of this, the Board of Directors established a Building and Accommodation Committee chaired by Dr. Athol L. Roberts. This committee met on a number of occasions and made its report to General Council in Regina in August 1990. The discussions led to the following recommendations, which were approved by the General Council:

- *That the CMA, MDM and MD Realty headquarters remain housed together in the long term.*
- *That the CMA and MDM build, buy or lease a new facility in the National Capital Region.*
- *That the existing CMA House be sold.*
- *That the CMA Board of Directors be empowered to proceed with whatever actions are required to carry out the three preceding resolutions with respect to the CMA/MDM/MD Realty headquarter facilities.*

In December 1990, the CMA decided to buy back MDM's 50% share in CMA House, based on the following reasoning:

- Benefits would be greater from the corporate tax perspective to have CMA own the property, given the expected increase in value, as a result of possible rezoning, should the building be sold.
- Risk exposure in MDM would be reduced by moving assets and investments to CMA and MD Investment Services.
- Intercompany loans between the CMA and MDM could be cleared up with the buy back.
- Compliance with the Goods and Services Tax (GST) would be made easier.

The CMA bought back MDM's 50% in CMA House by paying the fair market value of $3 601 725. Two components made up this sum — the unbudgeted revenue of $2 275 000 from MDM and $1 272 000 in loans receivable from MDM. With this effected, the CMA owned all of CMA House; the final part of the transaction was carried out in 1991 when CMA-owned shares in MDM were exchanged for additional shares of MD Investment Services.

Even though the passage of the resolutions appeared to have sounded the death knell for CMA House on Alta Vista Drive, there were many members who did not agree with the decision of the General Council, believing that the option of remaining in the existing building was the one of choice and that ways and means should be found to achieve this. In addition to those opinions, there were a number of signs that the time for buying and selling properties was not present and, all in all, the proverb about a bird in the hand seemed to be very relevant.

In 1991, the Building and Accommodation Committee reported to the General Council that its review during the preceding year had led it to the same conclusion as those who were unhappy with the proposal to sell and move. On the assumption that CMA House could be enlarged in some way the committee was recommending that CMA House not be sold and that the Association would continue to operate out of 1867 Alta Vista Drive. The rationale for the committee's decision was given as follows.

- The expansion recommended would provide enough space for the estimated needs of both the CMA and MDM to the year 2000.
- The likelihood was that the property zoning could be changed over the longer term, whereas there was very little chance that it would be changed to the CMA's advantage in the near future.
- In the opinion of the Building and Accommodation Committee, expanding CMA House would not detract from the potential to sell the building, should it be necessary in the long term.
- The construction of the expansion could be phased over 5 years to allow expansion into space more or less as required. This would facilitate the financing and would ease the situation during construction, causing as little disruption as possible.
- After discussion, the following motion was approved: "That the Canadian Medical Association consider, and if appropriate, pursue, as an option, expanding CMA House to accommodate the Canadian Medical Association and MD Management space requirements and that the Board of Directors be empowered to carry this out."

The committee reported to the General Council in St. John's in 1991 that significant progress had been made in the implementation of the previous year's resolution and that it had been found feasible to expand the facility. The expansion was planned to be carried out in two phases. Phase one was the addition of a further three storeys to the two-storey addition built in 1985 and 1986. The second phase would be a two-storey addition to the north end of the original building plus the creation of additional parking space. Cost estimates for phase one were \$3 200 000 and for phase two \$3 500 000. Those amounts included renovation and fit-up costs to the existing building. The cost of phase one was to be borne entirely by the CMA from its reserve funds. It was anticipated that by the time of construction of phase two, costs would be met from the same source.

The base building construction of phase one was completed in February 1993, 2 months behind schedule. The estimate to complete the base building was \$2 980 908; the budget for the fit-up, including renovations and purchase of new furniture and fittings, was \$2 700 000. The new upper three floors were completed in May, and basement renovations were completed by August when MDM moved into the top two floors and the ground floor. The Department of Publications occupied the third floor and Department of Information Technology was located on the second floor. The basement housed various administrative offices.

In 1993, the Building and Accommodation Committee re-examined the plan for phase two as it appeared that the need for renovations were more urgent than had been thought. The layout of administrative offices and units was not compatible with the need for a more efficient operation and, after review, the committee presented the following views to the CMA Board of Directors as the rationale for consideration of corrective measures.

◆ *The layout of offices and workspace had been altered radically a number of times over the previous 25 years and the current layout left much to be desired in terms of a good working environment.*

◆ *Mechanical systems, such as air-conditioning, air-circulation and heating were severely compromised.*

◆ *Fire and Safety Codes were not being adhered to.*

◆ *There were neither entrances to the building nor washroom facilities for the handicapped.*

◆ *MDM's new computer system was not compatible with the cabling in the main part of CMA House.*

The Board of Directors reviewed the committee's report when it met in March 1993 and authorized the committee to look into plans and costs for renovating CMA House to correct the shortcomings it had identified. Following this directive, a feasibility study was carried out, leading to a recommendation that the renovations be undertaken in a seven-phase plan. By doing this, some CMA staff would be able to remain in CMA House during the renovations; the remainder would have to be accommodated elsewhere.

The total cost of the renovations and fit-up was estimated at $3 217 599, and with additional anticipated costs the total would rise to about $4 million. The Board of Directors accepted the report of the committee in principle and directed the Committee of Finance and the Building and Accommodation Committee to carry out a joint study on the availability of space in CMA House and the urgency of correcting the deficiencies. The question of accommodating some of the staff outside CMA House had to be addressed, and authority was given to enter into discussions with the Canadian Dental Association, whose building was immediately adjacent to CMA House and where there was vacant office space for rent.

The outcome of the joint study was a recommendation that the renovations proceed as soon as was practical after the transfer of staff to the Canadian Dental Association and the reorganization of space within CMA House for the departments remaining there during the renovations. The Board of Directors had authorized the Executive Committee to give the final approval, and this was given after the Executive Committee reviewed the report of the joint study.

In the summer of 1994, the CMA began its sojourn in its new quarters. The ground and second floors south of the cafeteria and boardroom were closed off. Access to the building through the main doors was prohibited, except to the renovators, and staff access was through a newly-constructed side door. The secretary general and the senior secretariat moved into the ground floor of the Canadian Dental Association building, as did the departments of Ethics and Legal Affairs, Education, Membership, and Human Resources. The CMA boardroom became home to the departments of communications and government relations, finance, health care and promotion, printing and supplies, and maintenance. The Department of Health Policy and Economics was located in the Powell–Argue Room and the Department of Meetings and Travel in the room previously known as the T.C. Routley Library and Archives Room. The mail room was transferred to the basement of the five-storey annex. The renovations were expected to be completed in time for the displaced staff to return to a renovated CMA House before the end of the year, but at that time the renovations were not complete.

When the building committee first looked at the site in the 1960s, it was still part of the NCC's tree nursery. Across the road, in another part of the tree nursery, were several acres of trees and shrubs of many different varieties. For some years after CMA House was built, foxes, pheasants and grouse, beaver and muskrat continued to grace the scene, but they have long since departed, driven out by the construction of other buildings in the immediate area. CMA House now sits in a "medical community." Next door, on the north side, is the Canadian Dental Association and to its north are the headquarters of the Canadian Pharmaceutical Association. Across the road sit the headquarters of The Canadian Red Cross Society. On the other side of the small stream bordering the property to the east lie the National Defence Medical Centre, The Ottawa General Hospital, the Children's Hospital of Eastern Ontario, the University of Ottawa Medical School, and the Rehabilitation Centre, part of the Royal Ottawa Health Care Group.

None of the changes in its surroundings or in the building has diverted the aim of the CMA, as laid down in its mission statement:

> "TO PROVIDE LEADERSHIP FOR PHYSICIANS AND TO PROMOTE THE HIGHEST STANDARDS OF HEALTH AND HEALTH CARE FOR CANADIANS."

CMA House, Ottawa, 1994.

Chapter II

STRUCTURE AND ORGANIZATION

WHEN THE ASSOCIATION WAS FOUNDED in 1867, one of the first committees to be established was the Committee for the Framing of the Constitution and Bylaws. The committee presented its first report to the 1868 annual meeting in Montreal, and the records show that "this took a great deal of time and was attended by no little interruption, in addition to continued and general conversation in all parts of the room during the reading of the clauses" and, further, that "confusion ensued with motions and amendments being made in quick succession, and when at last the discussion was once more brought to the Bylaws, one member said that he could not understand how it was that if members did not sign their names in agreement to the rules, that they could be bound by them." Over the years, reaction to the presentation of amendments to the bylaws has not changed, and the exodus from General Council meetings when the bylaws are under discussion indicates that Association members act very much like their predecessors, believing that such matters are of little importance.

In 1909, the Canadian Medical Association (CMA) was incorporated under chapter 62 of the Statutes of Canada. During the next 48 years the bylaws underwent numerous revisions, mostly of a minor nature, more for clarification than for any other reason. In 1957, the General Council approved major changes and established a Committee on Organization to study the Association's structure and functions at the same time as further consideration of the bylaws. At the time of this decision, the Association was warned that it was venturing into areas and activities not contemplated when it was incorporated.

In 1958, the Committee on Bylaws recommended that the Association petition the Parliament of Canada for approval to amend the *Act of Incorporation*. The proposed amendments would apply to:
- Chapter II, Section 2 Objects of the Association.
- Section 7 Annual Value of Real Estate Held by the Association.
- Chapter VI, Section 1(c) Senior Members.

- ◆ Chapter X, Section 1 Functions of Sections Within CMA.
    Section 2 Authorization of Sections.
    Section 3 Organization of Sections.
    Section 4 Relationship of Sections to Other Professional Organizations.
    Section 5 Meetings of Sections.
    Section 6 Authority of Sections.
    Section 7 Dissolution of Sections.
- ◆ Chapter XIII, Sections 1 & 3 General Council Organization and Meetings.
- ◆ Chapter XIV, Sections 1, 2 & 3 Protocols for Amendments.

The proposed amendments to the *Act of Incorporation* were presented to the House of Commons and the Senate, and approved by parliament in March 1959. In 1961 the General Council approved the following.

- ◆ Chapter III The Seal. The Seal of the Canadian Medical Association as redesigned in 1961 shall be The Seal of the Association, shall be in the custody of the General Secretary and shall be affixed by him to all documents that require to be sealed.
- ◆ Chapter XIII Members of General Council to include Past Chairmen of General Council.
- ◆ Chapter XIV To Section 4 — Duties of Standing Committees added Committees on Aging, Child Health, and Physical Education and Recreation.

Two further recommendations were placed before the General Council:

- ◆ That this Council endorse the principle that the election of Officers of the Association need not be based on regional or geographic considerations.
- ◆ That this Council recommend that the Committee on Bylaws consider the concept that the Chairman of Council should be a member of the Association who is not on the Executive Committee and who is chosen for his knowledge of the rules of procedure and for the ability to hold the respect of Council in acting as its "Speaker."

The proposer of both recommendations was Dr. Patrick (Paddy) Bruce-Lockhart, speaker of General Council from 1987 to 1992. Both recommendations were approved and referred to the Executive Committee and the Committee on Organization for study and report to the General Council.

The 1962–63 committee studied a resolution it had received from the General Council after considerable discussion. The resolution read: "That representatives of Affiliated Societies be non-voting members of the General

Council of the Canadian Medical Association." The motion put before the General Council appeared to be motivated by concern that affiliated societies could exert undue influence because "the growth in the numbers of Affiliated Societies might result in their controlling the CMA delegates." In this context it was assumed that "CMA delegates" meant representatives from the divisions. At the time, the 213 membership of General Council was made up as follows:

Executive Committee 13
Officers and officials 8
Divisional representatives 110
Divisional presidents and secretaries 20
Chairpersons of standing committees 22
Past presidents of CMA 14
Deputy minister of health 1
Director general of health services, Department of Veterans Affairs . . . 1
Surgeon general Canadian Forces Medical Services 1
Association of Canadian Medical Colleges representative
    who is a dean of medicine and a member of CMA Representatives
    of affiliate societies 22

The study by the Committee on Bylaws found no evidence to substantiate the fears expressed, and the 1964 General Council approved that affiliate society members of the General Council should continue to be permitted to vote.

By 1965, the Committee on Bylaws, under its chairman, Dr. Hugh Arnold, had carried out a detailed study of the bylaws, and came to General Council with a number of questions as well as several proposed amendments. The questions were:

- Should a secret ballot replace the open vote procedure now authorized for the conduct of the business of the Nominating Committee? We recommend a secret ballot in respect of the selection of officers and an open vote of the Nominating Committee in the selection of Divisional representatives to the Executive Committee and their alternates. A suitable amendment to the Bylaw will be proposed.

- Should the custom of linking the nomination of the President-Elect to the location of the next Annual Meeting be continued or altered? Your Committee would point out that the Bylaw makes no reference to the place of residence of the President-Elect and imposes no geographic limitation in his selection. It has, however, been customary that the host Division for the Annual Meeting has the privilege of nominating the President-Elect.

CMA Executive Committee, May, 1959 – CMA House, Toronto.

Seated front row, L–R: Dr. T.C. Routley, Toronto; Dr. G.W. Halpenny, Montreal; Dr. A.F. VanWart, Fredericton; Dr. N.H. Gosse, Halifax; Dr. E.K. Lyon, Leamington, Ont.; Dr. M.A.R. Young, Lamont, Alta.; Miss M. Zoellner, Toronto

Standing second row, L–R: Dr. M. Dufresne, Toronto; Mr. B.E. Freamo, Toronto; Dr. A.F.W. Peart, Toronto; Dr. J.A. McMillan, P.E.I; Dr. C.D. Kean, Nfld.; Dr. G.M. White, NB; Dr. M.S. Douglas, Windsor; Dr. A.A. Haig, Alta.; Dr. P.O. Lehmann, BC; Dr. A.D. Kelly, Toronto; Dr. S.S.B. Gilder, Toronto; Mr. K.C. Cross, Toronto

Standing third row, L–R: Dr. E.F. Crutchlow, Montreal; Dr. R.O. Jones, Halifax; Dr. R. Lemieux; Dr. W.W. Baldwin, Brooklin, Ont.; Dr. R.W. Richardson, Man.; Dr. E.R. Stewardson, Sask.; Dr. R.K.C. Thomson, Edmonton

Standing back row, L–R: Dr. T.J. Quintin, Sherbrooke, Que.; Dr. Lorne Whitaker, St. Catharines, Ont.

The tradition has demonstrated the advantages of providing a local person who takes a leading part in meeting arrangements and of providing certain Divisions where Annual Meetings are not ordinarily held to propose a President-Elect. Your Committee does not suggest that the Bylaw specify where the President-Elect should come from but that all Divisions be asked in advance of the meeting of the Nominating Committee to propose the names of candidates for the elective offices of the Association. A suitable amendment to the Bylaw is proposed.

◆ Should the Nominating Committee meet one month in advance of its statutory meeting at the time of the Annual Meeting? Your Committee sees no advantage in such a meeting, particularly if the proposals of the Divisions are placed in the hands of the members of the Nominating Committee and the Divisions at the early date which we propose.

◆ Should the number and composition of the Executive Committee be changed? Your Committee feels that the current number of 18 voting members (5 Officers, 13 Divisional representatives) is approximately correct for the efficient conduct of business. However, the increasing membership of the Association makes it desirable that the larger divisions be represented in some proportion to their membership and we propose a numerical formula to replace the current statement on the Divisional representation on the Executive Committee. This would maintain the present numerical representation on the Executive Committee but would provide for the ultimate increase in representation from those Divisions where there is a progressive increase of members in the CMA.

The committee's proposals were discussed at some length, and the following statements are those approved by General Council for inclusion in the bylaws.

Chapter IX
Section 3. Duties and Powers of the Nominating Committee:
The Nominating Committee shall meet on the day of its election by the General Council and shall submit to a later session of that body:

1. Nomination of the following officers of the Association: a President-Elect, a Chairman of the General Council and an Honorary Treasurer.
   a) To assist the Nominating Committee, the General Secretary shall by February 1 preceding the Annual Meeting invite the Divisions to submit the names of candidates for the offices of President-Elect, Chairman of the General Council and Honorary Treasurer.

b) By March 15 preceding the Annual Meeting the General Secretary shall transmit to the Divisions and to their nominees to the Nominating Committee the names of any persons proposed by the divisions for the offices named in (a) above.

2. Nomination of an Executive Committee which, in addition to the President, the Immediate past president, the President-Elect, the Chairman of General Council and the Honorary Treasurer, shall consist of Divisional resident representatives to the number produced by the application of the following formula: each Division shall be entitled to one representative on the Executive Committee for their membership up to 2000 members of the Association resident in that Division, one additional representative for such membership up to 5000 and one additional representative for each 5000 members above 5000 or fraction thereof.

3. Nominations from members of the General Council of alternates for the elected members of the Executive Committee, there shall be one alternate nominated from each province for each Divisional representative. The function of the alternates shall be to act in the place of an elected member of the Executive Committee who is absent because of death or illness or from cause acceptable to the Chairman of the Executive Committee.

4. At its session, the Nominating Committee may receive in writing:
    a) Each Division's official nomination of the candidate or candidates for representation on the Executive Committee to which the Division is entitled; and also
    b) Each Division's official nomination of one alternate for each Divisional representative who will act in the absence by reason of death or illness or from cause acceptable to the Chairman of the Executive Committee, of the member or one of the members of the Executive Committee representing that Division. In the event of such official nomination by a Division being rejected by the Nominating Committee, the reasons for such action shall be incorporated in its report to General Council.

5. **Rules of Procedure**
    The Committee shall be called to order by the President as Chairman of the Committee. In the absence of the President, the General Secretary shall convene the Committee and request the Committee to

select, by open vote, the Chairman. The Committee shall then proceed to select nominees for President-Elect, Chairman of the General Council and Honorary Treasurer by secret ballot. It shall then select by open vote the nominees and alternates for the Executive Committee. In case of a tie vote, the Chairman shall have the casting vote in addition to the vote to which he is entitled as a member of the Committee. When called for, the report of the committee shall be presented to the General Council by the General Secretary.

Senior Members

Any member of the Association in good standing for the immediately preceding ten-year period who has attained the age of 65 years is eligible to be nominated for senior membership by an ordinary member of the Association. He shall be approved by the Executive of the Division in which he practised, but he may be elected only by the unanimous approval of the Executive Committee present and voting. Senior members shall be elected as follows:

i) Each Division is entitled to one senior member per year, notwithstanding the provisions in (ii). In the case of a Division acting as host to the Annual Meeting of the Canadian Medical Association, an additional senior member may be nominated.

ii) A Division may approve for election one senior member per year, in addition to (i) above, for each thousand members on its register for that year. Senior members shall enjoy all the rights and privileges of the Association but shall not be required to pay an annual fee.

Committees

The Standing Committees of the Association are named in the Bylaws and their terms of reference are briefly stated. In 1963 the Executive Committee reinstated the Committee on Mental Health after a period of time during which we depended on our Affiliate, The Canadian Psychiatric Association, for advice in this field.

To regularize the position we recommend the following addition to Chapter XIV Section 4: "Committee on Mental Health: This Committee shall advise the Association on all matters pertaining to mental health; shall advise the Committee on Economics insofar as that Committee is concerned with the economic aspects of the provision of adequate psychiatric and mental health services and shall maintain active liaison with the Canadian Psychiatric Association and with such other bodies as the Association may desire from time to time."

CMA Executive Committee, 1967.

L–R, back row: Dr. C.A. Cody, Dr. A.R. Mercer, Dr. W.J.S. Melvin, Dr. P.J. Banks, Dr. D.M. Aitken, Dr. H.G. Scarrow, Dr. R.M. Mathews, Dr. J.R. Anderson

L–R, centre row: Mr. B.E. Freamo, Dr. N.S. Skinner, Dr. D.N.C. McIntyre, Dr. G.W. Mylks, Dr. H.A. Arnold, Dr. H.J. Devereux, Dr. D.G. Cameron, Dr. R.G. Prefontaine, Dr. E.W. Barootes, Mr. D.A. Geekie

L–R, back row: Dr. A.D. Kelly, Mr. J.H. Maloney, Hon. Treasurer; Dr. N.J. Belliveau, President-Elect; Dr. R.D. Atkinson, Chairman of General Council & Executive Committee; Dr. R.K.C. Thomson, President; Dr. R.O. Jones, Past President; Dr. A.F.W. Peart, General Secretary

The bylaws were not changed during the next 3 years, but a number of comments were made that there were shortcomings in some of the sections, and in 1968 the Executive Committee established a committee with the mandate to review the bylaws, the organization, function and operations of the Association's many committees, and the establishment of work priorities. The committee, known as the Special Committee on Organization, chaired by Dr. Hart Scarrow, met on five occasions during the General Council year 1968–69 and presented its report to the General Council in Toronto in 1969. The report consisted primarily of a recommended draft of the bylaws and a number of major changes were proposed. The following changes were approved by General Council.

- ◆ The Executive Committee to be replaced by a Board of Directors.
- ◆ A new Executive Committee to be formed largely from the Officers of the Association.
- ◆ The 44 committees of the Association to be amalgamated into five Councils.
- ◆ The creation of a new office — Chairman of the Board of Directors.
- ◆ The creation of the offices of Speaker and Deputy-Speaker of General Council.

Executive Committee

The Executive Committee to consist of the President, the President-Elect, the immediate past president, the Chairman of the Board of Directors, the Honorary Treasurer and one member-at-large elected from the Board of Directors.

Terms of Reference of the Executive Committee

- ◆ The Executive Committee shall act on behalf of the Board of Directors between meetings of the Board and shall deal with such matters as require immediate decisions.
- ◆ The Executive Committee shall consider matters referred to it by the Board of Directors.
- ◆ The Executive Committee may consider and advise the Board of Directors on matters not currently before the Board.
- ◆ The Executive Committee may consider, act on and advise the Board of Directors on such other matters as may be agreed to by the President and the Chairman of the Board.
- ◆ The Executive Committee is responsible to the Board of Directors and shall report to the Board at each meeting of the Board.

The members of the first Executive Committee were:

Dr. Ross M. Matthews, president

Dr. Duncan L. Kippen, president-elect

Dr. Harold D. Dalgleish, immediate past president

Dr. Lloyd C. Grisdale, chairman of the Board of Directors

Dr. John H. Maloney, honorary treasurer

Dr. Hart G. Scarrow, member-at-large

Board of Directors

The Board of Directors was made up of representatives of the divisions of the Association, based on proportional representation. Each member of the board would have an alternate. The members and alternates of the first Board of Directors were:

	Members	Alternates
BC	Dr. Hart G. Scarrow	Dr. Robert M. Lane
	Dr. Archie M. Johnson	Dr. F. Sidney Hobbs
Alta.	Dr. Donald F. Lewis	Dr. John B.T. Wood
Sask.	Dr. Estathios W. Barootes	Dr. Frederick H. Wigmore
Man.	Dr. Garth E. Mosher	Dr. Donald A. McPhail
Ont.	Dr. Jim Small	Dr. Louis R. Harnick
	Dr. Jack H. Walters	Dr. James T. Colquhoun
	Dr. Bette Stephenson	Dr. Manning L. Mador
Que.	Dr. Germain Bigue	Dr. Arnold F. Jones
	Dr. George K. Wlodek	Dr. Claude Gendron
NB	Dr. J. Ray Boulay	Dr. S. Allan Hopper
NS	Dr. Anthony J.M. Griffiths	Dr. Charles L. Gosse
PEI	Dr. Athol L. Roberts	Dr. Ronald D. Drysdale
Nfld.	Dr. Augustus T. Rowe	Dr. Patrick Whelan

Speaker and Deputy Speaker of General Council

Both positions are filled by nomination and election by General Council. The holders of the positions are not officers of the Association. The first holders of these offices were Speaker: Dr. Reginald D. Atkinson and Deputy Speaker: Dr. Peter J. Banks.

Dr. Atkinson was a former chairman of General Council (1966–69).

Councils

With some exceptions, the Association's 44 committees were coalesced into five councils. These were:

> The Council on Medical Education
> The Council on Community Health Care
> The Council on the Provision of Health Services
> The Council on Personal Services to Physicians
> The Council on Economics

General Provisions for all Councils:

i)   The Chairman of each Council shall be appointed from the members of the Association by the Board of Directors annually.

ii)   Each Council shall be composed of a Chairman and one member from each Division. Members shall be chosen for their knowledge, ability, and interest in the work of that particular Council.

iii) A member of the Secretariat will be assigned to each Council and will act as Secretary to that Council.

iv)   The Councils shall determine their projects and priorities for the ensuing year, and prepare their programmes and budgets in time for presentation to the September meeting of the Board of Directors for approval. Projects will be carried out by the Council or councillors and subcommittees selected by the Council for knowledge and ability in the projected field. Each subcommittee will have a councillor as a member or chairman of the subcommittee. Subcommittees carrying out a specific project will automatically be dissolved with the termination of that project.

v)   Each Council shall gather routine statistics and other information associated with its area of concern.

vi)   Each Council shall meet from time to time at the call of the Chairman but at least once annually and at a time to be determined by the Chairman.

vii) All Councils shall report annually to the General Council and to the Board of Directors between meetings of the General Council.

viii) Any vacancy occurring among the members of any Council shall be reported to the Board of Directors.

ix)   Each Council shall recommend to the Board of Directors their detailed terms of reference as required and develop such regulations as are necessary to carry out these terms of reference.

The 1969 terms of reference of each of the five councils are described in the chapter on councils.

Committees

General Council approved two classes of committees — statutory and special. A special committee would be a short-term committee appointed by the Board of Directors or the General Council for a specific task and dissolved on completion of its task. Two statutory committees were appointed: the Committee on Finance and the Committee on Ethics. The respective terms of the two committees are outlined here.

Committee on Finance

i)   The Committee shall consist of the Honorary Treasurer as Chairman and five voting members of the Association. The Committee shall meet at least twice yearly.

ii) Three voting members of the Committee, including the Chairmen, shall constitute a quorum.

iii) The Committee shall be charged with the special duty of studying the immediate and long-term financial needs of the Association, including the establishing of reserve funds, and shall present to the General Council appropriate fiscal policies to meet these needs.

iv) The Committee shall assess the financial implications of all programmes and projects and make recommendations to the Board of Directors.

v)   The Committee shall prepare a tentative budget for the ensuing year indicating distribution of moneys to be made available for all purposes and shall receive regular reports to ensure that all committees and departments operate within this budget.

vi) All recommendations, financial transactions and minutes of meetings of this Committee shall be reported regularly to the Board of Directors.

vii) The Committee shall report annually to the General Council. Its report shall cover all the financial activities of the Association during the previous calendar year and shall indicate the revenues necessary for the subsequent year, including recommendations regarding the fee structure and assessments.

viii) The adoption by the General Council of the annual reports of the Committee on Finance and of the Auditor shall validate all the financial transactions of the Board of Directors, the Executive Committee, the Committee on Finance and other Committees of the Association during the year covered by the report.

The Committee shall recommend the appointment of Auditors to the General Council annually.

Committee on Ethics

i) There shall be a Committee on Ethics which will consist of a Chairman and two members of the Association.

ii) The Committee shall be concerned with the elaboration, interpretation and amendment of the Code of Ethics, and with problems related to ethics referred to the Association.

iii) The Committee shall report to the Board of Directors as requested and annually to the General Council.

The Association began functioning under the new format in 1970, and it became evident that the councils were having teething problems. Dr. Scarrow was asked to undertake a review of the councils and to come up with solutions to their problems. In his review, Dr. Scarrow recommended the following guidelines for establishing programs, priorities, budgeting, methods of referral and subcommittee chairmanship.

Programmes, Priorities and Budgets

It has become obvious that a programme for each ensuing year, with priorities and a realistic budget, must be ready for the September meeting of the Board of Directors. This means that each Council should settle on its programmes at the last spring meeting, probably with an updating by a nucleus before September. The Committee on Finance should see these programmes before presentation to the Board but should not suggest the abolition of programmes to the Council Chairmen. This function should belong to the Board of Directors. The presentation of programme and budget must be made by the Chairmen of Councils, not by Council Secretaries.

Once the budget is established the Council should be allowed to operate according to its own wishes within the limits of its budget items but must obtain approval from the Board of Directors for increases in previously approved or new project items.

Additional items are bound to come up during each year and if extra jobs are given to Councils, the budgetary aspect must be considered and reasonable allocation made for the work to be done. It is unreasonable to add extra work to a Council and at the same time ask them to live within a fairly rigid budget.

Referrals

The Executive Committee and the Board or Directors have tended to refer a problem to two or three Councils who may be involved in its solution. As a gen-

eral rule all referrals will now go to one Council. It appears to be both waste-ful and fragmentary to refer problems to more than one Council at a time.

Subcommittees

Every subcommittee should have a councillor as chairman or member. This is essential if the Council is to remain completely knowledgeable of all its activities.

Summary

The Board of Directors believes that the Councils have performed well in their first year. This is probably due to the calibre of the Chairmen and the mem-bers of Councils, as well as to the validity of the concept. Council activities are the main concern of the Board of Directors and must have first call on the monies we have available. Any economies should be made elsewhere.

The board also approved and recognized the following policies and rela-tionships between the councils, the General Council and the Board of Directors:

- ◆ *The Councils are Committees of General Council and not of the Board of Directors. Councils should report to the Board of Directors on any matters which have been referred to them by the Board.*
- ◆ *Councils should report to the Board on matters on which they wish the Board's opinion because the time interval is such that a decision cannot wait until the meeting of General Council.*
- ◆ *Board members receive the minutes of each of the Council meetings and any Board member may raise any item of Council business at a Board meeting.*
- ◆ *Councils report to General Council and the Board cannot make changes in these reports. The Board of Directors may, however, append recom-mendations or comments to these Council reports.*

By 1971 the new structure was fully operational and thought was given to the role that the Association should play, not only as it applied to the practice of medicine, but also to the place it should occupy within the social fabric of Canada. To this end, and after a lot of soul-searching, the Association took a decision, seen by some as fraught with danger and by others as an exciting chal-lenge, to invite a number of distinguished Canadians to meet with Association representatives, with the object of receiving criticism and advice on the path it should follow. It was believed that the words of the great Scottish poet, Robert Burns, in his poem *To a Louse* were appropriate for what was proposed: "O wad some Pow'r the giftie gie us, to see oursels as others see us! It wad frae mony a blunder free us, and foolish notion."

The Association's invitations were readily accepted, and participants met at the Seigniory Club at Montebello, Que., on Mar. 12 and 13, 1971. Criticism and constructive advice were forthcoming in good measure and in many ways contributed to a policy direction as relevant for the Association in 1995 as it was when it was conceived in 1971. Because of the perceived landmark importance, the report of the "think tank" as presented to the 1971 General Council in Halifax, NS, in June 1971 by the then general secretary, Dr. J. Douglas Wallace, is reproduced here.

On March 12 and 13, 1971 the CMA did something unique in its long and illustrious history — representatives of its Board of Directors and Secretariat met with a group of distinguished Canadians representing a wide spectrum of society that it had invited to come and criticize the Association and its activities. In the past one might consider that we have received our share criticism without inviting it. This time we asked for it on the basis that the Association really wants to know what and how the people of Canada think it is doing now, and what role they think it should play in society in the future.

The informal meeting was held in the Seigniory Club at Montebello, Quebec. Invitations were sent to a selected list of Canadian citizens whose opinions on sociological affairs were known to be positive and respected. To the credit of the past performance of CMA only two of these selected on the Number One list declined the invitation. They wanted to come but could not clear the time. The rest accepted with an enthusiasm that indicated to the planning group that it would be a lively and interesting gathering.

The background information provided to the participants covered a wide range of information concerning the Association. However, the one point that was stressed is a fact that is probably not recognized by many of our members — the CMA is a voluntary association of individual doctors and not a confederation of ten provincial divisions or a consortium of a large number of specialized and autonomous professional societies and associations. While for purposes related to the requirements of the constitution of our country it functions through ten provincial divisions, it is not a creature of those divisions. Under its national charter it is an autonomous organization that is said to represent the voice of Medicine in Canada as a whole. From the staff point of view — national and provincial — it was hoped that as a result of the "Think Tank" and the recent Secretaries' Conference, the CMA could identify specific areas of interest of its own at the national level that complement rather than duplicate or conflict with the responsibility of provincial divisions. We believe that there are important sectors of the health field on which the CMA can speak with authority without having to obtain prior approval of all its provincial divisions just as there are specific activities in each province in which it should not interfere. Between these two identifiable areas of decisive action there are a number of fields of common interest in which the national association can act in a coordinating and advisory role with its Divisions. Your CMA staff and the staff at divisional level sincerely hope that these roles can be properly identified as a result of the Think Tank and the deliberations.

To the surprise and delight of those that organized the meeting it took off on a constructive and positive note at the beginning and built up from there. On the whole the discussions in which all participants contributed with increasing vigour were frank and constructive. There were naturally moments of defensiveness when criticism narrowed in on sensitive areas, particularly those concerning incomes and economics generally. On this point the critics were quick to point out that we were unduly sensitive to such comments. The average Canadian doctor has no need to be defensive about the income that he earns through long hours of hard work, and society does not begrudge him that income. Unfortunately the publicity given to the relatively small percentage of medical incomes that are considered on a national basis to be excessive has created an overly defensive attitude on the part of the profession in the area of medical economics.

Time and again, on this and other topics, we were given the advice that the medical profession through its national and provincial associations should act instead of react. We should move in on known problem areas and do something about them rather than wait for some other group, usually government, to move in and make threatening noises that result in reaction rather than action. We were also told that we tend to underestimate the authority with which we can speak constructively on health and social matters because we are relatively few in number as compared with other elements of society. This major weakness was referred to on several occasions as a "group inferiority complex" and we were advised that we should have the intestinal fortitude to stand up and be counted on social and general health matters as well as on purely medical ones. When doctors as a group are acting rather than reacting their collective voice is heard and respected.

Another general criticism that was heard repeatedly concerned our traditional approach in attempting to reach a consensus of opinion that is acceptable to all Divisions if not all doctors in Canada on many issues, major and minor. In a nation as diversified as ours this was considered to be impossible.

This approach leads to unnecessarily long delays in decision and policy making and results in "watered down" statements that will not offend but at the same time are unlikely to give the impression of a leadership position.

The gathering came together without a detailed agenda of items for discussion. After a short general briefing session it divided into two discussion groups. When it returned to general session at the conclusion of the two days it was interesting to note that the two groups had covered almost identical topics of interest, and that they had very similar comments and recommendations. On that basis we must assume that these areas in which society as a whole has a primary interest in the CMA and its Divisions. These are therefore the areas to which we should devote most of our energy in the immediate future. The recommendations of the two groups are consolidated below as the consensus of opinion of the Think Tank as a whole.

Role of the Physician in Society and in his Community

Much of the respect in which medicine is held today stems from a past, less technological era in which the physician, because of his educational background and his interest in the welfare of people, was looked upon, and usually functioned, as a community leader. Rapid educational advances in other fields, and particularly in the technologies and social sciences, now preclude the inheriting of a community leadership role with the awarding of an M.D. Such a role must now be earned through individual and group performance in society as a whole, and in one's community in particular. The increasing science and technology of medicine is superceding the art and in an effort to maintain professional effectiveness most doctors have narrowed their areas of interest to purely medical matters.

It must be recognized that medical services are now part of the general social services provided to the public and that they cannot function effectively in isolation from the rest of those services. Physicians must therefore expand their areas of interest and must accept a major role at community level in becoming involved with others in the establishment of plans and priorities in broad social areas. If they wish to sustain, or hopefully improve, the quality of life in a community and in society as a whole they must become actively involved in activities organized to resolve social problems at the local level and thereby contribute positively to their resolution at the national level.

THE CMA HAS A RESPONSIBILITY TO STIMULATE GREATER INVOLVEMENT BY ITS MEMBERS IN THE IMPROVEMENT OF SOCIAL SERVICES AT THE COMMUNITY LEVEL.

Delivery of Health Services

It was generally agreed that the present patterns for the provision of health services are fragmented. They do not provide a satisfactory medium for either those providing the services or those receiving them. The lack of a team approach to the provision of health care results in the ineffective utilization of health service personnel and an overlapping of areas of responsibility that results in unnecessary conflict and confusion.

It was recommended that there should be a better organized division of labour in the health field, and that the team approach should be stimulated by the encouragement of group practice by both medical, other health professional and allied health personnel. Community health centres with health coordinators or ombudsmen were recommended as one potential solution. There should be more active participation in planning and operation by lay consumers, and greater attention should be given to the provision of health and social services in the home environment rather than in impersonalized institutions.

THE CMA SHOULD TAKE A LEADERSHIP ROLE IN JOINT PLAN-
NING AND DEVELOPMENT PROGRAMMES FOR HEALTH AND SOCIAL
SERVICES WITH GOVERNMENT AND WITH OTHER NATIONAL
HEALTH AND SOCIAL SERVICE ORIENTED ORGANIZATIONS.

Costs of Health Care

General concern regarding the escalating costs of health care is warranted and something must be done about it. The total cost is now being borne by government agencies and it is becoming increasingly evident that these agencies intend to apply realistic controls to health care expenditures with or without the help of voluntary agencies such as health oriented associations. There will be much less risk of adversely affecting quality if the voluntary agencies do participate in a constructive way in the establishment of controls.

Financing of health care is currently operating as a system of payment rather than a system of delivery. Payment is made on an input rather than on an output basis. Physicians generally are unaware of the indirect financial impact of their professional activities and have therefore shown relatively little interest in the establishment of utilization controls. This whole area of concern is being neglected by present medical education programmes at both the undergraduate and graduate levels.

THE CMA SHOULD STIMULATE ORGANIZED MEDICINE AT ALL
LEVELS OF THE SERVICE, EDUCATION AND RESEARCH FIELDS TO

STUDY AND DEVELOP COST EFFECTIVENESS PROGRAMMES, AND ENCOURAGE INDIVIDUAL PHYSICIANS TO BECOME AWARE AND KNOWLEDGEABLE OF THE COSTS THAT RESULT FROM THE UTILIZATION OF THEIR SERVICES BY THE PUBLIC.

Physician Incomes

Because of the length of their educational programmes, the pressure resulting from their responsibilities and the essential services provided to society, physicians are entitled to a good income. This becomes even more realistic and acceptable when considered on a life income rather than on an annual basis. Present schedules of fees for medical services were developed on the basis of a non-collection factor under a free enterprise system. They are therefore not satisfactory as schedules of payment for the medical care of a totally insured public. As a result there are marked disparities in income between various groups in the profession. Those that appear to be excessively high are attracting considerable attention from the public and are as well causing dissension within the profession itself.

Notice has been given by government paying agencies that we are at the end of the era of open-ended financing for medical services. It appears likely that in the near future provinces will begin operating on a "global budget" system under which a specified amount will be set aside each year for medical care. Total costs of medical services will be contained within that amount either through a joint effort by the provincial association and its paying agency, or by government alone if necessary. Budgetary provision will be made for new services and for population load factors but otherwise the funds available for total comprehensive medical services within a provincial jurisdiction will be fixed by the budget. The medical profession through its national and provincial associations should actively participate in the development and management of realistic budgetary and financial control procedures that will provide good medical care at an acceptable cost and equitably remunerate the physicians that are providing the necessary services.

THE CMA SHOULD ASSIST THE PROVINCIAL DIVISIONS IN THE DEVELOPMENT OF EFFECTIVE BUDGETARY AND FINANCIAL CONTROL PROCEDURES THROUGH WHICH THEY MAY WORK EFFECTIVELY WITH GOVERNMENT PAYING AGENCIES AND SHOULD ACT IN A COORDINATING AND CONSULTATIVE ROLE THROUGH THE DEVELOPMENT OF SYSTEMS, PROCEDURES AND DATA INFORMATION ON A NATIONAL BASIS.

Physician Requirements — Health Manpower

All aspects of health care, including education, now fall within the public domain. Organized medicine must accept the responsibility for the most effective expenditure of public resources and for the provision of an adequate supply and proper mix of medical manpower, including associates and assistants, to meet the public need. Many of our present problems appear to result from an improper distribution of medical manpower geographically and by specialty or type of practice. Because of the length of the medical education programmes, particularly in the specialties, the "law of the market-place" does not function effectively and the accidental mix of the products of undergraduate and postgraduate medical education programmes does not necessarily reflect the needs of society.

Methods and yardsticks must be found to predict the requirements of the future health care system for physicians in family practice and in the various specialties, and controls must be established to assure that the most appropriate mix of physicians is produced by the educational system and that individuals are not "specialized" into an already well-supplied market. Incentive programmes should be developed to encourage physicians into clinical fields and geographic areas that are in short supply.

THE CMA SHOULD ACTIVELY PARTICIPATE IN THE DEVELOPMENT OF NEW SYSTEMS FOR THE DELIVERY OF HEALTH CARE IN THE FUTURE AND SHOULD COORDINATE ITS ACTIVITIES WITH THOSE OF THE NATIONAL BODIES RESPONSIBLE FOR THE UNDERGRADUATE AND POSTGRADUATE EDUCATION OF PHYSICIANS, PHYSICIAN ASSOCIATES AND ASSISTANTS IN THE DEVELOPMENT OF PROGRAMMES THAT WILL ASSURE THE MOST EFFECTIVE UTILIZATION OF MEDICAL MANPOWER.

Periodic and Limited Licensure

It was noted that, while rapid advances are being made in all fields of medical science, and while medical education at the postgraduate level is becoming increasingly more specialized, there has been little if any interest in a requirement for continuing medical education, periodic assessment of medical competence or limited licensure. Present licensing regulations permit all qualified physicians continuing active practice privileges in a very broad spectrum of medical care. Controls, where they exist, are usually applied through the granting privileges and there is no assessment or accreditation of home or office practice.

While the CMA is not directly involved in the licensing of physicians and while its only involvement in the accreditation of physicians is in the intern-

ship programme, it was felt that it should use its influence to encourage a more realistic approach to an ongoing assessment of clinical competence in the interest of assuring the quality and safety of medical care.

The CMA should work at the national level with the authorities responsible for licensing, accreditation and continuing education of physicians in development of programmes that will ensure continuing clinical competence in areas of general and specialized medical care.

Role of the CMA

The primary purpose of the Think Tank was to provide an insight into the role that the CMA should develop for the future. We wish to develop realistic goals and objectives that will enable the Association to concentrate its efforts on specific areas of responsibility and to complement the activities of its Divisions, other health oriented associations and government in the planning, development and operation of comprehensive health and social services.

We were told that we are, and should continue to be, an important body of influence on the health scene. However, to accomplish this the CMA must become more of a leader and learn to act positively rather than react negatively or ineffectively. The comments of participants indicated that the CMA is regarded by many as a "Club" concerned primarily with doctors' incomes. We are accused of being oversensitive and reluctant to act. If the Association must wait for unanimity or a consensus of divisional opinion on all matters little will be accomplished.

A positive role must be established and this must be explained to a public that in the past has apparently been informed on what we are against than what we are for. The CMA is still regarded by many as an authority on health matters and its positive statements in that field are respected. However, it must broaden its views into the social services as a whole; work together with other professional, technological, government and lay organizations at all levels of society; and attain a positive leadership position.

The CMA should develop positive goals and objectives, and establish priorities for activities in specific areas of the health field in order that it may provide a leadership role in the provision of health and social services to Canadians now and in the future.

Consensus versus Leadership
While this problem was mentioned in many areas under discussion it was considered to be important enough to be brought out as a specific recommendation by one of the group reports. The premise contained in the recommendation was supported by the group as a whole.

THE GROUP CONSIDERS THAT IT IS A RESPONSIBILITY OF THE CANADIAN MEDICAL ASSOCIATION TO ESTABLISH LEADERSHIP IN THE STANDS IT TAKES IN VARIOUS MATTERS RATHER THAN TO LIMIT ITSELF TO A PRESENTATION TO THE CONSENSUS OF THE MEDICAL PROFESSION.

List of Delegates to the CMA Think Tank

Mr. A. Andras, research director, Canadian Labour Congress, Ottawa

Dr. John S. Bennett, director, CMA Scientific Councils, Ottawa

Mr. M. Bugera, treasurer, Pointe St.-Charles Community Clinic, Montreal

Mr. J. Cunnings, executive director, Manitoba Sanitorium Board, Winnipeg

Mr. E. Dunlop, executive director, Canadian Arthritis and Rheumatism Society, Toronto

Mrs. June (Callwood) Frayne, author and broadcaster, Toronto

Mr. Bernard E. Freamo, executive secretary, CMA, Ottawa

Mr. Douglas A. Geekie, director of communications, CMA, Ottawa

Dr. J. Gélinas, deputy chairman, Quebec Health Insurance Board, Montreal

Dr. Robert Gourdeau, CMA board member, Quebec City

Dr. Lloyd C. Grisdale, CMA board chairman, Edmonton

Dr. John Gutelius, dean of the School of Medicine, University of Saskatchewan, Saskatoon

Hon. James Henderson, minister of health, Edmonton

Ms. Joan Hollobon, medical science writer, Toronto

Mrs. Jean Jones, president, Consumers' Association of Canada, Toronto

Dr. Duncan L. Kippen, CMA president, Winnipeg

Dr. Maurice Leclair, deputy minister of health, Department of National Health and Welfare, Ottawa

Mrs. Grace MacInnis, MP, House of Commons, Ottawa

Mr. Stanley Martin, chairman, Ontario Hospital Services Commission, Toronto

Dr. J. Mount, president, Canadian Association of Internes and Residents, Toronto

Dr. Harry D. Roberts, CMA president-elect, St. John's

Dr. Bette Stephenson, CMA board member, Willowdale

Dr. J. Douglas Wallace, CMA general secretary, Ottawa

In 1972, the Board of Directors proposed a number of amendments to the bylaws with the intent of:

- clarifying areas of responsibility and authority in the Association;
- allocating duties and responsibilities more equitably among officers and senior CMA staff members;
- specifying more clearly the areas of activity to be undertaken by councils and their subcommittees;
- updating the bylaws to conform more closely with the organizational and activity patterns that had evolved.

A number of proposed amendments were referred back for further study. There were also some amendments to definitions and titles.

- *That General Council be designated as "The Governing Body and Legislative Authority of the Association."*
- *That the Board of Directors be designated as "The Executive Authority of the Association responsible for the management of the day-to-day affairs of the Association in accordance with the policies established by General Council.*
- *The title "general secretary" was changed to "secretary-general" and the holder's responsibilities spelled out more clearly.*
- *The Council on the Provision of Health Services was renamed The Council on Medical Services.*
- *The Council on Personal Services to Physicians was renamed The Council on Membership Services.*

All the councils had their terms of reference rewritten.

As a result of the referral back to the Board of Directors of a number of recommendations, the board established in 1973 a special committee charged with reviewing the existing bylaws and the referrals. This special committee's report, containing 25 proposed amendments, was presented to the General Council. Because of the legal connotations, Mr. Gordon Henderson, QC, legal adviser to the Association, was present at the discussions. The following major amendments were approved.

- *Representatives of the news media invited to attend and report on the proceedings of General Council.*
- *Criteria for the petitioning of a Special Meeting of General Council extended to a petition from fifty members of General Council.*
- *Requirement by the Board of Directors of regular progress reports by Councils.*

A number of the proposed amendments to the bylaws were again referred back to the Board of Directors for further study. The board set up a new Special Committee on Bylaws chaired by Dr. Guy Joron, with members Drs. F. Thomas Porter and W. James Corbett. This special committee's report was presented to the Board of Directors and, after approval by them, to the 1974 General Council. The Association's legal adviser pointed out that the Act of Incorporation was not a section of the bylaws and could not be changed by the Association unless approved by parliament. Amendments approved by the General Council included the following.

> *"The effective date of payment of annual dues to the Association to be Jan. 1 of the calendar year next but one following the year in which such dues had been determined by General Council.*
> *"The criteria for suspension of membership in the Association."*

The Executive Committee carried out a study of the councils' activities and the Association's operational goals and objectives, and presented the following report, which was approved by General Council.

Operational Goals and Objectives
- *To ensure that the Canadian public receives good and safe medical care.*
- *To maintain the CMA as the recognized "voice of Canadian Medicine".*
- *To coordinate the activities of the provincial Divisions and to provide them with central resources and consultative services that will be of assistance to them in their activities at the provincial level.*
- *To develop an organizational structure that can respond promptly and effectively on behalf of all Canadian physicians in areas of activity that are within the scope of federal jurisdiction.*
- *To cooperate with other professional, educational research and governmental organizations in the health field with the purpose of enhancing the health of Canadians.*
- *To provide a forum through which the Affiliates of the Association — the national specialist and generalist associations and societies — can bring their expertise to bear on the national health scene.*
- *To develop and maintain a variety of membership services that are beneficial to members and to coordinate other similar services developed at the provincial level in order to ensure that members moving from one provincial jurisdiction to another can maintain their professional rights and personal services.*

✦ *To work with, and to assist, appropriate national and international health agencies whose primary objective is to improve the health of people in other countries whose health services are not as advanced as those enjoyed by Canadians.*

The Board of Directors, having reviewed the outcome of the Executive Committee's study of the councils, concluded that three of the five councils were professional in nature and should continue in their present form, but that the Council on Economics and the Council on Membership Services did not fit into that category. With respect to the Council on Economics, General Council could not come to an agreement as to its category and referred the matter for further consideration by the Board of Directors. The discussion on the Council on Membership Services was lengthy and centred on the lack of means to development new services. To correct this, a recommendation was put forward that CMA input into the management of various savings funds of the Association become a staff function and that the Council on Membership Services restrict its activities to the development of new services.

MD Management Ltd., formally known as Lancet Management Ltd., was a subsidiary corporation owned by the CMA, and it was postulated that through it lay the most effective way to address and solve the perceived shortcomings in the services to members. In the end, General Council voted to abolish the Council on Membership Services and allocate its mandate to MD Management Ltd.

During 1975, the Board of Directors, as directed by the 1974 General Council, had reviewed the role and sphere of activities of the Council on Economics and presented the following recommendation to the June 1975 General Council in Calgary.

The Council on Economics shall have as its primary concern the collection, collation and interpretation of information regarding the costs of health services. It shall act as a source of information on medical economics for the Divisions specifically and may provide such information to other agencies which are involved in the provision of medical care to the public. It will study and make recommendations on developments in health insurance programmes and on all matters concerned with the methods of payment for medical services.

The recommendation was approved by General Council. In April 1976, the Board of Directors approved the creation of a unit within the CMA to be known as the Statistics, Systems and Economic Research (SSER) Unit with the mandate to respond to enquiries and requests from divisions on matters pertaining to medical economics. In 1976 the General Council approved an amendment to the resolution on the Council on Economics approved the previous year; the amendment inserted "appropriate information on medical economic matters to other national agencies" in place of "such information to other agencies."

In 1977, the Board of Directors appointed Dr. Lloyd C. Grisdale to carry out a study of the Association's organizational structure, with particular reference to the effectiveness of the Council structure. The study was wide-ranging, with advice and opinions being sought from many sources. The outcome of the study was as follows: "That the Council on Medical Education remain unchanged. "That the Councils on Community Health and Medical Services be amalgamated." and "That the Council on Economics become a Statutory Committee."

The Board of Directors agreed with the proposals, and after a long discussion on the matter, the General Council approved the amalgamation of the two councils. The matter of the Council on Economics engendered a debate that was not only long but was also emotionally charged, particularly when the views of the Newfoundland division were aired. The Newfoundland Medical Association had approved at its 1978 annual meeting,

> *That the members of the Newfoundland Division in Council hereby disagree with any recommendation which the CMA might propose which would change the status of the Council on Economics and instructs its representatives to the 111th Meeting of General Council to present this view to the General Council together with the position of the members of this Division that they would be satisfied with nothing short of full provincial representation on a Council representing each Canadian province individually.*

The chairman of the CMA Board of Directors, Dr. D. Laurence Wilson, commented on the criticism of the board's recommendation to change the status of the Council on Economics. He said that Dr. Grisdale had come to the conclusion that many of the activities undertaken by the council during the past year were now being carried out by the SSER Unit or through special conferences approved by the Board of Directors and that problems of policy on such matters as patient participation and the macroeconomics of health services should be pursued by a statutory committee elected by General Council rather than through a council. The Board of Directors, while recognizing that this format would lead to some divisions not being represented on such a committee, was of the opinion nevertheless that a reduction in numbers would not necessarily be a negative factor and that no adverse inference should be drawn from the proposed change in status of the council.

The motion to change the Council on Economics to a statutory committee named the Committee on Economics, made up of a chairperson and five members representing the regions of Canada, was defeated and the matter referred once again to the Board of Directors.

In 1979, the General Council approved terms of reference for the new Council on Health Care: "The Council on Health Care shall be concerned with the provision of comprehensive health care in the protection and promotion of the health of the individual, the family and the community. Within this framework, the Council shall concern itself with the role and scope of activities of physicians and other providers of health care."

At the same General Council meeting the mandate of the Council on Economics was discussed, following the previous year's referral back to the Board of Directors for clarification of the council's role and its terms of reference. The General Council approved that the first sentence of the council's terms of reference be amended to read as follows: "The Council shall be concerned with matters relating to the economics of medical care."

The Committee on Archives was approved as a statutory committee not elected by General Council and made up of five members of the Association, preferably past presidents, elected by the Board of Directors. The committee's terms of reference were:

The Committee on Archives is to advise on the collection and maintenance of archival material relating to Canadian medicine, including the accumulation, preservation and indexing of documents pertaining to the history of the Association. The Committee shall report annually to General Council and shall prepare and present a listing of those members of the Association who died subsequent to the preceding Annual Meeting of the Association.

In 1978, the General Council resolved that a special committee be appointed to review its procedure. Dr. Reginald D. Atkinson was given the task "with power to consult as widely as he wishes." His report indicated that he followed this part of his mandate to the letter! Thirteen recommendations were submitted for consideration by General Council and seven were approved, with the remaining six being referred to the Board of Directors for further consideration.

Those approved were:

i) *That a manual be prepared for the use of Chairmen of Councils and Committees which will provide guidelines to assist them in Association activities, including the preparation and presentation of reports for General Council and the Board of Directors.*

ii) *That Reports to General Council be distributed at least six weeks prior to the date of the Annual Meeting, beginning in 1983.*

iii) *Members of General Council who intend to introduce amendments to recommendations, motions supplementary to reports, and/or motions under New Business, be instructed at the time of distribution of the Reports to forward them at the earliest possible date to the Secretary-General; and that such amendments or motions relating to reports shall, subsequent to the approval of General Council, take precedence over New Business motions.*

iv) *The Affiliate Societies be permitted to submit formal reports to the General Council with the approval of the Board of Directors.*

v) *The General Council reaffirm its approval of the general procedures currently used in the conduct of its meeting, recognizing that it has the authority to set aside or modify the order and rules of procedure.*

vi) *The content of the section "Conduct of Meetings of General Council of the Canadian Medical Association" found in Reports to General Council be reviewed and revised where appropriate by the Speaker and Deputy-Speaker with staff assistance.*

vii) *Wainberg's Company Meetings including Rules of Order (2nd Edition) be the basis for orders and rules of procedure for all meetings of the Association.*

An interesting viewpoint of General Council, written by Ms. Joan Hollobon, science writer for the Toronto *Globe and Mail,* had appeared in that newspaper as a lead article on July 11, 1974.

The General Council is always a good show... And the level of debate is often vastly superior to that of the many more pretentious Houses, too. Each year the familiar faces, the familiar format, often the familiar subjects, give a sense of déjà vu — a continuing play, staged each year in a different theatre, but that is wrong. Despite the familiarity and similarity, every

General Council has its own distinctive atmosphere, reflecting changing and professional issues and evolving professional attitudes. In discussing health, economic or social issues today, doctors unquestionably accept a corporate responsibility for the profession's activities, not just to the profession, but to society. Traditionally, the CMA saw its role as one of reaching consensus among doctors in ten provincial divisions, a suitable role for a leisurely age. As the pace of life and medicine increased, with governments in the health picture, it was not enough. A few years ago , the CMA sought to develop a leadership function, but gently, because CMA too, faced a dilemma of provincial rights and jurisdiction. The CMA's committees and Councils have also moved toward more thoughtful studies, even if these take two or three years, rather than reporting to General Council every year with recommendations of little real value.

Twelve years after writing that article, Ms. Hollobon was awarded the CMA Medal of Honour.

The General Council of 1980 was noteworthy because it was at that meeting that the bylaws were amended to include one representative each at General Council from the Yukon Medical Association (YMA) and the Northwest Territories Medical Association. In 1989, the YMA was granted divisional status, followed a year later by the Northwest Territories Medical Association.

In 1972, the CMA had received a request from the Canadian Bar Association (CBA) that a liaison committee be formed by the two associations to discuss mutual problems. After examination by the Board of Directors and General Council, the concept was approved and the CMA/CBA Liaison Committee was established. This committee functioned up to 1988 providing both associations with many valuable reports and recommendations for consideration at their respective annual meetings.

The CMA Committee on Ethics had been in existence since 1867 and in the ensuing years it had been active in maintaining and updating, when indicated, the Association's *Code of Ethics*. The scope of its activities increased considerably *pari passu* with advances in technology, and more and more the committee found that its resources required inclusion of advisers on legal and ethical matters, in particular when these related to bioethical issues and concerns.

In 1988, the Board of Directors considered a staff proposal that a division of ethics and legal affairs be established to strengthen the Association's leadership in current and emerging ethical and legal matters relating to medical

CMA Board of Directors, 1988–89.

L–R (standing): Dr. Judith Kazimirski, Dr. Barry Maber, Dr. Edwin Coffey, Dr. Harry Callaghan, Dr. Lloyd Bartlett, Dr. Ken Kolotyluk, Dr. Arun Garg, Dr. Lorne Bellan, Dr. Richard Railton, Dr. Bruno L'Heureux, Dr. Léo-Paul Landry, Dr. John Anderson, Dr. Neil Gray, Dr. Paige Emenau, Dr. Hugh Scully, Dr. Ed Moran, Dr. Paddy Dobbin, Dr. Basil Johnston, Dr. Georges Hooper, Dr. Carole Guzmán, Dr. Henry Gasmann, Dr. Ruth Collins-Naki, Dr. Richard Kennedy

L–R (seated): Dr. Marcien Fournier, Dr. John O'Brien-Bell, Dr. Athol Roberts practice, such matters being of interest to the profession and others. The proposal recommended that the department's objectives be:

- ◆ To assist in CMA policy formulation.
- ◆ To influence legislation.
- ◆ To develop and implement informational/educational activities.
- ◆ To act as a resource to divisions and members and to national and international medical associations.
- ◆ To encourage, monitor and interpret current research in ethics.
- ◆ To provide a forum for discussion of ethical and legal matters of mutual concern to the CMA and the CBA.

The Board of Directors approved the concept. The setting up of the department is described in the chapter on ethics.

In 1988, the Association once again took an in-depth look at what it was, where it was going and what its role should be. It was decided that if the CMA were to maintain a strong leadership role it would have to adopt different methods of operation. In February, the Board of Directors received a proposal from the secretary general, Dr. Léo-Paul Landry, titled *Looking to the Future of the CMA — A Strategic Management Process.* Following a review by the board, the secretary general was authorized to develop and propose a plan of action to establish a strategic management process for the Association. In its review the board was of the opinion that the medical profession was being increasingly influenced by external events. The development of a management philosophy arising from the strategic management process would enable the Association to be more disciplined and more aware of goals and priorities, and as well serve to visibly link the Association's activities with the desired goals and priorities of its members. Late in the year the firm of Redding and Associates of Chicago was appointed as the consultant organization for the CMA in its strategic management process.

The strategic management project titled, "Focus on the Future," continued throughout 1989 and 1990 and involved many meetings and discussion groups. The whole structure of the CMA was exposed to critical examination with both positives and negatives examined in depth. The Board of Directors stressed that the focus of the Association be to serve the needs of its members, divisions and other key stakeholders and, based on those needs, that work be directed to institute effective methods to systematically establish corporate directions.

General objectives were achieved in three distinct task-oriented phases:

1. Background research, general data-gathering, situational analysis and market research.

2. Analysis and interpretation of the research data.
3. Development of a mission statement, and resulting objectives and implementation strategies on the basis of the research.

Core service and product strategies were established and refined to meet the needs of each of the three segments of the membership — members, divisions and affiliate societies. It was seen that some of the services and strategies would be non-revenue-producing and available to all members, whereas others would be revenue-producing and targeted to specific segments of the membership.

Mission Statement

> To provide leadership for physicians and to promote the highest standard of health and health care for Canadians.

On the basis of recommendations arising out of the strategic management process there was a restructuring of the CMA secretariat. During 1991, CMA staff made a number of presentations to the Board of Directors as to how they believed the Association could function in more scientific and strategic ways within the organization and with other bodies. The following key roles were emphasized.
- Representation of physicians federally.
- Consensus building within the profession.
- Facilitator of change.
- A national resource for information and expertise.

The strategic plan itself became the means whereby three goals might be reached.
- Enhancement of the quality of management of issues of importance to the Association and its main stakeholders.
- Development of strategic alliances with other organizations to achieve common objectives.
- Enhanced collaboration and decreased competition and duplication inside and outside the Association.

In 1991, both the Board of Directors and the Committee on Finance shared the opinion that there needed to be within the CMA secretariat a committee whose mandate would be to review the need for the performance and terms of reference of councils, committees and working groups. Such reviews would be done on an annual basis or as necessary, and the findings would be reported to the Board of Directors. A Committee on Committees, made up of members of the Executive Committee, was set up in March 1991.

The committee met six times during 1991 and 1992 and examined the policy-making mechanism of the Association. From its deliberations it acknowledged four basic principles that the Association should follow.

- ◆ The need to enhance programs in the management of the affairs of the Association on an ongoing basis.
- ◆ Recognition of the need for strong divisional representation on the CMA's core committees (councils, the Committee on Ethics, the Political Action Committee and the MD Advisory Board) through which the majority of issues are handled.
- ◆ The need to build into the policy developmental process additional expertise, as the need arises, into expert groups such as subcommittees and ad hoc committees, and liaison committees with other organizations. Normally such groups and committees allow input from affiliate societies and express the outcome of their deliberations through core committees.
- ◆ The need for fiscal responsibility.

As described earlier, Dr. Atkinson had undertaken a review of the General Council and made a number of recommendations in his 1980 report. The much sought-after "perfection," or at least something akin to it that was acceptable to everyone concerned, had not been achieved, and once again the parliament of Canadian medicine was subject to critical scrutiny. Over the years the General Council had seen a number of changes in the way it operated. Some of those changes had been proposed and rejected a number of times before they had become part of the proceedings. The current use of large projection screens on which recommendations, amendments, and so on, could be displayed and seen by everyone in the room, as opposed to the long-time custom of passing out hundreds of sheets of paper for each recommendation and amendment, was opposed for a number of years after it had been suggested. A more recent change (1993) was the introduction of the "traffic lights," which have been an effective means of curbing verbosity and which have not, contrary to expressed misgivings, restricted the freedom of expression. This device was first proposed in 1973 for use in General Council and other CMA meetings!

Changes also occurred in the format of General Council proceedings. In 1992 the Board of Directors approved a revised format for reports to General

Council and a modified approach to General Council deliberations in order to enhance discussion and debate on issues of strategic importance to the CMA and the medical profession in general. It was the wish of the Board of Directors that the new methodology provide more time for issue-oriented debate and give the General Council greater opportunity to enhance policy development through better use of the wisdom and expertise of its members.

The new format was introduced in 1993, and delegates, divisions and affiliate societies were asked for their views on its effectiveness. Feedback confirmed approbation of the new format in which the chairman of the Board of Directors would report in detail on strategic issues; council and committee activities would continue to be included in the reports to General Council but would be limited to summaries of important activities in which they had been involved but which were not contained in the board's report. The idea of having information sessions on specific issues enhanced the level of debate and met with widespread approval.

One of the recommendations from the 1971 think tank bears repeating here: "The Group considers that it is the responsibility of the CMA to establish leadership in the stands it takes in various matters rather than to limit itself to a presentation of the consensus of the medical profession." There is no better place than General Council, the governing body and legislative authority of the Association, for that responsibility to be demonstrated.

In 1994, the General Council approved the following recommendation: "That, as a matter of urgency, the CMA's strategic management review process, begun in 1988, be completed by subjecting the Board of Directors, Committees and Councils of the Association and the composition, role and function of General Council to the same review process as experienced by other facets of the Association."

A companion resolution directed the Board of Directors to reconsider the composition of the Committee on Structure in light of the expanded mandate foreseen in the above motion and that consideration be given to the inclusion of appropriate regional and affiliate society representation.

Affiliate Societies

The Committee on Bylaws was asked in 1947 to consider giving affiliated societies membership in the General Council. After due consideration it recommended that such privilege not be granted, basing its decision on the fact that not all societies could be given membership and that drawing a distinction between which should be approved and which should not would be difficult and probably contentious. The matter was raised again in 1949 when the role of sections within the Association was studied by the Executive Committee. The impetus for raising the topic again came from the movement within the Association to form a section of general practice.

The Committee on Bylaws presented a paper in which nine points outlined the role of sections and their relationship to the Association as a whole, and the General Council in particular. This paper, reproduced below, demonstrated foresight on the part of the committee, and its arguments were such that the General Council approved it and amended the bylaws to allow the sections General Council representation.

1. A national medical association such as The Canadian Medical Association is committed to the responsibility of representing every practitioner in Canada in every phase of his activity. It must therefore adopt such administrative machinery as will facilitate the development of all the phases of every department of medicine.

2. Sections of the Association have become increasingly important and valuable in the presentation of the scientific programme of the Association. There is every indication that their function will become more necessary in the future because the magnitude and complexity of modern medicine necessitates its subdivision into departments (specialties) for many purposes. The work and problems of these fields can best be dealt with by the groups who are interested in them. It is conceivable that some of the work now performed for Council by Standing Committees might advantageously be delegated to a suitable section of the Association — e.g. the work of the Committee on Industrial Medicine might be delegated to the Section of Industrial Medicine; that of the Committee on Public Health to the Section of Preventive Medicine; that of the committee on Maternal Welfare to the Section of Obstetrics and Gynaecology.

3. Growth in population of Canada and corresponding growth in membership in The Canadian Medical Association may make it necessary to delegate much of the programme of the annual meetings to Sections. In the American Medical Association, the great numbers attending the annual meetings have necessitated the presentation of nearly all papers before sectional meetings. In the American Medical Association, Sections are indispensable units of the administration necessary for the presentation of the scientific programme and the discussion of problems related to their special fields.

4. *Sections need not be limited solely to scientific fields of medicine. Provision should be made for the establishment, where necessary, of sections in non-scientific fields, e.g. Medical Economics.*

5. *There is no conflict between national associations representing special fields of medicine and Sections of The Canadian Medical Association. Each has different but equally important functions to perform. Since these responsibilities are complementary to one another, the same individuals can function to good purpose in the national association representing a specialty and in the corresponding section of The Canadian Medical Association.*

6. *Sections should be organized in such a manner as to ensure continuity from year to year. Consideration should be given to the possible advantages of Sections of The Association continuing their activities between Annual Meetings. It should be recognized that sometimes the place of the annual meeting will lack the space necessary to permit all Sections to hold their annual sessions, and Sections should be so organized as to ensure their continuity of existence from meeting to meeting even though this interval may be a period longer than one year.*

7. *Sections should have the authority and the right to pass resolutions directed to the General Council or the Executive Committee. For this purpose, some machinery must be developed to indicate who is entitled to vote as a member of a Section.*

8. *Difficulties have been encountered in the past in ensuring that Sections elected officers for the ensuing year. This has compelled the Executive Committee to assume this responsibility. It is desirable that Sections elect their own officers and means should be devised to ensure that they do this without fail.*

9. *It should be recognized that a Section is an integral part of The Canadian Medical Association and the members of a Section, first and last, are members of the Canadian Medical Association. The function of a Section is to advance the interests of The Canadian Medical Association and all its members. The use of a Section to develop an independent group within the Association committed to the interests of one group of the membership, to the detriment of others, must be avoided.*

In 1952, the Committee on Constitution and Bylaws was of the opinion that, where a section was weak and unorganized, and where a national body had been set up in a particular field of medicine and had become affiliated with the Association, the possibility of a working arrangement with the affiliate had to be explored whereby it might represent the specialty in the scientific program at the Association's annual meetings. This arrangement would continue until such time as the section could assume the duty itself.

The committee presented the 1953 General Council with a revised version of the bylaws. Part of the preamble to the document read:

> *Your Committee, in the Section on Affiliations, has endeavoured to pro-vide, in general terms, that those of our children who have grown to have their particular and varied aspirations and who, because of them, have felt it desirable to set up housekeeping for themselves, may be able to retain a firmer connection with the parent household and a more significant place in the body politic. While we may not in such association be able to assume the cohesion of a matriarchy, there are features of that form of association which many of our specialist bodies feel we might do well to emulate.*

Sixteen sections were named in the revised bylaws and the methods whereby new groups could be designated as sections of the Association were spelled out in Chapter X. In Chapter VII the criteria for a group to be considered an affil-iate were laid out. One class was described as "Canadian Medical Specialist Soci-eties whose members are members of the CMA or whose membership is composed of members of the CMA along with others from some other med-ical organization." This class was entitled to one seat on the General Council for each affiliate society.

In 1958, Section X dealing with sections of the Association was reviewed by the Committee on Bylaws, concerns having been expressed over the grey areas between sections and affiliate societies, the risks of trespass, the risks of frag-mentation and the need to provide channels for the expression of sectional opinion. The review led the committee to reluctantly come to a conclusion that sections *per se* should not be represented on the General Council. It was also opined that the activities of sections would be confined to areas that did not conflict with the responsibilities of the divisions or those of the affiliated national medical societies.

No changes were recommended over the next 5 years, but in 1963 there was a long debate at the General Council meeting over the appropriateness of rep-resentatives of national affiliated medical societies being represented on standing and special committees of the CMA. The argument in favour of allowing such membership was that there was representation on General Council by a number of affiliates who had no representation on CMA committees, and the Association of Canadian Medical Colleges — a member of General Council prohibited from membership on the Committee on Medical Education — was given as an example. A recommendation that representatives of affiliated societies be non-voting members of the General Council was referred to the Committee on Bylaws. In 1964, the Committee on Bylaws recommended to the General Council that delegates representing affiliated societies should be allowed to vote at General Council meeting, and the General Council approved the recommendation. At that time there were 22 representatives of affiliated societies on General Council out of a total membership of 213.

In 1971, the Board of Directors reported that it had involved a number of affiliate societies in the study of various scientific problems; one example was the great assistance they had provided the Association in establishing a position on the oral contraceptive. The board also hosted a meeting with representatives of affiliate societies and considered subsequent steps the Association might take to improve relations between the two parties, particularly in areas in which the expertise of the affiliates would be of assistance in formulating the Association's positions and policies. It was further agreed that the Department of Communications be allotted extra staff and facilities for dealing with affiliate affairs, and that CMA House in Ottawa be used as a mailing address and meetings site for affiliate societies, should they so wish. In 1975, it was agreed that the Executive Committee and representatives of affiliate societies, along with chairpersons and coordinators of CMA councils, would meet annually.

By 1979, the number of affiliate societies had risen to 34, 30 of which were represented at a meeting held in Montreal with the Executive Committee on Feb. 6. The president of the CMA, Dr. Kenneth O. Wylie, presented a paper on the subject of CMA/affiliate society relationships; this was followed by discussion on a number of subjects of mutual concern, including improved liaison between the parties, recommendations to General Council and the role of allied health professions. On the latter subject, many of the representatives expressed the concerns of their respective societies over the proliferation of disciplines in allied health, believing there was a definite need for role definition and determination of professional and legal responsibility for services undertaken by allied health personnel.

The meeting was told that the CMA planned to study the perceived problems and that it was important that the affiliate societies contribute by detailing their concerns. The Board of Directors formed a committee with a mandate "to assume the responsibilities related to the rational utilization of allied health workers, namely manpower needs, identification of emerging disciplines and recognition of new ones."

The affiliate societies and the CMA met in September 1979, and in 1980 the Board of Directors presented a paper outlining policies designed to improve liaison with the affiliates. The policies included annual meetings between the CMA Executive Committee and representatives from the affiliate societies; their involvement in CMA studies and other activities; special time at General Council for affiliate society business; attendance at each other's meetings; designation of certain CMA staff as liaison officers with affiliate societies; and the convening of a meeting between the CMA Publications Committee and those affiliates interested in the matter of publications and mailing privileges.

On Sept. 15, 1981, the Executive Committee met in Toronto with representatives of the affiliate societies. Details of the report of the Task Force on Federal/Provincial Fiscal Arrangements were provided and delegates asked to provide the CMA with evidence of underfunding in Canadian hospitals. A major topic of discussion was medical manpower, and delegates were urged to have their members complete the CMA Physician Manpower Questionnaire. Other items discussed were allied health personnel and medicare, the CMA's Political Action Committee and the use of the affiliate society expertise by the CMA. A follow-up meeting was held in Ottawa in June 1982.

The 1987 General Council meeting approved a change in the bylaws as they pertained to affiliate societies. Section 16.1 was amended to read: "Any Canadian medical organization, the majority of whose members are physicians and the majority of whose members are members of The Canadian Medical Association may, subject to the approval of General Council, become affiliated with The Canadian Medical Association."

The Executive Committee met with representatives of the affiliate societies on Oct. 29, 1988, and agreed with a proposal that a committee of affiliate societies be formed with the intent to enhance communication and liaison between the Association and the affiliate societies. In March 1989 the Board of Directors approved the concept and directed the establishment of such a committee to function as a Committee of the Board of Directors. The terms of reference of the committee were:

- *To provide a means whereby issues common to Affiliate Societies could be discussed.*
- *To enhance communication between the CMA and the Affiliate Societies.*
- *To submit to the Board of Directors its nomination for Chairperson of the Committee.*
- *To report periodically to the CMA Board of Directors.*

It was agreed that the chairperson or designate would have observer status at meetings of the Board of Directors. The Executive Committee and the Committee on Affiliate Societies met annually and discussed a number of matters; in 1991, for example, discussion included quality assurance, physician resources, euthanasia, status of the fetus, women's health issues and the Goods and Services Tax.

In 1994, there were 38 affiliate societies, each regarded as a repository of expertise upon which the Association may draw when occasions so demand.

Chapter III

MEDICAL CARE INSURANCE

THE CONSTITUTION ACT OF 1867 has little to say about health services and social services, but it was not long before a number of private national voluntary organizations came into being with the aims of providing health care and social services for the residents of Canada. Many of those organizations still exist today — the Red Cross, the Canadian Council on Social Development and the Victorian Order of Nurses. Such groups formed the basis for the subsequent development of Canada's health and social services, but the onus for planning, organization and coordination moved away from the voluntary private sector to the public sector.

In the 1920s, the CMA established a committee to examine health care insurance, and over the next 3 decades it actively studied the subject and made presentations to the various commissions and committees set up by the federal government. In 1943, a House of Commons Committee on Social Security was appointed to examine health care insurance based on a national scheme, and the CMA made a presentation to the committee outlining the Association's views on the subject. After World War II, interest in developing a comprehensive health insurance plan for all Canadians reasserted itself, and in 1956, the federal government proposed to the provinces a health insurance program beginning with hospital and diagnostic services.

On Apr. 1, 1957, the *Hospital Insurance and Diagnostic Services Act* was passed. The CMA welcomed the plan whereby Canadians could be insured against the costs of hospital and diagnostic services but expressed concern over the interpretation of some parts of the legislation. The implementation of the Act (i.e., the provision of federal grants to the provinces) required six provinces totalling one-half of the population of the country to have entered into agreement with the federal government.

The CMA discussed the Act at its 1957 General Council and the following motion was approved:

That the CMA Executive Committee, through the Association's Advisory

Committee to the federal government, request from the Minister of National Health amplification of item "f(iii)" in the Definitions in Bill 320 and in particular regarding: (a) the portion "necessary interpretation for the purpose of maintaining health, preventing disease and assisting in the diagnosis and treatment of any injury, illness or disability"; (b) the portion "laboratory, radiological and other diagnostic procedures" with clarification of the relation of these services in aid of diagnosis when rendered in the office of physicians and these services when rendered in hospitals.

Concern was also expressed over the fact that the federal government had ignored the views of the Advisory Committee and, in particular, the statement approved at the 1956 General Council, viz., "Whereas discussions regarding health insurance would convey the impression that only the compulsory form is being considered, the CMA reaffirms its position in support of health insurance of a voluntary nature, with financial assistance from public funds where necessary." In its report to the General Council in 1958, the Advisory Committee stated that, although the Association's concerns were comprehended by the federal government, it was disappointing to find that they were not addressed in the Regulations under the Act.

In March 1959, the CMA issued its first *Information Bulletin* whose purpose was "to impart current information on the opinions and policies of organized medicine in Canada." In the publication the CMA pointed out that for many years it had espoused the principle of health care insurance and issued a number of policy statements on the matter in 1945, 1949 and 1955. The CMA's position on cost participation by individual recipients of health care was emphasized, as were the need for awareness by governments and the public of increasing health care costs, the application of the fee-for-service principle to remuneration of physicians for services rendered and the necessity for expansion of medical education and research facilities within the hospital setting.

In the village of Birch Hills, Sask., on Apr. 25, 1959, Premier Tommy C. Douglas announced in an electioneering speech that his government intended to establish a medical care insurance plan for the province. At the time there were a number of health care insurance plans in operation in Saskatchewan; one of these was the plan established by the medical profession itself that covered about 40% of the province's residents. In the view of physicians any increase in medical care insurance should have to be through the existing voluntary nonprofit plans and not through the introduction of a new plan.

The proposed program in Saskatchewan was a major topic in the discussions at the General Council meeting in Toronto at the end of May 1959, and after much debate the following motion was approved:

That a Special Committee, appointed by the Executive Committee of the CMA, to be known as the Committee on Prepaid Medical Care, be established for a continuous study of all matters pertaining to health insurance and medical service, among which shall be: (a) to study and make available to the CMA, facts, data and recommendations with respect to timely and proper provision of prepaid medical care for the people of Canada; (b) to investigate matters pertaining to the economic and social aspects of prepaid medical care; (c) to study and resolve matters of health insurance of common interest to the CMA and prepaid plans in Canada, in order that each may assist the other to provide the best possible medical service to the people of Canada; (d) to utilize the functions and personnel of the Bureau of Medical Economics, to hold meetings as frequently as necessary for the proper completion of the terms of reference and to maintain a close liaison with the Economics Committee and the Executive of the CMA.

In the meantime, relations between the medical profession in Saskatchewan and the provincial government had deteriorated. At the annual meeting of the College of Physicians and Surgeons of Saskatchewan on Oct. 29, 1959, a motion was passed *nem. con.* to the effect that the college opposed a compulsory, government-controlled, province-wide medical care plan and that it endorsed an expansion of medical care programs, using the existing nonprofit prepayment programs. In December the premier announced that he intended to strike an advisory planning committee on medical care comprising three representatives from the provincial government, three from the general public, three from — and to be named by — the medical profession, and an appointee from the University of Saskatchewan School of Medicine.

Between Dec. 16, 1959, and late March 1960, numerous letters were exchanged between the college and the government, based on the college's maintenance of its position as had been expressed in the resolution of Oct. 29. With the understanding that its representatives would maintain that position, the General Council nominated Dr. Jack F.C. Anderson from Saskatoon, a past president of the CMA, Dr. Estathios W. Barootes from Regina and Dr. Clarence J. Houston from Yorkton. With the announcement of the names of the other members of the committee on Apr. 25, and the announcement by the premier that Saskatchewan would go to the polls on June 8, the medical profession entered into open confrontation with the provincial government.

A major plank in the government's platform was the proposed medical care plan. On June 8, the Cooperative Commonwealth Federation Party was declared re-elected with a gain of two seats but with the lowest proportion of total votes cast in the 16 years of its mandate. The CMA was getting ready to hold its General Council meeting in Banff, Alta., when what was described as a "crisis" was created, and the CMA was in newspaper headlines from one end of Canada to the other. The triggering factor had been a headline in the *Saskatoon Star-Phoenix* on June 10 — "CMA DROPPING OPPOSITION TO SASKATCHEWAN MEDICAL PLAN," and an accompanying Canadian Press report read: ". . . the CMA, in a statement Thursday, said the decision of the voters would be honoured by the profession and that the Association would drop its opposition and cooperate in devising the best possible plan. Dr. Arthur D. Kelly, CMA General Secretary, said there could be constituted an endorsement of the plan for Saskatchewan."

The article went on to attribute to Dr. Kelly the following statement:

"This is a democracy. The CMA accepts the decision in this light. Our efforts now will be bent on avoiding the defects we see in government plans elsewhere."

When Dr. Kelly arrived in Banff he was roundly taken to task, first by Saskatchewan physicians and then by physicians from the other provinces, all of whom were extremely unhappy with the statements attributed to him. In addition to the verbal attacks, there were many telegrams and letters from physicians who would not be attending the General Council meeting. There were 2 days of meetings of the Executive Committee in which the whole question of what had been reported in the news media was studied in depth and whether or not Dr. Kelly had indeed said what had been reported. In the end it was agreed that incorrect inferences had been drawn from what Dr. Kelly had said in a telephone conversation with a reporter from the Toronto *Telegram*. General Council, including the physicians from Saskatchewan, accepted Dr. Kelly's explanation, but, although oil had been poured on troubled waters, not everything was calm and serene.

Much of the 1960 General Council meeting was taken up with the situation in Saskatchewan. It was reported to the meeting that over 90% of physicians in private practice were opposed to the proposed governmental medical care plan. It was agreed by General Council that the terms "health insurance" and "health care" were capable of too broad an interpretation and that they should be replaced with the term "medical services" or "medical services insurance" where applicable. The Committee on Economics put forward a draft of a policy statement on medical services insurance for consideration by General Council and, after much debate and a number of amendments, the following was approved as CMA policy:

The CMA believes that:
- *The highest standard of medical services should be available to every resident of Canada.*
- *Medical-services insurance to prepay the costs of these services should be available to all, regardless of age, state of health or financial status.*
- *Certain individuals require assistance to prepay these costs.*
- *Efforts of organized medicine, governments and all other interested bodies should be coordinated towards these ends.*
- *While there are certain areas of medical services in which tax-supported programmes are necessary, a tax-supported comprehensive programme, compulsory for all is neither necessary nor desirable.*

The CMA will support any programme of medical services insurance which adheres to the following principles:
1. *That all persons rendering services are legally-qualified physicians and surgeons.*
2. *That every resident of Canada is free to select his doctor and that each doctor is free to choose his patients.*
3. *That the competence and ability of any doctor is determined only by his professional self-government.*
4. *That within his competence, each physician has the privilege to treat his patients in and out of hospital.*
5. *That each individual physician is free to select the type and location of his practice.*
6. *That each patient has the right to have all information pertaining to his medical condition kept confidential, except where the public interest is paramount.*
7. *That the duty of the physician to his individual patient takes precedence over his obligations to any medical-service insurance programme.*
8. *That every resident of Canada, whether a recipient or provider of services, has the right of recourse to the courts in all disputes.*
9. *That medical-service insurance programmes do not in any way preclude the private practice of medicine.*
10. *That medical research, undergraduate and postgraduate teaching are not inhibited by any medical-services insurance programme.*
11. *That the administration and finances of medical-service insurance*

programmes are completely separate from other programmes and that any board, commission or agency set up to administer any medical-services insurance programme has fiscal authority and autonomy.

12. *That the composite opinion of the appropriate body of the medical profession is considered and the medical profession adequately represented on any board, commission or agency set up to plan, to establish policy or to direct administration for any medical-services insurance programme.*

13. *That members of the medical profession, as the providers of medical services, have the right to determine their method of remuneration.*

14. *That the amount of remuneration is a matter for negotiation between the physician and his patient, or those acting on his behalf; and that all medical-services programmes make provision for periodic or automatic changes in remuneration to reflect changes in economic conditions.*

The strong feelings of the members of General Council were reflected in their approval of the following motion: "The CMA believes that a single government-controlled scheme of medical care is not the answer to our health problems."

The face-off between the profession and the Government of Saskatchewan continued throughout the balance of 1960. In June 1961, the chairperson of the Advisory Planning Committee on Medical Care requested members of the committee to draw up an interim report for presentation to the provincial minister of health by September 1961. This request was contrary to the understanding of the three representatives of the College of Physicians and Surgeons of Saskatchewan, and they protested the chairperson's action. The pressure to have this interim report appeared to have originated with government officials and seemed to have been influenced by an announcement by the premier that the *Medical Care Insurance Act* would be created in a special session of the legislature after the report had been received. Another factor that seemed to have a bearing on the request for the report was the intention of the Cooperative Commonwealth Federation Party to hold a leadership convention in early August 1961.

Since its inception in April 1960, the committee had held meetings and public hearings and received many briefs. The report asked for was in three parts: two minority reports and one majority report. The three representatives of the college along with one other member of the committee filed one of the minority reports. In it they recommended government support and enhancement of existing insurance programs and the provision of financial assistance by the government to those who were unable to meet the cost of the premiums.

This position was in keeping with CMA policy and could not be seen to be surprising inasmuch as the CMA had provided the services of the CMA secretariat to assist in the preparation of the minority report as well as providing financial assistance, gestures that were gratefully acknowledged by the Saskatchewan delegates to the 1961 General Council meeting in Montreal.

At that same General Council meeting the following motion was approved:

> *The CMA wishes to express its concern that political pressure in the Province of Saskatchewan may be exerted on the Advisory Committee on Medical Care of that province to hasten its recommendations concerning med- ical-services insurance before the studies and deliberations of the committee have been brought to an orderly conclusion. It is the opinion of the CMA that medical-services insurance can only be considered properly in its relationship to all other aspects of health services. It is also our opinion that it might not be in the best interests of the citizens of Saskatchewan or to [sic] the citizens of the rest of Canada if a pattern of governmental medical-services insurance should be established prematurely in that province.*

The Executive Committee of the CMA had received the following recom- mendation from the Committee on Economics:

> *That the CMA approach the federal government to ask it to establish a committee to study the existing and projected health needs and health resources of Canada and to study methods of ensuring the highest standard of health care for all citizens of Canada, bearing in mind the CMA Statement on Med- ical-Services Insurance.*

The Executive Committee accepted the recommendation and in turn recommended to the federal government that a Royal Commission on Health Services be established. On Dec. 21, 1960, the Rt. Hon. J.G. Diefenbaker announced that he would set up such a commission and publicized the fact that he had received a letter from the CMA over the signature of Dr. Kelly, assuring the cooperation of the CMA in the commission's work.

In January 1961, the Hon. Emmett M. Hall, QC, was named chairman of the Royal Commission. Six members were named, of whom two were physicians — Dr. David Baltzan of Saskatoon and Dr. Arthur F. VanWart of Fredericton. Dr. Baltzan was a past president of the Saskatchewan Medical Association and Dr. VanWart was a past president of the CMA. Following the announcement of the formation of the Royal Commission, the CMA set up a subcommittee of the Executive Committee to obtain data and information from, *inter alia*, CMA divisions and affiliate societies, such information to be used in the CMA's presentations to the Royal Commission. The subcommittee was chaired by Dr. George E. Wodehouse of Toronto; the other members were Dr. Joe McMillan of Charlottetown and Dr. Lawrence Rabson of Winnipeg.

Meanwhile, in Saskatchewan, relations between the medical profession and the government were deteriorating rapidly. The premier had announced that the medical care plan would come into effect in 1962. The College of Physicians and Surgeons of Saskatchewan told the government that the medical profession would not cooperate in a compulsory government-administered plan. At a meeting of the college two resolutions were passed: the first stated that the proposals contained in the majority report of the Advisory Committee were not acceptable to the college and the second supported the views of the physicians as expressed in their minority report. The college held its annual meeting on Oct. 17 and 18, 1961, at which time the following were approved: "The College of Physicians and Surgeons of Saskatchewan and the Saskatchewan Division of the CMA reiterate their refusal to accept a government-controlled medical scheme as outlined in the legislative draft sent to members by the Minister of Health and declares they cannot cooperate in such a plan" and "The members of the Association will continue to give service to their patients and agree that they will sign no individual contracts to service an overall health plan as presented in the draft Bill."

In early November 1962, Premier Douglas resigned and was succeeded by the Hon. Woodrow Lloyd. On Nov. 17, the *Medical Care Insurance Act* received Royal Assent. Letters continued to pass between the college and government but there were no signs of any rapprochement. The CMA, as well as several other divisions continued to give support to the doctors in Saskatchewan.

The Saskatchewan Medical-Care Insurance Commission was formed in January 1962. Among its members were two physicians: Dr. Orville K. Hjertas and Dr. Sam Wolfe. Ongoing meetings between the profession and the government made no headway in resolving the impasse. On May 3, the premier addressed a meeting of 550 doctors in Regina in an attempt to change the profession's opposition to the plan. His words fell on deaf ears, as later in the same meeting approval was given for a withdrawal of office-based medical services, effective 12:01 am on July 1. The meeting did approve the planning of hospital-based emergency services. Dr. Jack F.C. Anderson reported at the end of June that many doctors had left the province to seek work elsewhere and that many others planned to follow suit. Replacements were coming into the province from the United Kingdom and the Republic of Ireland and, after being licensed by the college, were being directed by the commission to areas of need.

In July, the Government of Saskatchewan brought in Lord Taylor from the United Kingdom to act as mediator between the profession and the government. General Council, meeting in June in Winnipeg, was given a first-hand account of the situation in Saskatchewan by Dr. Harold D. Dalgleish of Saskatoon. Following his presentation, General Council approved the sending of a letter to the premier over the signature of the CMA president, Dr. Gerald W. Halpenny, in which the CMA asked that the Act not be implemented and urged immediate discussions between the two parties. Meetings were held and, although there was a hint that some concessions might be made by the government, there were not sufficient grounds to avoid the withdrawal of office private practice on July 1.

Dr. Kelly met with Lord Taylor in Saskatoon and briefed him on the CMA's policies and their applicability to the situation in Saskatchewan. The CMA established a small subcommittee that would hold itself ready at the disposal of the college council; its services were used right up to the last minute before resolution of the dispute. On July 23, Lord Taylor presented a document that came to be known as The Saskatoon Agreement, and acceptance by both parties terminated the impasse. It was agreed that the document held imperfections and was a compromise not entirely acceptable to either party, but it did provide for the resumption of normal medical services. A special session of the Saskatchewan Legislature, held on Aug. 2, 1962, implemented the agreement by passing 22 amendments to the Saskatchewan *Medical Care Insurance Act.*

Disagreement existed then — and it could still be found in 1994 — as to whether or not the compromise outcome was in conflict with the CMA's 14-point policy. Be that as it may, with the signing of the agreement, the Saskatchewan Medical-Care Programme became a reality. Being the first of its kind, it was watched very carefully by other provincial governments and by the profession right across the country.

The Royal Commission on Health Services began its public hearings in Ottawa in September 1961. From there it travelled across the country where more than 400 briefs were presented to it. The CMA attended almost every hearing and made known its opposition to a government-controlled medical services program and its support of insurance programs already in operation. Although the main purpose of the commission was medical services insurance, at almost every hearing other matters related to medical care were the subject of discussion. In addition to the hearings, the commission arranged for 26 research studies to be undertaken.

The report of the commission was released in June 1964. It recommended a universal, compulsory, tax-financed insurance covering a wide spectrum of health services. The CMA's position on private health care insurance was rejected in toto. The report did recommend that the profession remain self-governing, that patients would still have choice of doctors, that remuneration for services rendered by a physician would be on a fee-for-service basis and that the federal government should pay 50% of the program costs through health grants to the provinces.

The 1964 General Council meeting was held in Vancouver from June 22 to 25; the 4 days were more than its usual length, but the Executive Committee believed that the extra time was needed for adequate discussion of the commission's report. Copies of the 200 recommendations contained in the report were circulated to members of General Council, but not every member was aware of the circumstances by which the CMA had got the report.

The CMA had asked for copies of the report in advance of its general release so that it might be in a better position to respond to it at the General Council meeting. The request was denied. Copies were sent from Ottawa and reached the CMA's office in Vancouver late in the evening of Sunday, June 21. *All of the copies were in French!* CMA officers and members of the CMA Secretariat were up for most of the night translating the recommendations into English and preparing a preliminary statement for the Executive Committee to present to General Council.

Toward the end of 1963, Dr. Kelly had written to Mr. Justice Hall inviting him to address the General Council. The invitation was declined on the grounds that his position as a judge of the Supreme Court precluded him from taking part in any discussions that arose after the publication of the report. A further invitation was sent by Dr. Kelly around Christmas, but the response from Mr. Justice Hall was unchanged. The CMA was at a loss to understand why its invitation had been turned down when it learned that the commissioner had addressed the annual meeting of the Canadian Nurses Association in St. John's, which took place at the same time as the CMA General Council!

The profession's reaction to the report was mixed, but the two physician members of the commission — Drs. Baltzan and VanWart — were the recipients of many unfavourable comments from their colleagues. To be fair to Dr. Baltzan, he had disagreed with the commissioner over several points and had even considered writing a minority report. It was also reported that both of them were soundly berated by Senator Wallace McCutcheon, who had been a member of the commission before his appointment to the Senate in August 1962. The preliminary report that had been prepared by the Executive Committee was presented to General Council where, after much discussion and a number of amendments, it was approved as the official response of the CMA to the commission's report. It was released on June 22 at a mid-morning press conference and, in part, read as follows:

> *The CMA maintains as its prime concern the quality of health care for all Canadians. We agree that the public interest is paramount and demands measures which will result in the highest quality of medical care. The CMA believes that the commission has an identical concern, but we have found, on the basis of experience, that the method of providing medical services recommended by the Commission will, in the long run, impair the quality of medical care.*
>
> *The people of Canada should be aware that similar plans, which are operative in other countries, have led to excessive demands for services which have overtaxed the ability of health workers to provide. The consequence has been to substitute quantity for quality and has sacrificed, in many instances, the interests of the sick patient.*
>
> *We believe sincerely in the availability of health care services for all Canadians, but we are opposed to the creation of a single compulsory plan in each province, administered by a Commission but, in effect, controlled by the government of the day.*

At the end of more than 2 days of debate, the General Council approved the holding of a special meeting in early 1965 to consider further, inter alia, the Report of the Royal Commission on Health Services. As more and more physicians read the report, negative reaction to it by the profession increased. To counteract this negativity, Mr. Justice Hall began accepting public-speaking engagements in which he criticized the CMA for its opposition and for, in his opinion, the fallacious arguments that it was using to bolster its case. In February 1965, to reinforce his beliefs that the commission had produced a viable health care blueprint for the country, he published the second volume of the report, consisting of a summary of the 26 commissioned research papers.

A special meeting of General Council was held in Toronto on Jan. 29 and 30, 1965. For consideration were the following: the reports of the Association's three special committees (the Special Committee on Policy, the Special Committee on Prepaid Medical Care and the Special Committee on the Australian Plan) in their interrelationship to each other and to the Report of the Royal Commission on Health Services. The intended outcome of the deliberations was to arrive at an expression of Association policy.

It was the view of the Executive Committee that the General Council's attention be focused on the single large area of health insurance but that consideration of other recommendations in the commission's report would not be ruled out. The meeting was told that the CMA believed that its "Statement on Medical Services Insurance," issued in 1960, was still valid and represented the consensus of the medical profession in Canada but that, in light of experience and studies conducted in the interval, the statement should be reviewed for possible modification and restatement.

The Special Committee on Policy presented its report, which contained two major proposals. The first was that it be recognized that health services encompass more than the services of physicians and that insurance to cover the services rendered by a physician, or under the direction of a physician, was necessary. The second proposal was that the CMA encourage its sponsored plans to evolve from its existing concept of total prepayment to the "sounder, more economical and logical one of patient participation."

Early in its studies, the Special Committee on Policy had become interested in the Australian approach to medical services insurance and had recommended to the Executive Committee the formation of a special committee to study the merits and shortcomings of Australia's plan and to report on features that could be adopted for the Canadian scene. The Special Committee to Adapt the Australian Plan of Medical Services to Canadian Conditions was formed; three of its members had the advantage of seeing the plan in operation. One of the major components in the Australian plan was a system of federal subsidy in terms of a contribution per item of service, available to subscribers who enrolled voluntarily with one of the many approved carriers. All subscribers had the option of co-insurance, although this could be waived by the physician in the case of low-income contributors. The committee's report outlined in detail how certain aspects of the Australian plan might be incorporated into the Canadian context.

The Special Committee on Prepaid Medical Care presented its report, which contained no specific recommendations but commented on a variety of topics — continued sponsorship by CMA divisions of the plans they had originated, pro-rationing, extra-billing, assignment and the obligation of plans to their participating physicians.

The General Council then moved on to consider the Report of the Royal Commission on Health Services, which presented a case for the transfer of expenditure for all health services from the private to the public economy, and by so doing demolished many of the arguments the medical profession had put forward at the commission's public hearings. The CMA agreed that public financing was necessary to improve medical and paramedical education, medical research, upgrading of mental health services and provision of assistance to inadequately supported basic health services but did not agree with the use of tax funds for the individual in respect of his or her own health.

The studies arising from the five documents led to a number of specific areas for in-depth consideration: compulsion, comprehensiveness of benefits, funding of health services, patient participation, fee schedules, subsidy rationale and philosophy. All of these topics were discussed in great detail and a number of recommendations arising therefrom were approved. The conclusions of General Council were summarized as follows:

> *We have postulated much of this appraisal on the assumption that voluntary methods of medical services insurance will continue to receive the opportunity to develop their full potential. We strongly advise that a single, compulsory, tax-supported plan, operated by government, or any plan that is dependent on a single source of funds, will not maintain and develop adequate medical care of high quality.*
>
> *If government does propose a plan of this type, certain minimal conditions should be assured before the medical profession could consider extending cooperation. The first of these conditions is that physicians, as individuals, must be afforded the freedom of practising partially or wholly outside the plan and patients should be permitted to utilize the services of such doctors under private arrangements without loss of benefits which have been paid for through taxes and/or premiums. We should also reaffirm the right of patients and doctors to freedom of choice in seeking and supplying health services, the freedom of doctors to choose the type and location of their practice, and the confidentiality of information received in the doctor–patient relationship.*
>
> *Furthermore, any governmental agency administering medical services insurance should be responsible for that function alone, should be appointed by the Legislature and should report directly to that body. Fiscal authority and autonomy should be granted to the administering agency which should include as members representatives of the medical profession. A desirable degree of flexibility would be provided in such a tax-supported plan if, in place of a single carrier, the insured person were afforded a choice of several approved agencies and possibly more than one range of benefits.*

The General Council had referred the 1960 CMA "Statement on Medical Services Insurance" to the Committee on Economics, and it was the object of major study by that committee at its meetings of Mar. 5 and 6, and Apr. 9 and 10, 1965. At the time of reporting to General Council in Halifax in mid-June, the chairman, Dr. Victor C. Goldbloom, pointed out that the draft policy presented for discussion was the outcome of many consultations with the executive committees of the divisions and other committees of divisions as was deemed necessary. He further stated that in the practical application of the statement of policy the most important consideration was the quality of care, not simply the quantity of care provided by the physician but the quality of care that the patient receives, and that this should be made clear to the public. The draft statement of policy on medical services insurance was then placed before the General Council and after debate and amendments was approved in the following form.

The Need for Insurance

The Canadian Medical Association believes that it is in the public interest that medical services insurance be available and accessible to all Canadians.

The need for such insurance arises out of the increasing complexity and effectiveness of medical care, and the growing demand for medical services. This insurance should cover the services of the physician in home, office, or hospital, and also, under separate accounting, the services of paramedical personnel working under his direction and professional services and therapeutic agents otherwise ordered by him.

Personnel

Canada will continue to experience a shortage of physicians and of associated health personnel for at least the next generation. It will not therefore be possible to envisage unlimited availability of medical and paramedical services in the foreseeable future.

The mere provision of insurance will not of itself solve the problem of personnel, or ensure the availability of their services. In fact, the extension of the coverage to the whole population, especially on a total prepayment basis, will place a considerable strain on available personnel and may endanger the quality which the public receives.

The Dangers of Restrictions and Conflicts

If a system were created which undertook to pay the total cost of health services, and were dependent for this on a single and therefore potentially limited source of funds, it could be obliged through lack of restraint to do one of two things:
(a) to impose restrictions on the coverage of people or of services, or
(b) to be in continual conflict with the providers over working conditions and
remuneration.

We believe that such restrictions or conflicts would impair the quality of care, and we believe that it is not in the public interest that a plan be established which cannot be readily adjusted without restriction or conflict.

Flexibility and Progress

We therefore believe that alternative types of insurance, those which offer total prepayment and those which offer various forms of patient participation, must be maintained.

Time may bring into sharper relief the differences in value to the insured between various types of insurance, as well as the distinction between insurance against catastrophic costs and budgeting and prepaying of other health expenditures.

Each type of insurance has advantages and disadvantages and medical services insurance is not the only economic protection which society requires. It would be most unfortunate if a well-meaning decision today deprived the Canadian people of choice and progress in the future.

Freedom

The Canadian Medical Association believes that every resident of Canada should have as free a choice as possible among different carriers and different plans, as well as a free choice of physicians, and that every physician should have free choice of patient except where humane considerations dictate the contrary, and be free to participate, or not to participate, in any plan or with any carrier.

There must be no discrimination by any insurance plan against the non-participating physician, or against the subscriber who consults him. The subscriber who consults a non-participating physician must not be obliged to relinquish any benefits for which he has directly or indirectly paid, and clear provision for his indemnification must be assured.

We believe that it is in every sense in the public interest that these freedoms must be preserved. If the insurance plans devised are satisfactory to all concerned, both receivers and providers of service, then private arrangements will be relatively rare. If, on the other hand, a plan is for any reason unsatisfactory, then the freedom to conclude private arrangements will be an alternative to conflict and an incentive towards improvement of the plan.

Administration

We believe that it is in the public interest that the administrative structures of medical services insurance programmes be non-political in nature; that the medical profession be satisfactorily represented therein; and that the medical profession be fully consulted at all stages of planning and preparation.

The Role of Government

The development of medical services insurance is the responsibility of the provinces, and financial contributions to the federal government should not interfere with the self-determination of the provinces.

We believe that it should be the responsibility of provincial governments:

(a) to ensure that adequate insurance coverages, with appropriate safeguards for the public, are available, and accessible to every resident; and

(b) to provide, preferably as fixed-dollar subsidies, enough financial assistance to persons in need to enable them to purchase insurance — using the annual income-tax declaration as the basic criterion.

We believe that through cooperation between governments, insuring agencies, the public, and the health professions, voluntary insurance can in fact be made accessible to every resident of Canada.

The Protection of the Public

Among the safeguards which should be given to the public, one of the most important is that of privacy. Payment for any insured service has to be justified by a diagnosis and often by other medical information. The relationship between patient and physician must nevertheless be kept as private as possible, and any information provided to the insurer must be used solely for the assessment of claims and must be handled consistently in a confidential manner.

Insurance should be offered on a universally available, guaranteed renewable basis without penalty, and provision must be made for portability and the continuation of coverage despite unemployment, illness or the death of the wage-earner.

Conclusion

The Canadian Medical Association confidently believes that the people of this nation can develop insurance programmes which will preserve freedom of individual choice and action, foster personal initiative and responsibility, and while doing so make adequate insurance coverage possible for every Canadian.

The General Council was given an account of an important meeting held at CMA House on Aug. 17 and 18, chaired by Dr. Frank A. Turnbull, president of the CMA. There were representatives from the CMA, the Association of

Canadian Medical Colleges, the Royal College of Physicians and Surgeons of Canada, the Association des médecins de langue française du Canada and the College of Family Practice of Canada. Present as observers were: Dr. R.F. Farquharson, chairman of the Medical Research Council, Dr. G.D.W. Cameron, deputy minister of national health and Dr. K.C. Charron, director of health services, Department of National Health and Welfare. The meeting studied the 25 recommendations of the report of the Royal Commission pertaining to medical education, and participants found themselves in general agreement with those recommendations. The proceedings of this meeting were embodied in 20 pages of detailed discussion and circulated to the CMA Executive Committee and the principals of the other organizations represented at the meeting. After studying the report, the Executive Committee authorized the Advisory Committee to the federal government to present it to the highest authority in the federal government.

On Nov. 16, 1964, the Advisory Committee, amplified by the chairperson of the Committee on Medical Education and representatives of the four organizations that had attended the meeting in August, met with the Hon. Judy LaMarsh, minister of national health and welfare, and the Hon. C.M. Drury, chairman of the Privy Council Committee on Scientific and Industrial Research. The prime minister and the minister of finance were not present. The gist of the presentation was that the implementation of many of the recommendations in the Report of the Royal Commission on Health Services would require an increase in medical manpower and that the maintenance, to say nothing of the extension, of health services depended greatly on new measures being taken in medical education and medical research. No commitment was made by the federal government.

One of the recommendations in the Royal Commission's report was the calling of a federal–provincial conference to discuss the findings and implementations. The Executive Committee deemed it advisable for the Advisory Committee to the federal government to meet with appropriate ministers before any such conference, and on June 8, 1965, the advisory committee met with the prime minister, the Rt. Hon. Lester B. Pearson, the minister of finance, the Hon. Walter Gordon and the Hon. Judy LaMarsh. The CMA's position on medical services insurance was presented, and a number of specific items were discussed, such as the right of patients to receive full benefits whether or not the attending physician was a participant in the plan, and the need for the CMA to have regular consultations with the federal government. By and large, there was very little firm commitment by the government. Some comfort had been found in the following excerpt from the recent throne speech:

> *My government believes that public policy should be directed to improving the quality of health services and to ensuring that all Canadians can obtain needed health care, irrespective of their ability to pay. Accordingly, my government will, at an early date, meet with the governments of the provinces in order to discuss with them the way in which federal and provincial action can most effectively contribute to programmes that will provide health services to Canadians on a comprehensive basis.*

The federal–provincial conference took place in Ottawa on July 19 and 20, 1965. The prime minister outlined four criteria under which the national medical services insurance plan, now known as medicare, should operate:

(a) *The scope of benefits should be, broadly speaking, all the services provided by physicians, both general practitioners and specialists.*

(b) *The plan should be universal, viz., it should cover all residents of a province on uniform terms and conditions.*

(c) *Public administration, either directly by a provincial government or by a non-profit agency.*

(d) *Full transferability of benefits when people are absent from their province or when they move their residence to another province.*

At the end of the 2-day conference the prime minister announced that the federal government would share the cost of comprehensive, compulsory, government-administered, transferable insurance and would make funds available to provincial governments, commencing July 1, 1967. There had been no inkling of the imminence of such a decision at the time of the June 8 meeting with the prime minister and his ministers, and the CMA had not been consulted prior to the announcement.

In response to this announcement, the CMA issued a statement to the federal government and to the news media, drawing attention to the Association's concerns over the compulsory aspect of the proposal as well as mandatory government administration. The CMA also cautioned against the precipitous action in introducing the plan as early as 1967 and drew attention to the shortage of medical and other health personnel.

The Advisory Committee met with the minister of national health and welfare on Sept. 16, 1965, just a week before the Federal–Provincial Conference of Ministers of Health, and gave her a document outlining the Association's grave concerns over the prime minister's announcement. From the Association's point of view the meeting was an unsatisfactory one, and it was not until Oct. 1 that the minister replied in writing, giving the government's interpretation of the four criteria enunciated by the prime minister on July 20. In the Executive Committee's report to the 1966 General Council the minister's reply was described as "vague."

The minister indicated that, under the compulsory aspect of the plan, 90% to 95% of the population would be required for the provincial governments to receive federal funds and that a provincial-government program would be acceptable so long as the plan was administered, either directly by the provincial government or by provincial agencies appointed by the provincial government. Such agencies would be responsible to the provincial legislature and would operate on a nonprofit basis as well as being subject to a governmental audit. As to the right of a physician to practise outside the plan and for a patient to receive reimbursement for medical services received, the minister indicated that this would not be ruled out of the federal program but pointed out that she had concerns over the possibility of extra-billing and that if too many doctors operated outside the plan or if the amount of extra-billing violated the principle of universality, then the federal contribution would not apply.

Following the federal election on Nov. 8, the Advisory Committee met with the new minister of national health and welfare, the Hon. Allan MacEachen, on Jan. 25, and Mar. 10, 1966. On Apr. 30, the Executive Committee sent a strongly worded telegram to the prime minister with a copy to the Mr. MacEachen, indicating the Association's concern that the government had not seen fit to consult with it before the announcement by the prime minister on July 20. On June 8, the Advisory Committee met again with Mr. MacEachen, and on June 10 the Executive Committee sent him the following telegram, over the signature of the president, Dr. Robert O. Jones:

> My understanding of your statement at our meeting on June 8, 1966 was that federal legislation having to do with the insurance of physicians' services would contain nothing to prohibit patients receiving any benefits to which their insurance entitles them when they consult any qualified physician. May I have your agreement to this principle by telegram, with permission to announce same at our sessions of General Council which will be open to the press.

The minister replied:

> Re. your telegram June 10, I wish to affirm my statement to you that on your assurance that the medical profession accepts responsibility for avoidance of abuses and excess which would impair universality, or access of patients to

services, it is not intended to prohibit the doctor billing his patient directly and patient claiming benefits. No objection to announcement to this effect being made to General Council.

Deputy Minister of Health Dr. J.N. Crawford addressed the General Council on the matter of the four criteria outlined by the prime minister in July. He stated that the principles were the principles of universality wanted by the people of Canada and that federal legislation would in no way prohibit the reimbursement of patients. There was considerable discussion on the question of opting out and extra-billing. Dr. Crawford pointed out that the CMA had received assurance that extra-billing would be permitted as long as it did not interfere with the availability of service or violate the principle of universality. He reiterated that questions dealing with the design, detail and operation of any plan were matters to be decided between the medical profession and the provincial governments, not the federal government, and that the federal government, except for the enunciation of broad principles, had no intention whatever of limiting or designing any plan that a province might bring into effect.

On his first day in office as the new president of the CMA, Dr. R. Kenneth Thomson wrote to the Hon. A. MacEachen on the matter of obtaining flexibility in the government's medicare proposal by allowing greater latitude in the use of private administering agencies; part of the letter contained a memorandum prepared by Mr. Bernard E. Freamo in response to the minister's request.

The Advisory Committee met with the minister on June 27 and was told that he was adamant on the matter of the 90% requirement for provincial plans to qualify for federal funds. He agreed to consider more flexibility in the administration of the plan and to work more closely with the CMA, but when the medicare bill (C-227) was introduced in the House of Commons there was very little evidence of flexibility. Further meetings between the CMA and the federal government produced no changes in the latter's position, and letters from Dr. Thomson to the prime minister did not change the mindset of the government. On Dec. 8, 1966, the bill received third and final reading in the House of Commons.

In summarizing the CMA's negotiations with the federal government on Bill C-227, it is believed that the following points are significant, taking into account the history of medicare since its inception:

1. The CMA was not consulted before the federal government made known the details of its medical services insurance plan.
2. The federal government, having made its announcement, rejected the advice of the CMA on the need for changes in the proposed legislation.

3. By omission in the bill, physicians are permitted to practise outside federal legislation but, to do so, a similar provision is required under provincial legislation.

Further concern was expressed by the Association over the inclusion in the bill, just before its passage, of an amendment (Section 4[3]) giving the government authority by order-in-council to include various other medical services under the bill. It was the association's position that Bill C-227 had not been designed to include other health services and that if further health programs were to be implemented, it should be done under separate legislation and with separate funding. Following the meeting of the Executive Committee on Dec. 9, 1966, the following statement was released by the CMA:

> *The major concern of Canadian doctors with the passing of the Medicare Bill is to see that it provides the best quality of medical care possible for the people of Canada.*
>
> *With the third reading of Bill C-227 in the House of Commons yesterday, Dr. R.K.C. Thomson, President of the CMA, says that discussions and negotiations will now shift to the provinces in an attempt to develop provincial medicare programmes in the best interests of the public.*
>
> *With the Bill's inflexibility and with the requirement for total coverage of the population, there will be problems. As Dr. Thomson puts it, "the inflexibility will make it difficult for the provinces to tailor medical services to the special needs of the different parts of the country. Yet this is exactly what must be done to provide the people with the best of medical care."*
>
> *Total coverage means the loss of one more civil liberty. All must take part in the programme.*
>
> *The Association's position is that patients will have complete freedom to choose their own doctor. Each person can go to the doctor of his choice, whether the doctor directly participates in the scheme or not, and have his medical bills paid.*
>
> *It is the strong opinion of the CMA that benefits under medical care acts and programmes should be limited to those services performed by or under the direction of a properly qualified physician. Other health benefits should be provided by separate legislation and separate funding.*
>
> *The Association believes that the cost of the programme will soon become a major concern to all Canadians. Tax funds will now pay for medical services previously paid for by employer-employee contributions to prepaid plans. Taxes will also have to bear the cost for all the additional services that will be demanded.*

Dr. Thomson is concerned that the medium and medium-low income groups will feel the tax increases required to pay for the programme most. Equally, scarce funds will be diverted from the vital areas of medical research and training of health personnel. The need for more physicians, nurses and other paramedical personnel to fill the increased demands that inevitably follow such programmes is also a concern. The already existing shortage of such people will be increased.

Dr. Thomson summarized the feelings of the Association by saying, "Our concern is to see that the people of Canada receive the highest quality of medical care. The object of our provincial divisions will be to ensure, as far as possible, that Canadians will continue to receive the best medical care and that obstacles are not placed in the way of continued improvement."

Two provinces, British Columbia and Saskatchewan, joined medicare on July 1, 1968; four other provinces indicated that they would join in 1969. The remaining four provinces gave no commitment, and both Ontario and Quebec went so far as to say that medicare was far down the list of their priorities. A number of provincial leaders had expressed concerns similar to those of the Association and this, coupled with misleading and inaccurate statements made by members of the federal cabinet, led to the CMA writing to the prime minister asking for a meeting with him to discuss the government's policy on health care. The prime minister did not accede to the request, but the CMA did meet with minister of national health and welfare, the Hon. J.C. Munro, on Aug. 26 and Nov. 11 and found that he was committed to medicare. The minister indicated that he saw no reason to change the government's policies in the matter of health care nor would he accept the concept that different approaches in provincial programs, in the initial stages, would enable a judgement to be made as to which was the best method.

The Association believed it would get nowhere by attempting to change the inflexibility shown by the minister, and the decision was made to write to the prime minister, the Rt. Hon. Pierre Elliott Trudeau. On Jan. 3, 1969, a letter was sent to the prime minister over the signature of Dr. Harold D. Dalgleish, president of the CMA, asking for a meeting at which the concerns of the Association might be expressed and clarification provided on some of the points in the legislation. The letter was acknowledged by a member of the prime minister's staff, but later the CMA general secretary was told that the prime minister did not wish to meet with the Association.

On Mar. 6, the president wrote again to the prime minister asking for a meeting and noting that the prime minister had held meetings with representatives of other segments of the community, including leaders in business, finance and labour. The letter also reviewed the many contributions made by the CMA over the years, including the fact that it was the CMA that had recommended the formation of a study that became the Royal Commission on Health Services, that the CMA had an important role in the development of health services in Canada and, as such, would be a source of counsel for government policy and programs.

On Apr. 4, the prime minister replied to Dr. Dalgleish:

In response to your telegram and other correspondence already acknowledged, with respect to your request to present a brief to myself and the Cabinet, I must regretfully decline this opportunity at this time. It is helpful to be able to see many important associations such as yours, but unfortunately the heavy demands on the Government have made it impossible for now. I hope your Executive will understand this position.

In any event, the important thing is that your views do receive a hearing, and in this connection I understand, as you mention in your letter, that your Association has met with the Minister Of National Welfare, the Honourable John Munro, in late August, and again on November 11, and with the Minister of Finance, the Honourable E.J. Benson on February 10, concerning a variety of topics. I believe that this was the best route for you to take, and I assure you that my colleagues and I have similar views about the importance of your organization's recommendations. I know they will be happy to see you again if there are any further matters you wish to discuss.

I hope you will convey my regrets to your membership, and at the same time my assurance that through the responsible Ministers your views will continue to receive the attention of the Government.

Yours sincerely,
Signed by Pierre Elliott Trudeau
Prime Minister of Canada

This response was not welcomed with any degree of satisfaction by the Executive Committee, which believed that a meeting with the prime minister and senior members of his cabinet was a reasonable request. As the voice of organized medicine in Canada, the CMA believed that it had a responsibility to present the views of the profession to those who collectively establish government policies on a wide range of matters extremely important to the profession.

On Apr. 1, 1969, the provinces of Newfoundland, Nova Scotia and Manitoba introduced medical insurance programs that qualified under the federal act. Alberta announced that a similar program would be instituted in the near future. By the time the General Council met in Winnipeg in mid-June, all provinces, except New Brunswick, had either implemented plans for medicare or had announced a date for its implementation. In Quebec, legislation precluded reimbursement benefits from the plan for patients of opted-out physicians.

The following statement on medical services insurance was approved by the General Council at its meeting in June 1969.

Statement of Principles on Medical Services Insurance (1969)
The Canadian Medical Association believes that all medical services insurance programs should be based on the following principles:
1. *Medical services insurance should be available and accessible to all Canadians.*
2. *Insurance programs should be sufficiently flexible that, in the light of experience, changes can be made in administration, benefits or financing.*
3. *The ideal insurance mechanism is one wherein the contractual relationship exists between the insurance agency and the subscriber, and not between the agency and the physician.*
4. *The most responsible relationship exists when the professional and financial agreements are between the physician and the patient.*
5. *The best method of paying for the great majority of personal medical services is on a fee-for-service basis.*
6. *The patient should be aware of, and wherever possible pay part of, the cost of medical services he receives.*
7. *The patient should have the right to choose his physician without loss of benefits.*
8. *The patient has the right to expect that the information disclosed to the physician will be held in confidence.*
9. *The physician should have the right to choose his patient, subject to humane considerations, and to choose the type and location of his practice.*
10. *The physician should have the right to determine his method of remuneration. In determining his fee, he should be guided by the fee schedule approved by his provincial association.*
11. *The physician must have the right to practise with professional freedom and must accept the responsibility to practise according to the rules of ethical behaviour established by his professional organizations.*

On Nov. 24, 1969, the federal government made public the report of its Task Forces on the Cost of Health Services. The report came in three volumes and contained 337 recommendations. The Association studied the reports, and on Apr. 8, 1970, after much input from the CMA councils and divisions, a preliminary statement was sent to the minister of national health and welfare in response to a deadline set by him.

It is interesting to note that on Jan. 15, 1970, the Executive Committee was invited to meet with the minister of national health and welfare, the minister of finance, the president of the Treasury Board and their senior officials to discuss voluntary restraint on increases in professional fees of physicians. The ministers stressed the fact that they were approaching the medical profession first as a responsible profession whose action they hoped would set an example and give leadership to other professions. This attitude was very much at variance with their attitudes toward organized medicine, and the CMA in particular. The CMA agreed that inflation was an urgent national problem and that the medical profession would assist in contributing to a solution but pointed out that the establishment and revision of fee schedules were the prerogatives of the provincial governments and that fee changes tended to follow changes in the economy rather than precede them. On Jan. 16, 1970, the Association issued a statement, which said in part: "The Canadian Medical Association will urge its members to practise voluntary restraint to help curb inflation."

In 1971, New Brunswick instituted a medical services insurance plan and became eligible for federal funding.

Over the next 2 years relationships between the Association and the federal government improved, and there were many instances of meetings between CMA senior staff and senior officials of the various government departments. The president of the CMA, Dr. Harry D. Roberts, met with the minister of national health and welfare on a number of occasions in 1971 and 1972 and reported that there were frank exchanges of views on many current issues at those meetings. He reported to the Board of Directors that the Department of National Health and Welfare was very concerned about increasing expenditures in the area of health care and that it believed it must have a more direct control over costs.

This philosophy was the basis on which the federal government made a proposal to the provinces to control the increase in federal expenditures in cost-shared programs by limiting annual increases based on a percentage, itself based on the gross national product. If implemented, this form of financing would be a radical departure from the way funding had been provided and could present problems for the provinces if the sum produced by the gross national product formula were insufficient to offset increases in the provinces' costs. The provinces might then impose controls of their own in order to remain within budget. The Association was concerned that health care could fall victim to decisions made by financial comptrollers and called a conference of representatives from the divisions to discuss the implications of the proposed changes in greater detail.

At a joint meeting of the federal and provincial health and finance ministers on Jan. 19, 1973, the federal government presented a revised proposal for cost-sharing of the medicare and hospital insurance programs. The new formula did provide for some additional funding for the provinces but made no change in the basic philosophical approach, i.e., to control future increases in health care costs. Reports from the meeting indicated that very few of the provinces were willing to accept funding based on the gross national product formula.

In 1973, the General Council passed the following resolutions:

> *Resolved that this Association urge the federal government to share with the provinces the costs of existing programmes, as well as future programmes embracing ambulance services, home care, nursing homes, and services for all handicapping conditions.*
>
> *The Council on Economics with the Secretary-General of the Association pursue the problem of payment of out-of-province benefits with the Department of National Health and Welfare in order to obtain a standard method of paying in each province for services rendered to out-of-province patients and thus increase the portability of benefits for the patient.*

Throughout the balance of 1973 and the first 4 months of 1974 a number of meetings were held between the CMA and the departments of national health and welfare and finance to try to resolve the problems arising from reimbursement to out-of-province patients. The Association had no success in obtaining helpful solutions to the problems of health insurance portability and the matter came before the General Council again in 1974 when, after much discussion the following was approved: "The CMA, through its Divisions, urge all provincial health care insurance plans to adopt a common policy that would allow direct payment to out-of-province physicians for insured services rendered to out-of-province residents."

In late 1974 and early 1975, the Association's Department of Research and Development along with the Council on Economics undertook a study of the status of health insurance portability. With the exception of one jurisdiction, all provinces and territories had accepted, in principle, an interprovincial agreement on eligibility and portability of health insurance coverage, but the necessary legislative and regulatory changes for full implementation of the agreement were slow in coming.

In his 1975 federal budget, the minister of finance, the Hon. John Turner, announced that legislation would be introduced to restrict federal government expenditure with respect to the shared costs of the medicare program and that it was the government's intention to terminate existing cost-sharing arrangements for hospital insurance.

The CMA president, Dr. Lloyd Grisdale met with the minister of national health and welfare, the Hon. Marc Lalonde, and his deputy minister on July 25, 1975, at which time the minister explained in detail the government's rationale for the proposed legislation, designed to force provincial governments to take actions necessary to bring health care costs under control. At the meeting the minister expressed his frustration over the lack of such action on the part of the provinces.

The tocsins rang at CMA House and the president called a meeting of divisional presidents for Aug. 22 to discuss how the proposed legislation would affect the delivery of health care in their respective provinces. Following the meeting at which a unified position was agreed upon, the Executive Committee arranged to meet with the health and finance ministers on Sept. 12, 1975. However, Mr. Turner resigned on Sept. 10, and the Department of Finance was represented at the meeting by the Hon. C.M. Drury. Prior to the meeting Dr. Grisdale had submitted the following letter to the prime minister and the two ministers on Sept. 10:

> Gentlemen:
> The Canadian Medical Association is extremely concerned, indeed distressed, by the Government of Canada's introduction of Bill C-68.
> The introduction of Bill C-68 has the potential for major irreparable harm to the quality of medical care and Canada's medical care insurance programme. Internationally, Canada's medicare system has been highly regarded. Contrary to the expectation of many experts, cost increases have been maintained at reasonable levels. We have been able to point with pride to a system which has worked well and was responsive to demonstrated needs. Must we now view the programme as one in which the primary concern is financial and that in future the programme will be tailored to the financial exigencies of the moment, not medical care requirements? Such a policy poses a major threat to the health of Canadians.
> Medical care insurance in Canada has had a very satisfactory cost experience. If criticism is warranted, it is because provincial governments have not allocated sufficient funds in recent years to adequately compensate physicians for inflation. Nationally, and in each province, actual costs have been consistently

within projected budgets. Even the current year's projected increase (16.6%) is very reasonable in view of the minimal medical services fee for schedule increases, the rate of inflation, recent salary awards, increased costs of practice, newly developed medical procedures and increased utilization initiated by patients.

We are concerned because press reports on this legislation and statistics and projected costs in the budget speech, perhaps inadvertently, have misled the public. By combining medicare and health insurance costs and then singling out the medicare programme for specific action via the imposition of unrealistic cost restraints, the inference is that increased medical care insurance costs are the major factor in escalating health care costs.

We know, and are sure that you know, that this not the case. The proportion of Canada's gross national product spent on medical services in Canada has actually declined from 1.3% in 1971–72 to 1.1% in the federal government's forecasts for 1975–76. The average annual federal payment increase for this period is less than 12%, much less than increases in overall federal government spending; whereas your contribution has increased at an annual rate of 18% during the comparable 4 year period. While we believe that these increases are not unrealistic in view of wage awards which hospitals have been forced to accept (often on court order), we strongly object to your government's inappropriate decision to control health cost increases by placing unwarranted expenditure restraints on medicare — a programme which has not been responsible for undue cost increases.

We cannot escape the conclusion that the proposed medical care insurance funding restrictions essentially constitute a tactic to force the provinces to accept new cost-sharing agreements at the risk of endangering Canada's medical care insurance programme.

Secondly, the physicians of Canada view this proposed legislation as the introduction of price controls on physicians' services and therefore physician income controls. We would point out that no other sector of the economy has been subjected to wage or price controls — a concept we believed your government had rejected. In addition, the proposed ceilings make no allowance for the several variables which directly affect the physician's real income, such as the increases in utilization or patient demand for services, substantially increased overhead costs and the persistent high level of inflation.

The Government of Canada must be as aware as we of the methods of financing medical services in Canada. Most of the finances come from the Federal Government and direct public participation through premiums and programme specific taxes. The net cost to the provincial treasuries is in many instances nominal. The effect of the proposed restriction of federal contributions is predictable. Increases in direct provincial costs could be astronomical, inevitably resulting, for some provinces, in curtailment of services or the placing of undue restrictions on payments made to physicians.

This Association has not and will not deny the vested interest of its membership in federal government budget restrictions for medical care insurance. However, we ask that you do not regard this request to withdraw Bill C-68 as a simple reflection of that vested interest. We must disagree with the statements of the Minister of Health relative to the potential effect of this legislation on the quality of medical care. Bill C-68 will endanger the quality and the availability of medical care for Canadians. The permanent cost of increase ceilings proposed will result in the rationing of medical care. The cost increase ceilings will inhibit, if not prohibit, the introduction of new medical procedures, and make it impossible for them to be made available to all Canadians who would benefit from them. This will be particularly true for those Canadians who live in less wealthy provinces — frequently those areas where improvement in the health care delivery system is most needed. This effect on the "have-not" provinces is particularly significant. Since the introduction of medicare, these provinces with less developed health care systems have benefitted from the federal-provincial cost-sharing formula. The impositions of a ceiling on federal contributions will deprive these less wealthy provinces of further opportunity to improve the level of medical services in their communities. It will be impossible to evolve a uniform programme of equitable availability and quality.

To put the vested financial interest of the profession in proper perspective, we suggest that a review of the record re increases in physicians' fee schedules, relative net and disposable income increase data will lead to the inevitable conclusion that price and earning controls on physicians are unwarranted. In view of the profession's demonstrated economic responsibility, including adherence to your government's request for voluntary cost increase restraint in 1971, we would respectfully suggest that the singling out of the medical profession for de facto permanent price and income controls is unjust. Reconsideration of this legislation may not allay the fears of physicians about the future orientation of the medical care insurance programme, but it would remove the spectre of impending income restrictions, without protection from the effects of inflation and cost increases, a concept that no other segment of Canadian society has been forced to accept.

We concur with the expressed opinions of the federal and provincial governments, that improved health care cost efficiency is indicated and that *the rate of health care cost escalation can and must be controlled. There is no doubt that positive steps towards such objectives can and should be taken. To cite a few simple examples of what might be done, we suggest that the introduction of compulsory seat belt legislation and highway speed limit restrictions, combined with appropriate and effective education programmes, would markedly reduce this country's hospital and medical care insurance costs. Legislative changes allowing the profession to provide less expertise demanding services by utilizing paramedical personnel, while protected from related liable legal liability and provided with a means to be compensated for such services — at a commensurately lower level, is yet another. The introduction of programmes to promote many of the indicated lifestyle changes proposed in the Government of Canada's working document A New Perspective on the Health of Canadians is yet another. Toward the achievement of such rational, indicated objectives, I pledge the support of the Canadian Medical Association, but we must oppose Bill C-68.*

The Canadian Medical Association urgently requests that the federal government reconsider the amendments to the Medical Care Insurance Act proposed in Bill C-68. We look forward to discussing this with you at 10:30 a.m. Sept., 12, 1975.

Yours very truly,
L.C. Grisdale, MD, President

That letter formed the basis for discussion at the 2-hour meeting at which the acting minister of finance assured the CMA delegation that the cabinet would consider the following points:

1. The profession had voluntarily adhered to the prices and wage restrictions recommended by the federal government's commission in 1971;
2. medical care insurance costs remained well within federal and provincial government budgets;
3. medical care insurance costs, averaging about 12% since the introduction of medicare, have been consistently lower than the cost increases related to hospital care insurance;
4. costs of medical care insurance have declined from 1.3% of gross national product in 1971–72 to 1.1% for 1975–76 according to federal government estimates;
5. fee schedule increases enacted by the profession since the introduction of medicare have exhibited a considerable degree of economic responsibility;
6. federal medicare cost-sharing restrictions would be reflected inevitably in provincial government-medical profession payment-level negotiations and

result in some degree of control in the price of medical services and, in turn, of physicians' income controls.

A further meeting with the two ministers on Nov. 13, 1975, did not produce any changes in the proposed legislation acceptable to the CMA. Subsequently, three amendments to Bill C-68 were introduced by the minister, viz.,
1. the establishment of specific ceilings for 1976–77 and 1977–78;
2. the establishment of a mechanism to ensure appropriate direction of federal medicare contributions;
3. a 36-month exemption from ceilings for new insured services.

The CMA launched a campaign at federal and provincial levels to inform politicians and the general public of the Association's misgivings should the bill be passed. In the words of Dr. Grisdale:

> *Unquestionably, the introduction of Bill C-68 and serving the required five year notice relative to the termination of current hospital insurance cost-sharing agreements are major planks in the federal government's programme to realise [a] new cost-sharing formula with the provinces (for both hospital and medical-care insurance programmes), but are also instruments to force a reorganization and rationalization of Canada's health care delivery system. These actions are of even greater significance than the major financial implications involved. Much more than the financing of health care and financial health of Canadian physicians is involved. The entire future of health and medical-care delivery is at stake. The CMA will govern and direct its action relative to Bill C-68 accordingly.*

On Feb. 26, 1976, Dr. Grisdale wrote to the chairperson of the House of Commons Health, Welfare and Social Affairs Committee, outlining the Association's position on the bill and asking an opportunity for representatives of the Association to appear before the committee. The request was granted, and a CMA delegation appeared before the committee on Mar. 25. The Association's concerns were aired in great detail, bolstered by reliable statistical evidence that showed in fact that, while the health expenditures as a percentage of the gross national product remained at about 7.3%, the percentage of gross national product spent on medical care insurance had actually decreased from 1.33% to 1.19% over the same period.

Although the delegation was of the opinion that it had been given a fair hearing, there had been no indications that any of the concerns expressed would be reflected in any changes to the bill, or that the proposed amendments would be changed in any way when the bill was presented for third reading in the House of Commons.

At the 1976 General Council meeting it was approved that the CMA seek to discuss the broad-based aspects of Canadian medical care services with the prime minister of Canada on a regular basis, and on Sept. 20 Dr. Estathios W. Barootes, CMA deputy-president, wrote to the prime minister requesting a meeting. On Oct. 12, the following reply was received:

> *Dear Dr. Barootes,*
>
> *Thank you for your letter of September 20, 1976. I am pleased that your meeting with the Honourable Marc Lalonde on September 14, provided a forum for a useful exchange of information.*
>
> *I can only reiterate the comments made to you by the Minister of National Health and Welfare, that the federal government has no intention of either diminishing or withdrawing from its responsibilities in the health care field. Indeed, this year, during the federal/provincial discussions of Deputy Ministers and Ministers of Health, held respectively in March and April and at the June meeting of the First Ministers, the Federal concern was made abundantly clear. We are and will continue to be vitally concerned with improving the health care delivery system in respect of its comprehensiveness and cost effectiveness. There is no question of abdicating or diminishing our responsibilities in this field.*
>
> *I would like to meet with you and members of the Association, but regrettably my schedule of commitments for the foreseeable future is very tight. This, added to my planning responsibilities for the next session of the House, unfortunately, precludes an appointment at the present time. I am encouraged that satisfactory channels of communication have been established with the Honourable Marc Lalonde. I am certain the Minister will continue to keep me well informed of the concerns which the Association may have.*
>
> *Sincerely,*
> *Signed by P.E. Trudeau*
> *Prime Minister of Canada*

During 1976 and 1977 the federal and provincial governments had held discussions on the subject of new cost-sharing arrangements for medicare, hospital and post-secondary education funding. Bill C-37 — the *Established Programmes Fiscal Arrangements Act* — had been put forward as a method of turning over to the provinces monies that would otherwise be contributed by the federal government as its portion of cost-shared programs. In part of the preamble to the bill, the Act was described as "An Act to provide for the making of certain fiscal payments and of established programmes financing contributions to provinces, to provide for payments in respect of certain provincial taxes and fees, and to make consequential and related amendments." The proposed formula was a very complicated one, but the CMA was assured that monies allocated to medicare and hospital insurance would exceed the amounts that the provinces would have otherwise received under the cost-sharing agreements.

The 1977 General Council expressed its concern over the proposed legislation, even though it was perceived that greater flexibility might bring benefits to providers and users in the health care area. The major concern was the possibility that the provinces might direct monies allocated for health care away from that and into other competing provincially funded programs. The General Council passed a motion directing the Association to recommend to the federal government that those tax credits and monies transferred to the provinces by the federal government under federal Bill C-37 in lieu of hospital and medical care cost-sharing be specified for the use of health care in those provinces.

At the same meeting concern was expressed over the matter of portability of medicare benefits. In spite of repeated efforts by the medical profession to correct the problem, serious difficulties were being encountered by physicians attempting to be reimbursed for services rendered to patients from out-of-province. Two motions on the matter were approved:

> *That the CMA, with the help of the provincial Divisions, enjoin the provincial paying agencies to issue benefit cheques payable to the physicians for services rendered to out-of-province patients.*
>
> *That the CMA favours direct patient participation in payment for medical services by physicians.*

On Sept. 16, 1977, Marc Lalonde resigned and was replaced by Monique Bégin. The first meeting between the CMA and the new minister took place on Apr. 4, 1978, at which time the Association's concerns, particularly as they related to Bill C-37, were drawn to her attention. On Dec. 14, 1978, the CMA president, Dr. Kenneth O. Wylie, wrote a 15-page letter to the minister outlining the CMA's views on a number of matters: medical research funding in Canada, cooperation between the CMA and the federal government in health care matters, confidentiality of medical records, patient participation in health care costs and the federal government's philosophy on that matter, eligibility of continuing medical education expenses for income tax deduction, professional and service corporations, and national immunization policy. Shortly after receiving the letter, the minister met with Association officers and senior officials.

By the time the General Council convened in June 1979, there was a new federal minister of health, the Hon. David Crombie, and although he was afforded a standing ovation following an address to General Council, members' concerns over the federal government's direction in health care policy were reflected in the debate following his speech. *The Canadian Medical Association Statement of Principles on Medical Services Insurance* (1969) was a focus for the deliberations and led to a resolution reaffirming the principles outlined in the document and further resolving that Principle 6 be understood to embrace hospital and other institutional services as well as services provided by physicians.

The perceived increasing politicization of health care and the general dissatisfaction with the basic concepts of medicare engendered a lengthy and a sometimes emotional discussion, which led to General Council approval of the following:

> *Whereas physicians across Canada are more than ever indicating their dissatisfaction with the basic concepts of Medicare, and whereas Medicare has once again become a political issue as evidenced by the former Minister of National Health and Welfare and the Leader of the NDP, and whereas the Association is of the opinion that the basic concepts should be subject to national discussion, therefore the CMA requests a federal/provincial conference of governments and the profession to discuss the basic concepts of Medicare and their implementation and application.*

After further debate a second motion was approved: "That the CMA believes that the principle of universality of health care is not violated by the practice of selected billings of patients beyond a schedule of government benefits."

On July 13, 1979, a letter over the signature of the CMA secretary general, Dr. Robert G. Wilson, was sent to the federal minister of health, outlining the need to discuss some matters including "the present status of funding of health-care in Canada; the controversy regarding agreements with the provinces, particularly as they relate to the expenditure of medical funds on medical services; and the desirability and the utility of a national conference on the Canadian health-care system."

A meeting between the president of the CMA and the minister was held on Sept. 7, 1979. Shortly thereafter, at the Conference of Ministers of Health, David Crombie announced the establishment of a commission to undertake a review of the medical care insurance system in Canada.

The minister appointed Mr. Justice Emmett Hall to conduct the review which, it was hoped, would answer the concerns of the medical profession as well as respond to the criticisms being levelled at the government by the Liberal Party Opposition in the House of Commons, particularly by the former minister of health, Monique Bégin. The one-man commission was given 8 months to complete its task. The commissioner appointed Dr. Malcolm Taylor, who had been the research consultant on the 1964 Royal Commission on Health Services, as his research director. Five independent studies were commissioned.

Following the appointment of Mr. Justice Hall, the CMA representatives met with him to discuss and make suggestions with respect to the terms of reference of the commission. The CMA prepared a draft of its proposed submission to the commission and then convened a meeting attended by its board of directors, presidents and secretaries of its divisions, and representatives of the College of Family Physicians of Canada, the Royal College of Physicians and Surgeons of Canada and the Association of Canadian Medical Colleges to review the draft and to draw up a strategy relative to the submissions to the commission. There was a general agreement over the tenor and thrust of the brief, but because the divisions wished to present their own submissions, it was agreed that the CMA would make its submission first and the divisions would make their presentations when the hearings were held in their respective provinces.

Following the meeting a second draft was prepared and submitted for critical review to secretaries of the divisions at a meeting on Jan. 14 and 15, 1980. The finalized version was approved by the Executive Committee on Feb. 16, 1980. The 36-page brief was presented to the commission on Feb. 27, in Saskatoon, by a CMA delegation led by the president, Dr. D. Laurence Wilson.

The brief was 1 of 450 submissions made to the commission over a 5-month period. By and large, the submissions from the public indicated that there was opposition against extra-billing, insurance premiums and user fees, all of them being seen as barriers to accessibility.

The commissioner handed his report, titled *Canada's National–Provincial Health Program for the 1980's — A Commitment for Renewal*, to the minister on Aug. 29, 1980. One chapter — "The dominant issues" — dealt with perceived barriers to accessibility. Governments were adamant in their opposition to extra-billing whereas the medical profession was just as insistent that it had the right to maintain the practice. The review pointed out that these positions were in conflict, inasmuch as the profession could not unilaterally fix fees for its services and the state did not have the right to conscript the services of physicians.

The commissioner concluded: "The real point is the right of physicians to be adequately compensated for their services; no more, no less."

He went on to say:

I reject totally the idea that physicians must accept what any given Province may decide unilaterally to pay. I reject too, as I did in the Report of the Royal Commission, the concept of extra-billing. My conclusion and recommendation is that when negotiations fail and an impasse occurs, the issues in dispute must be sent to binding arbitration, to an arbitration board, consisting of three persons, with an independent chairperson to be named by the Chief Justice of the relevant province and one nominee from the profession and one from the government.

The Medical Care Act should be revised to provide: (i) That extra-billing by physicians inhibits reasonable access to services and is contrary to the intent and purpose of the Act, and (ii) That the provinces should develop a mechanism to ensure reasonable compensation to physicians.

The CMA noted that if extra-billing were to be banned in all jurisdictions, changes would be required in the *Saskatchewan Medical Insurance Act* (1978) and, if this were to be done, the overall requirement that extra-billing be banned would override the right of Saskatchewan doctors to continue that practice.

Another chapter in the commission's review dealt with portability, comprehensiveness, accessibility, universality and public administration, and it was the commissioner's view that the provincial ministers and their counterparts meet and work out a solution to the problems associated with portability, such problems being a source of great annoyance to many Canadians.

The commissioner concluded that allegations levelled against provinces, accusing them of diverting funds from federal sources, earmarked specifically for health care, to other non-health areas within their respective jurisdictions, were unsubstantiated.

The review was discussed by the Executive Committee and the presidents of the divisions at a special meeting in Vancouver on Sept. 13, 1980. The outcome of their deliberations was the creation of a small ad hoc committee charged with producing a position paper for discussion at General Council 2 days later. The ad hoc committee was chaired by Dr. D. Laurence Wilson; members were Dr. Jacob Dyck, president of the Manitoba Medical Association, Dr. Robert M. MacMillan, president of the Ontario Medical Association, Dr. Marc A. Baltzan, chairman of the CMA Council on Economics, and Mr. Douglas A. Geekie, director of the CMA Department of Communications.

On Sept. 15, the General Council convened as a committee of the whole and the following position paper was put before the meeting by Dr. Wilson.

The CMA will support several of Mr. Emmett Hall's recommendations in his review of health services, but categorically rejects his package of proposals to resolve what he calls "the dominant issue". Mr. Hall's proposals that all direct personal responsibility for the payment of health care costs be eliminated, that all health care costs be paid for by government from taxation revenues, that payment for physicians' services come from that one source and, if necessary, be determined by compulsory arbitration, are not in the best interests of the public or the profession.

Mr. Hall's proposals would infringe on the patient's right to select a physician of his choice. Under the proposals, patients choosing an opted-out doctor would be denied their share of the financial benefits of the medical care insurance program. In effect, Mr. Hall would severely restrict the patient's right to retain the advice and services of the physician of his choice on a mutually agreed basis. At the same time, the doctor would no longer be his patient's advocate, and an independent provider of health care — an employee legally and otherwise responsible to the patient. Instead he would become, in labour relations terminology, a government-retained dependent contractor — a de facto civil servant. In a very real sense Mr. Hall is recommending that Health Care Insurance which the medical profession of Canada has pioneered and strongly supports, be abandoned in favour of state medicine.

Several provincial ministers of health oppose this recommendation. They have acknowledged that the responsible manner in which doctors have billed their patients directly has not threatened the principles or the function of health care insurance. Their opposition to Mr. Hall's proposal is, no doubt, also influenced by his stipulation that the level of government payment for physicians' services would be subject to binding arbitration — that the spending of tax money be removed from Cabinet control.

The CMA has strongly supported medical care insurance for many years. It has been a fundamental CMA principle that "the patient should be aware of, and wherever possible pay part of, the cost of medical services he receives". That principle applies not only to the cost of services provided by physicians but includes hospital and other institutional services. It has always been subject to the financial ability of the patient to pay. We believe that the patient should be protected from catastrophic health care costs, regardless of their cause, but that he should retain some direct responsibility for the cost of personal health care. It also provides a most important safety valve for unsatisfactory medicare benefit negotiations, a means whereby the physician can oppose naked fiscal power exercised by provincial governments without harm to his patients.

The Association believes that a health care insurance program that pays all costs for some of the population and most of the costs for the rest is a pragmatic solution infinitely preferable to a state health care system, one that provides "free medical services" for all. It protects the independence and freedom of the physician to serve as the patient's personal advocate free to criticize on his patient's behalf the deficiencies of governmental or institutional policies detrimental to health care. Finally, it allows the patient more freedom to decide how much of his personal resources he will spend on health care.

In its submission to Mr. Hall the CMA has supported the insurance principles which form the basis of our present legislation, and has argued against Mr. Hall's determination to end all forms of extra billing — all forms of direct patient participation in the costs of health care. We will continue to defend our position by forceful presentation of our views to the public and to our legislators.

If the people and governments of Canada reject our advice, if they accept Mr. Hall's proposal, deny physicians the right to serve as self-employed professionals, direct that state medicine be introduced, convert physicians to dependent contractors or civil servants, it will be a sad day for patients and doctors alike. Regrettably, it will make it inevitable that physicians seek the protection of some form of union organization rather than our current voluntary association of self-employed professionals. In case that unfortunate decision is made by governments, we recommend that this meeting of General Council direct the Board to explore the potential benefits of unionization of the profession with attention to such issues as defined hours of work, premiums for hours on call, overtime, weekend and holiday service, standardized working conditions and grievance procedures, indexed pensions and other fringe benefits that are available to state employees.

Mr. Hall's proposals could result in considerable benefits to the profession. However, it is our belief that they would be realized only at the expense of professional freedom and to the detriment of future health care of the people of Canada.

At the conclusion of his presentation, Dr. Wilson was given a standing ovation. The committee of the whole then discussed the motion "That the report of the ad hoc committee be approved in principle and adopted as the official position of the CMA." There followed what has been described by many long-time attendees at General Council meetings as "one of the best discussions that had ever taken place in that setting." The quality of those discussions is well reflected in the General Council proceedings of 1980. When the meeting reconstituted itself as General Council, the following motion was approved unanimously: "That the Statement presented by the CMA President, Dr. D. Laurence Wilson, on the Hall Health Services Review Report be approved in principle and adopted as the official position of the Canadian Medical Association."

On Oct. 25, a meeting of the Executive Committee with the presidents and secretaries of divisions was held in Ottawa. The Hall Review was discussed, and the consensus was that the primary problems of the health care system had not been addressed. It was agreed that a position paper be developed, concentrating on two factors: underfunding of the system and the lack of medical input into health care decisions. The paper was developed and, after approval by the parties concerned, was used as the basis for a speech given by the immediate past president, Dr. Wilson, to the Canadian Labour Congress Health Coalition on Dec. 15. The Canadian Labour Congress agreed with a number of the concerns presented by the CMA, particularly those related to government underfunding and the implications of the recent federal budget.

Following the release of the Hall Review, the minister of national health and welfare strongly advocated the banning of extra-billing and repeatedly stated that the current expenditures on health care were adequate. The federal government set up a parliamentary task force, made up of seven members of the House of Commons, to study federal/provincial fiscal arrangements. On May 12, 1981, the CMA made a submission to the task force; included in the document were the following recommendations:

(i) *That the Government of Canada, while recognizing the primary responsibility of provincial governments for health care, continue to play an active role in financing health care insurance.*

(ii) *That the Government of Canada and provincial governments take collaborative action to correct the underfunding of health care in Canada.*

(iii) *That the financial support for governments for health care be increased to reach a level of 8.2 per cent of GNP by 1985; and further that the increased federal government payments be conditional on appropriate increases in health expenditure by the provinces.*

(iv) *That the EPF Act formula be revised to provide increased funding for the less affluent provinces.*

(v) *That government recognize the important role of private funding for health care services.*

CMA responds to Extended Program Financing Task Force proposal, Sept. 4, 1981.
L–R: Mr. Douglas A. Geekie, Dr. John S. Bennett, Dr. Robert A. Wilson, Dr. Léon Richard (President), Mr. Bernard E. (Woody) Freamo, Dr. Normand P. DaSylva.

On June 18, 1981, CMA President Dr. William D.S. Thomas wrote a letter to Mr. H. Breau, chairman of the task force, in response to some questions raised by the task force. On the same day he sent a long letter to the Hon. Allan MacEachen, minister of finance, reiterating the Association's concerns and apprehensions over the policies of the federal government in the matter of health care. Copies of the letter were sent to all members of the federal cabinet, deputy ministers of finance and national health and welfare, members of the task force, opposition parties' critics on health and finance, and provincial governmental ministers of health and finance.

It had been hoped that the report of the task force would be released in time for it to be discussed at the General Council meeting but this was not the case. The absence of the report did not prevent General Council from debating the topics of extra-billing and underfunding, which led to the resolution: "The CMA is unalterably opposed to any government action which could prevent direct patient billing and is prepared to resist any such government action by every means at its disposal."

The report of the task force was released on Aug. 31, 1981, and 4 days later the Executive Committee met with divisional presidents and secretaries to review the report and its recommendations. There was unanimity in the criticism of the primary objectives in the report, i.e., to control costs at the expense of the availability and quality of health care, to eliminate political embarrassment caused by governmental inadequacy in providing funding, and to destroy the economic and professional freedom of the medical profession.

In view of the inability of the Association to convince governments that underfunding of the health care system was indeed a reality, the Board of Directors approved in principle, on Oct. 31, the commission of a study to determine the degree of underfunding of hospitals in Canada. On Nov. 12, the federal minister of finance brought down the budget, one outcome of which was Bill C-97 — An Act to amend the Federal/Provincial Fiscal Arrangements and Established Programs Financing Act of 1977. The existing established programs fiscal arrangements were extended for a further year without any substantial change. During that year the provinces were to negotiate a further 5-year agreement with the federal government.

The CMA's study on hospital underfunding was carried out by Mr. Milan Korcok, acting as an investigative reporter for the *Canadian Medical Association Journal*. The study was designed to be a short-term one with the aim of producing evidence of underfunding that could be used by the CMA and its divisions in discussions with governments. From the study it was determined that major financial problems existed in teaching hospitals, that serious underfunding problems existed in many large community hospitals providing secondary level health care, but that there did not appear to be any major funding problems in smaller hospitals.

The CMA proposed that a long-term study be carried out, and the accounting firm of Woods, Gordon was commissioned to do this. This study was to have three major thrusts: (a) a 5-year picture of the funding of Canadian hospital services; (b) a 5-year picture of changes in hospital use, particularly where there was a clear fiscal relationship; (c) projections of funding and utilization trends over 5 years. Included in the study would be the identification of two indicators — service and financial — that were representative and capable of being tracked.

The federal minister of health, the Hon. Monique Bégin, continued to express her opposition to the practice of extra-billing, and it was reported that this stance annoyed some of the provincial ministers of health who saw it as an interference in provincial affairs. To help the divisions counteract the federal minister's statements, the CMA provided assistance in their meetings with their respective ministers of health. At the end of May 1982, at a federal/provincial conference of ministers of health, agreement was reached that direct billing not be prohibited but that control of extra-billing be addressed to protect accessibility. The question of user fees was also addressed and a study of their impact on accessibility was proposed.

It was the Association's stated position that not enough of the gross national product was being spent on health care and that governments were applying financial constraints, leading to the rationing of health care services. In September 1982 the General Council debated a recommendation put forward by the Board of Directors: "That General Council approve the establishment of a task force to study the existing and potential effects of the rationing of health services which result from government policies." The motion was approved. The General Council was also told that a new *Canada Health Act* was to be presented to the House of Commons before the end of the year and that the proposed legislation had already been drafted.

The Conference of Provincial Ministers of Health was held in Vancouver in late September, and at the end of the conference a communique setting out the provincial governments' opposition to the proposed legislation was issued. In the ensuing months the CMA and its divisions stepped up their opposition to the bill in public. The federal minister rebuffed all attempts by the CMA to meet with her and the war of words continued until she agreed to meet with the CMA on July 14, 1983. The meeting did nothing to resolve the differences in policies between the two parties. At the time of the meeting, Alberta and New Brunswick announced the introduction of hospital user fees.

The task force proposed by General Council in 1982 had been formed with Ms. Joan Watson, a nationally known consumer advocate from Toronto, as chairperson. Other members of the task force were the Hon. Pauline McGibbon, past lieutenant-governor for the Province of Ontario, Mr. Roy Romanow of Saskatoon, M. Lucien Saulnier of Montreal, Dr. Léon Richard from Moncton and Dr. John O'Brien-Bell from Surrey, BC. M. Lucien Saulnier resigned in the very early stages of the work of the task force. The operation was called Task Force on the Allocation of Health Care Resources and given the following terms of reference:

The Canadian Medical Association is committed to the provision of the highest possible quality of health care for all Canadians. Further demands on the health care system are likely to focus on increased aging population and health problems associated with occupation, environment and lifestyle. New technological advances bring an important added dimension to the question of costs and the capacity of the health care system in Canada to adequately absorb them.

The Task Force will be given 18 months to conduct its study, although it will be free to determine its own time requirements.

Within this context, the Task Force has been asked to study and report on the following:

A) The expected costs and impact of the introduction of new procedures and technologies on the health care system.

B) The demographic changes within Canada and their expected impact on the demand, availability and nature of appropriate medical services.

In order to better examine these issues, the Task Force will be asked to study and report, as necessary, on the following:

a) i) The present
  - *the quality of Canada's current health care and resources in comparison with other developed countries;*
  - *preventive services;*
  - *treatment facilities and personnel;*
  - *research capabilities and yield.*

ii) The future
  - *the expectations of the public;*
  - *the level the medical profession considers desirable;*
  - *the level the governments consider affordable and/or practical;*
  - *the level of the quality of care that the Canadian population can achieve.*

    b) The costs of the provision of health care will depend on such factors as:
- *quality standards;*
- *geographics;*
- *demographics and organization of the health care delivery system.*

C) *To examine the methods by which such costs could be met.*

D) *a) To recommend action necessary to achieve the best possible health care for Canadians.*

    b) To develop a critical path based on identified priorities for change.

In June 1983, the task force conducted a search conference in Toronto at which a number of professionals covering a broad spectrum of health care expertise were challenged to provide the task force with specific areas and topics that it should address. Two major research projects were commissioned. The first, "Investigation of the impact of demographic change on the health-care system in Canada," was conducted by Woods, Gordon; the second, jointly funded with the Institute for Research and Public Policy, was carried out by the Departments of Economics and the Department of Clinical Epidemiology and Biostatistics at McMaster University in Hamilton, Ont. In January 1984, the task force began its cross-country open hearings and private meetings.

Since the 1983 General Council meeting, the CMA had expended much time and energy, along with the divisions, in developing policy and implementing tactics with respect to the proposed new *Canada Health Act*, scheduled for first reading in December 1983. Consultants were retained to conduct a public-opinion survey to determine the attitude of Canadians toward the proposed legislation and to look at the attitudes of the medical profession, different levels of government and the health care delivery system in general. A series of videotapes were produced for the public and the profession, and advertisements were placed in Canadian national newspapers. The CMA conducted its own survey of the opinions of its membership; the response indicated overwhelming support for the actions and policies of the Association.

In January 1984, the Association learned that the federal legislators were considering removing a clause in the Act requiring the provinces to provide reasonable compensation for insured services. The officers of the Association met with the minister of national health and welfare to express grave concern and point out that such an action would remove an important negotiating position from the profession and eliminate its financial protection. The minister took the position that the clause was being removed at the request of provincial ministers of health.

The CMA submitted for consideration an amendment to the clause to include a section on binding arbitration but, in the February debate in the House of Commons, the CMA's recommendation was rejected. During February and March the newly formed House of Commons Committee on Health, Welfare and Social Affairs held hearings. In the first instance, a decision had been made that the committee would not entertain any presentations from representatives from divisions of any national organization; this decision was subsequently reversed. On Feb. 16 the CMA presented its brief to the committee and followed this with a further presentation on Mar. 7. All 10 CMA divisions made their presentations on Feb. 21. Presentations were also made by a number of CMA affiliate societies.

When the *Canada Health Act* was finally approved, the clause that had caused the CMA so much concern had been amended by the government members of the committee and now read:

12(2) In respect of any province in which extra-billing is not permitted, paragraph 12(1)(c) shall be deemed to be complied with if the province has chosen to enter into, and has entered into, an agreement with the medical practitioners and dentists of the province that provides;

a) for negotiations relating to compensation for insured health services between the provinces and provincial organizations that represent practising medical practitioners or dentists in the province;

b) for the settlement of disputes relating to compensation through, at the option of the appropriate provincial organizations referred to in paragraph (a) conciliation or binding arbitration by a panel that is equally representative of the provincial organizations and the province and that has an independent chairman; and

c) that a decision of a panel referred to in paragraph (b) may not be altered except by an Act of the legislature of the province.

In late March and early April, the Senate committee held hearings and the CMA made a submission, stressing that Section 12(2) did not protect the profession adequately. The senators did not agree and refused to amend the Act, and on Apr. 9 the *Canada Health Act* was unanimously approved in the House of Commons. On Apr. 17, 1984, it received Royal Assent.

The CMA sought expert legal opinions as to the possibility of challenging the Act, based on the Constitution and the proposed charter of rights that would come into effect in 1985. In the many discussions at the CMA level it was noted that the Canadian Association of Internes and Residents had been, in large part, responsible for having the word "all" added to "insured health services" in Section 9 of the Act. That association had done this because it believed that the phrase "all insured health services" might provide a basis for testing the legislation in the courts. The 1984 General Council approved: "Be it resolved that the CMA Board of Directors take all reasonable steps to preserve the professional freedom of the medical profession through the courts."

The Task Force on the Allocation of Health Care Resources submitted its report to the CMA in 1984. Meetings and hearings had been held in 14 major cities across the country; 260 written submissions had been received, and 236 groups and individuals had expressed their views at the hearings and in private meetings. One of the major topics brought to the task force were matters relating to health care of the elderly, especially the threat of institutionalized care; other topics were the dilemma of increasing technology, "turf wars," the concept of "wellness" and funding problems.

On the question of funding, the task force report stated that

> *The resolution of the "adequacy of funding" debate is hindered by the conflict that exists between the federal and provincial governments. There is a dichotomy between those who are responsible for health-care budgets and those who make the decision as to how the monies are spent. There is little information to guide us in reaching the conclusions about the adequacy of funding; we do not know the extent of the inefficiencies in the system, and to establish that the Canadian health-care system is underfunded requires convincing that spending more money will indeed provide a measurable improvement in health, and that this improvement is greater than that which can be achieved by spending the money in some other way. There is a basic conflict between consumers, health-care professionals and governments over the concept of "scarcity" which insists that all societies must ration resources. All these problems are compounded by common misunderstandings with respect to health-care expenditures which are not borne out by the data.*
>
> *Because the evidence is contradictory and inconclusive, the Task Force does not support the contention that there is underfunding generally in Canada.*

The report of the task force was well received and more than 11 000 copies were distributed. After reviewing the report the Board of Directors believed that many of the points raised were of major interest to the divisions and that there should be discussions between them, their respective provincial governments and other health organizations on the contents of the report and its recommendations.

In the fall of 1984 a general election was held, and the Hon. J. Epp became minister of national health and welfare. The disagreements between the profession and the federal government had not disappeared, but the climate of discussions between the CMA and Mr. Epp were considerably more amicable than they had been with his predecessor. To the dismay of the CMA, the minister of finance, the Hon. Michael Wilson, announced in his budget speech his intention to effect a reduction of $2 billion in expected transfers to the province before 1990. The Association communicated its concerns over the likely adverse effects on health care in several letters to the minister. An additional concern was the imposition of a new tax on health products, which would substantially increase the costs of private practice, especially in practices such as radiology, ophthalmology and laboratory medicine.

In August 1985, General Council approved: "That the CMA General Council request the Minister of Finance to rectify the inequities and discriminatory changes in federal taxes affecting medical supplies used in physicians' private offices."

At the same meeting there was much debate on the matter of the 1984 resolution on the question of challenging the *Canada Health Act* in the courts and a review of the actions taken by the CMA to date. The CMA's legal consultants had analysed the legal opinions on the Act obtained by the CMA and the Ontario Medical Association and offered the opinion that a challenge to the legislation could be undertaken, based on the dictation of provincial government programs by the federal government and on the fundamental freedom of the profession provided by the *Charter of Rights and Freedoms*. After due consideration, the CMA Board of Directors requested the minister of national health and welfare to refer the legislation to the courts for a ruling on its constitutionality. The minister stated that he was not willing to take this step.

The General Council was told that the Association's counsel had filed a Statement of Claim in the Supreme Court of Ontario, with the CMA, the OMA and a lay person as plaintiffs, and the attorneys general of Canada and the Province of Ontario as defendants.

On Dec. 20, 1985, the Government of Ontario introduced Bill 94 — legislation to eliminate extra-billing in compliance with the requirements of the *Canada Health Act*. The Act received Royal Assent on June 20, 1986. The CMA's solicitors then filed declarations on behalf of the CMA and the OMA, challenging the *Canada Health Act* and the validity of the recently passed legislation in Ontario.

The federal budget of early 1986 had indicated the government's intention to further limit future contributions to provinces under the Established

Programmes Fiscal program, and once again the CMA expressed its concerns in the strongest possible terms to the minister of finance. On June 3, the CMA submitted a brief to the House of Commons Legislative Committee on the matter of Bill C-96 — An Act regarding the Federal/Provincial Fiscal Arrangements and Federal Post-Secondary Education and Health Contributions Act 1977.

The brief outlined the deleterious effect of the legislation on all aspects of health care, particularly in areas of the country where there was less than national average fiscal capacity. The head of the CMA delegation, CMA President Dr. William J. Vail said that the Association's views received a sympathetic hearing but that the committee indicated that it was not inclined to amend the legislation.

There followed meetings between the CMA and the national health minister and his senior officials, but no rapprochement was reached, and it was a very frustrated General Council that met in Charlottetown in August 1987. Some of the frustration arose from the slowness in the litigation of the challenge to the *Canada Health Act*. The federal government and the Government of Ontario were said to be cooperating, but on the other hand there was a delay in the CMA's solicitors obtaining some of the Ontario background documents. It was reported that, after the complete set of 15 volumes, containing thousands of documents, plus other documents yet to be received from the attorney general of Canada, had been studied by the lawyers, discovery of the provincial government and the federal Crown would be concluded. The CMA had delivered the appropriate background documents to the defendant attorneys general, and those from the OMA were expected in the near future.

Portability, or the lack thereof, was another topic that led to a lengthy discussion at the meeting and produced the following resolution, very similar to the one that had been approved by General Council in 1973: "That the CMA vigorously petition the Minister of National Health and Welfare to resolve the problem of payment to physicians for services provided to out-of-province patients as outlined under the portability clause of the *Canada Health Act*."

The minister addressed the General Council meeting and then met with the Executive Committee to discuss a number of vexatious problems, including portability, and pointed out that agreement on portability had been reached by nine provinces, the Province of Quebec being the exception. He also said that active negotiations were taking place between his department, the provinces of Quebec, New Brunswick and Ontario, and the three medical associations from those provinces.

On June 21, 1988, a delegation headed by CMA President Dr. Athol L. Roberts presented a brief to the House of Commons Committee on Health, Welfare and Social Affairs on the future of the Canadian health care system and its funding. The general direction of the brief is summarized here:

1) *The CMA continues to support the role of the federal government in the provision of an adequate level of funding to the provinces to allow for a national character and a reduction of inequities in the health care system.*

2) *The CMA calls on the federal government to sit with provincial governments to re-examine the established Programs Financing Arrangements with the objective of seeking a mechanism that will contribute directly to reducing the disparities in the health care system.*

3) *The CMA believes that objective study of viable private sector involvement must take place.*

4) *The CMA supports the investigation and development of alternate delivery mechanisms that are cost efficient and provide clinically effective care. The CMA is concerned, however, that alternate modes of delivery might be promoted by governments in the name of cost containment without adequate emphasis on the maintenance of quality of care.*

5) *The CMA strongly believes that there is a need for better integration and coordination of the different levels of care for the general population and the elderly in particular. This must apply for community as well as institutional care.*

6) *The CMA believes that a national conference, hosted by the Department of National Health and Welfare, should be organized for 1990. The conference should make use of the many studies that are currently under way across the country.*

7) *The CMA supports ongoing assessments of the clinical effectiveness of services not only to the aged but also in the health care system as a whole.*

8) *The CMA believes that there is an opportunity for the federal and provincial governments through their federal/provincial health care committee structures to work with the medical profession and other interested parties to develop an appropriate mechanism that will begin to seriously address issues of technology assessment.*

The CMA accepted an invitation from the minister to prepare a response to the federal government document, *Achieving Health for All: a Framework for Health Promotion.* Further meetings with the minister examined the implications for health care that might arise from the proposed Free Trade Agreement between Canada and the United States. The minister gave assurances that the effects would be minimal.

The process of litigation in the matter of the *Canada Health Act*, begun in 1985, was still wending its way through the legal labyrinths, and an increasing number of members expressed their concerns over the length of time of the process and the escalating costs. It was reported to the 1989 General Council meeting that $586 000 had been expended to date. In answer to many questions, it was explained that both the federal government and the Government of Ontario were using the many resources at their disposal and wished to portray the medical profession as the villain threatening medicare. The General Council was told that the legislation had brushed aside the professional freedom of medical practitioners to contract for their services, and governments, having established the reality of a single source of funding, could not only dictate the financial return to all practitioners (as suggested by the current statements on income capping in some provinces) but through their fiscal constraints directly affect the quality of health care being provided to the people of Canada.

By the time the General Council met in Regina in August 1990, it was obvious that many members believed that to continue the litigation was not a viable option. The General Council was told that the anticipated date of the case being tried in early 1990 had been rendered void, largely due to the delaying tactics by the governments involved. In mid-April the OMA informed the CMA that its board of directors would, in June, be recommending its council to defer and ultimately drop its challenge against the legislation banning extra-billing, if and when the profession in Ontario were awarded fair and independent binding arbitration as a means of solving fee disputes.

At their meetings in April and May, the Executive Committee and the Board of Directors of the CMA discussed whether or not the constitutional challenge should be continued and opinions were sought from more than one legal source; these opinions were circulated to the divisions. After much discussion the General Council approved:

> *That the CMA withdraw its legal challenge to the Canada Health Act, provided that the legitimate concerns of the public, the CMA and its Divisions, with respect to the implementation of the Act, are respected.*
> *That the CMA reaffirm its opposition to those aspects of the Canada Health Act that restrict adequate funding for excellence in health care for Canadian citizens.*

To provide guidance and strategy for the CMA Board of Directors to implement these resolutions, an ad hoc steering committee, also representing the OMA, was set up. The steering committee, together with a CMA staff working group, identified and assessed the following issues of concern:

1. From the CMA's perspective, accessibility quality, portability, levels of funding and future funding strategies are essential components in implementing the *Canada Health Act.*
2. From the perspective of the divisions, additional issues of concern include reasonable compensation and acceptable dispute mechanisms.
3. From the public interest perspective, accessibility, quality and comprehensiveness of services.

These perspectives were then developed:

(a) That a continuation of the court action at this time would not serve the best interests of the medical profession or government. Discontinuing the court action was in the best interests of all concerned and would bring to a close an unhappy chapter in government–profession relations.

(b) That both the profession and government are committed to the basic principles of national health programs as set out in the *Canada Health Act.* An entire generation of post-medicare Canadians has come to view access to necessary health care services as a right, not a privilege, of citizenship. As the free trade debate amply demonstrated, medicare programs are considered by many to be integral to our national identity and must be protected, especially at this crucial point in our history. The CMA is prepared to work with other stakeholders and to redouble its own efforts to preserve the national health programs the profession helped to build.

(c) That discontinuing the court action can be seen as having reopened channels of communication and cooperation. With the court challenge behind us, the CMA, the OMA and the Department of National Health and Welfare can look forward to renewed opportunities for collaboration in such areas as quality of care and human health-resources planning that demand priority. A stronger working alliance on key health issues — substance abuse, native health, family planning and environmental health — can be seen as a positive outcome of resolving the issue.

In March 1991, the CMA Board of Directors approved the three propositions put forward by the ad hoc steering committee as the basis for requesting a ministerial statement on the *Canada Health Act.* The Board of Directors also authorized the committee to proceed with the necessary actions for withdrawal from the court action, provided that: (i) every reasonable effort had been made to coordinate CMA and OMA actions; (ii) the taxation of CMA costs did not exceed the threshold amount established by the Board of Directors; and (iii) the minister of national health and welfare agrees to provide the CMA with a public statement of intent consistent with the board-approved propositions.

The three basic propositions were accepted in a May 1991 letter from the deputy minister of national health and welfare, and the CMA undertook the actions necessary to end the legal challenge to the *Canada Health Act*. On Aug. 13, the minister, the Hon. Benoit Bouchard, addressed the General Council. Here are excerpts from his speech:

> *In the context of increasingly limited governmental financial resources and escalating health service costs, many Canadians are wondering about the ability of governments and various bodies involved in the health care field to provide in future a quality of care at least equal to what they have known. Nevertheless, our health system is required to evolve, and probably undergo transformations.*
>
> *It would be a delusion to believe that the federal government will be in a position to allocate substantial new financial resources. If we wish our health system to continue based on the principles of universality and accessibility, we have no choice but to ensure that health costs remain affordable. To do so, we must be able to count on the participation of all parties seeking and implementing solutions.*
>
> *If there is one responsibility that lies with the federal government, it is to safeguard the key principles set out in the Canada Health Act: universality, accessibility, portability, comprehensiveness and public administration. In this connection, the federal government is still as determined as ever to ensure maintenance of these principles in the entirety within the provincial health systems.*
>
> *It is urgent for us to collaborate with the provinces and territories to help them solve the problems being faced by the provincial health systems. It is an obvious prerequisite to have a sustained dialogue between governments, health professionals or health service consumers. All the stakeholders in Canada's health care system must collaborate in the search for greater efficiency in an ever-improving system. For this reason, I am especially pleased to note that the Canadian Medical Association has withdrawn its legal challenge to certain provisions of the Canada Health Act.*
>
> *Indeed, there are many issues on which health professionals and governments agree. There are issues on which our differences will challenge us. But this is a time for conciliation and collaboration.*
>
> *Money is not our only problem. We need to look critically at the quality of our health care, human resource planning and problems related to environmental health and other issues. All the stakeholders have unique and important perspectives to bring to bear. It is important that we all have an opportunity to be heard.*

I would be remiss if I did not take the time to emphasize the important link that exists between Canada's health and national unity. We are all aware that Canada is passing through a critical point in its history, a national identity crisis without precedent. While Canadians are hard put to identify the symbols that hold us together, our health system, with its key principles applicable to every region of the country, constitutes without a doubt one of the institutions which makes the greatest contribution to Canada's distinctiveness, to its being a real country. Like national unity, our health system remains a fragile thing to which we must give every attention, onto which we must focus a collective desire for its continued survival. Canadians have their country at heart, their health system at heart. In the months to come we shall see whether this desire is a real one, and if it can be translated into concrete actions.

The concerns of the profession were not allayed, as was evidenced by the debate at the 1992 General Council meeting. Members believed that the enactment of the five principles as enunciated in the *Canada Health Act* was too restrictive, inflexible and inclusive.

To this end approval was given to the following:

That the CMA recommends changes to the Canada Health Act to allow creative problem-solving initiatives and to permit the additional funding measures that are necessary for the continued implementation of these principles and the survival of high-quality health care to all Canadians.

To address the resolution, the Board of Directors established a working group on health care system financing under the aegis of the Council on Health Policy and Economics to conduct a detailed study of health care financing in Canada. The study and related analysis were to include who should pay for physicians' services and how the health care system should be funded.

In 1993, the group presented the General Council with a detailed working discussion paper titled *Toward a New Consensus on Health Financing in Canada.* Five primary policy principles were approved (described in the chapter on the CMA councils under the work of the Council on Health Policy and Economics). These principles were accepted as the basis for developing specific CMA policy. A draft policy paper was submitted to the Board of Directors in March 1994 and referred to the Council on Health Policy and Economics, the Political Action Committee, divisions and affiliate societies for input and reactions.

A sample survey of members for opinions on the recommendations in the paper was conducted by the staff of the Association.

The draft policy paper, titled *Health Financing in Canada: Meeting the Challenge of Change*, was placed before the General Council in August 1994 by Dr. Hugh Scully, chairman of the working group. In his opening remarks Dr. Scully said that, based on the opinions received from a wide spectrum of the profession and public, the working group had determined that the current system of health care funding was not sustainable over the longer term and that the group had looked at all available options against the criteria of desirability and achievability.

The report contained 12 recommendations, and these were discussed by General Council. The following nine were approved:

◆ *That the CMA support national standards for publicly financed health insurance.*

◆ *That the CMA recommend that the federal government take immediate steps to arrest the decline in federal cash transfers to the provinces and territories for health care by establishing a basic cash contribution floor for a fixed period of not less than five years.*

◆ *That the CMA recommend that the federal government administer the national principles of publicly funded health care insurance in a fair and non-preferential manner.*

◆ *That the CMA recommend that the federal government, with the full involvement of the provincial/territorial governments, assume a leadership role with the physicians of Canada through their provincial and national medical associations and other stakeholders, in developing a social consensus on national health goals and strategies.*

◆ *That the CMA recommend that, over the next five-year planning horizon, governments at least maintain, in real terms, the level of public sector health care funding.*

◆ *That the CMA recommend that government take the lead in developing an ongoing public consultation process for reviewing and defining the range of publicly financed health care benefits.*

- *That the CMA recommend that the governments of Canada review and where necessary, revise current health legislation or regulations that unnecessarily restrict the personal choices of consumers and providers regarding alternatives in private insurance and other health care financing arrangements.*
- *That the CMA recommends that governments, the CMA and its Divisions and the private health industry explore, on a priority basis, methods for appropriately accessing private health insurance benefits.*
- *That the CMA recommend that Canadians be permitted by law to contract with a physician for the provision of health care services outside the constraints of provincial/territorial health insurance plans.*

Several other motions on the subject were referred to the Board of Directors for consideration.

Given the state of the Canadian economy at the end of 1994, it is clear that the funding of the Canadian health care system is going to be a subject of ongoing discussion for some time to come.

Chapter IV

SAVINGS PLANS

IN THE EARLY 1950s, the CMA's Income Tax Committee had looked at potential ways whereby there might be a measure of income tax relief for physicians purchasing pensions and annuities for retirement. Presentations had been made to the federal government on the subject of introducing legislation whereby such relief would be available, but these had not changed the government's mind. Indeed the Association had been told bluntly that any change in the legislation was extremely unlikely. Similar presentations by the Canadian Bar Association and other professions had been met with the same attitude and governmental decision.

A multidisciplinary committee was formed in 1951; members were lawyers, chartered accountants, architects, engineers and other professionals. The objects of the committee were to frame a specific amendment to the *Income Tax Act* and to have the amendment accepted by parliament. The CMA Executive Committee approved CMA cooperation with the committee in its furtherance of a mutual aim and authorized expenditure of up to $500 for that purpose. It was held that a major concerted effort be mounted to change the legislation, which permitted deductions for approved pension plans only when there was an employer–employee relationship.

The services of an eminent counsel were retained, a brief was prepared and presented to the minister of finance. In 1953, the General Council learned that the most recent federal budget made no reference to legislation changes suggested by the CMA and other organizations but that the presenters of the brief had inferred from statements made during its presentation that the legislators now saw merit in the claim and that the way might be paved for further attempts to have the legislation changed.

In June 1954, the CMA general secretary, Dr. Arthur D. Kelly, told the Executive Committee that no progress had been made in the matter during the preceding 12 months. The minister of finance had said that he was still unwilling to change the Act and that the Department of Finance was not in a position to administer a program of tax deduction for the individual taxpayer. The relevant debates in parliament had done nothing to make him change his mind.

Dr. Kelly reported to the Executive Committee that the Canadian Bankers Association and the Canadian Institute of Chartered Accountants had jointly presented a brief to the minister, asking for recognition of small groups, such as a principal, a partner and a few employees, as an approved pension plan. The presentation received a sympathetic hearing, but the 1955 federal budget showed no changes to the Act.

On Jan. 4, 1956, the CMA made a three-part presentation to the minister. The first part asked for restoration of the privilege of charging, as a current expense, the costs of attending medical conventions. The second part requested amendment of the *Income Tax Act* to permit self-employed persons to deduct from current taxes payments made for annuities or an approved plan similar to the method by which employees were allowed tax exemptions for payments for annuities, under approved plans, made by their employers. The third part asked that the cost of continuing medical education be considered a capital expenditure, amortized and chargeable as an exemption during the period of amortization.

Members of the delegation who met with the Hon. Walter Harris and his assistant deputy minister, Dr. A.K. Eaton, were Drs. R. Morrison Mitchell, chairperson of the Income Tax Committee, and Kelly, representing the CMA, and Drs. Jean M. Laframboise and Armand Rioux, representing l'Association des médecins de langue française du Canada (AMLFC). The submission read as follows:

> The Canadian Medical Association and l'Association des Médecins de Langue Française du Canada submit herewith a brief on behalf of the medical profession of this country in respect of an anomaly of the Income Tax Act. We refer to the position of the self-employed taxpayer respecting his personal contributions to annuities or other forms of retirement income. On several previous occasions, attention has been called to the favoured position of the participant in registered pension plans whereby he is afforded the advantage of tax deferment on his own and his employer's contributions. It is our belief that the time is now opportune to extend this privilege to members of the professions and other taxpayers who by the nature of their work have not been eligible for inclusion in registered pension plans.
>
> We respectfully suggest that the situation of the practising physician is typical of many other self-employed taxpayers, but since we undertake to speak only for doctors, our argument will be confined to considerations which affect the medical profession.

We of the medical profession must take some responsibility for the extra-ordinary increase in longevity which has occurred within living memory and which is an important reason for the widespread concern for provision in retirement. Although doctors have not shared the increasing span of life to the degree which is applicable to the population generally, we do survive longer than our professional forebears and must consider means for support following our earning years.

The long and expensive education of a doctor at both undergraduate and graduate levels results in his entry into gainful employment at a relatively late age. His earnings reach their maximum only after a period of years, they are briefly sustained and they decline in a manner which is related to his advancing age. A medical practice, laboriously built up, does not represent a capital asset which may be disposed of on death or retirement and the doctor's income is absolutely dependent on his personal efforts and ceases when he becomes incapacitated. None of these factors operate to this degree in the case of taxpayers employed in business and in industry and, in sum, they constitute the essential reasons why members of the profession should be encouraged and aided in their efforts to build up a retirement income.

As citizens we share your concern at the present inflationary trends which reduce the real value of our currency. We suggest that the proposal which we are advancing would encourage saving and would act in some measure as a deterrent to further inflation.

Effective saving out of income is made increasingly difficult by the current high cost of living and the heavy load of taxation applied during the most productive years. Evidence is not lacking that economic uncertainty and the necessity of continuing to work beyond the usual retirement age is having an adverse effect on recruitment to the professions where self-employment is the rule. In the medical profession, particularly, the public interest will only be served by removing one of the handicaps inherent in the present situation.

It is our understanding that one of the conditions for registration of a pension plan is that employer contribution to the fund must be made in addition to the tax-deferred employee contribution. It is our further understanding that more than four thousand such plans have been recognized and registered. In the case of self-employed persons, the element of employer contribution is, of course, lacking but it is our view that the self-employed taxpayer should be permitted to contribute the equivalent of both elements.

If in the interests of administration it is necessary to group self-employed doctor taxpayers into one or more registered pension plans, our Associations will give consideration to organizing such groups and to establishing either a trustee pension fund or a group-deferred annuity contract. We observe with interest, however, that the 1956 Finance Act of the Parliament of Great Britain does not require the formation of such groups, but confers on the tax-payer the right to select the deferred annuity which he prefers from among the policies which comply fully with conditions of the Act. This is reminiscent of the compulsory savings provisions of wartime taxation and it is suggested that its application to contributions by the self-employed in Canada would not present insuperable administrative difficulties.

We recommend most urgently, then, that in justice and equity the self-employed taxpayers be granted tax deferment on their personal contributions to their own retirement funds. We suggest that the Income Tax Act be amended to give effect to this wholly desirable means of saving and that the following conditions be incorporated:

(a) That the Department of Finance recognize and register retirement funds established

    (i) on the basis of a group contract provided by the relevant professional or other Association for its self-employed members, or

    (ii) on the basis of the purchase by the self-employed taxpayer of a deferred annuity of approved type.

(b) That the age of retirement and maturity of the contract be not earlier than 60 years or later than 70 years.

(c) That the benefits be taken as a pension for life or for a guaranteed number of years whether by the annuitant or his designated next-of-kin under a joint survivor option.

(d) That the retirement policy be non-assignable and that it not be surrenderable for cash except with the occurrence of total and permanent disability.

(e) That in the event of the death of the participant before reaching retirement age, return of premium and profits be made to his estate.

(f) That the tax deferred contribution of the participant be up to 10% of his gross income or $3,000 per annum, whichever is the lesser. In the case of older entrants to the plan, these amounts should be increased by a factor which takes account of their age and diminished years of contribution before retirement.

It is unnecessary to elaborate further that self-employed taxpayers need the encouragement to make provision for retirement income which could be provided by placing them on terms of equality with members of registered pension plans. We recommend most earnestly that appropriate action be no longer deferred

*and that at the upcoming session of Parliament legislation be passed to amend the
Income Tax Act to permit tax deferment on personal contributions to pension plans.*

Following the presentation, Dr. Mitchell reported to the Executive Committee that if the Act was to be changed, the CMA should be ready, willing and able to set up either a trusteed pension fund or a group annuity contract. The Committee on Income Tax was given the authority to make enquiries about knowledgeable consultant sources and to select one, should the budget speech give indications that doctors would be permitted to make before-tax deductions.

It was with great pleasure that the CMA welcomed the inclusion in the budget speech of Mar. 14, 1957, the long-sought-after changes for which it had lobbied so hard, viz., that self-employed taxpayers would be afforded tax relief for deductions for pension contributions.

The essentials of the new legislation were that, effective Jan. 1, 1957, self-employed taxpayers would be permitted to claim as deductions from earned income, sums up to 10% of income or $2500 per annum, whichever was the lesser, which had been contributed to approved annuities or other specified forms of retirement funds; and employed taxpayers who were members of registered pension plans could supplement their existing coverage by a separate annuity contract and deduct personal contributions up to $1500 per annum.

The Wyatt Company of Ottawa was hired as consultants for the CMA. On June 20, 1957, 2 days after the General Council meeting in Edmonton, Dr. Mitchell met with the Executive Committee. Present at the meeting by invitation was a staff member of the Ontario Medical Association, who had studied business administration at the University of Toronto after leaving the Royal Canadian Air Force at the end of World War II and who had joined the Association's Department of Economics in 1947 as its secretary. From that day in 1957 on his name would be synonymous with the CMA savings plans. He was Bernard Ellwood Freamo, known to everyone as "Woody."

Dr. Mitchell presented the following memorandum:

1. *The Canadian Medical Association set up a Group Retirement Savings Plan for its membership and that of the AMLFC, if the latter wishes to accept our invitation to join with the CMA.*
2. *The plan to have dual avenues for investment:*
    (a) A fixed dollar fund underwritten by an insurance company and that the recommendation of the Committee is that the National Life Assurance Company of Toronto be the company. A somewhat long-second choice would be the Industrial Life Insurance Company of Quebec.

Bernard Ellwood Freamo, known to everyone as "Woody."

b) *A common stock fund administrated by a trust company and that the first choice of the Committee is the Royal Trust Company, with second choice the Montreal Trust Company.*

3. *Administration be according to the method described in the memorandum to the Committee.*

   a) *This entails an administrative cost at the commencement of 1.25% of the yearly premium from the insurance company fund and 0.5% from the common stock fund.*

   b) *The acceptance of the offer of the National Life Assurance Company of Canada to process the common stock data on their IBM equipment at little or no cost to the CMA.*

   c) *An arrangement which the Royal Trust has developed with the Bank of Montreal to accept payment in any branch of their Bank or in any bank in Canada where there is no branch of the Bank of Montreal, and to transfer this money at no cost to the participant or the Association.*

   d) *Administration costs to the CMA are projected liberally at a figure of $28,000, which it is expected will be met in a period of two or three years, recoverable in a period of four or more years. Certain additional personnel will be required in CMA House.*

4. *The administration of the Savings Plan be under the jurisdiction of a separate committee of the CMA rather than that of the Committee on Income Tax. It is further suggested that the membership of the Committee be more or less constant.*

5. *As soon as contracts have been signed, the Committee on Income Tax or the new committee investigate the field of appointing an agent or agents of record.*

Much discussion followed this presentation. Among the matters raised were the mechanics of promoting the Canadian Medical Retirement Savings Plan (CMRSP); the vehicles to be used for publicity purposes; and the role of the divisions. Mr. Freamo said that the average contribution would be at its lowest during the first 2 years but that it would rise after that.

The Executive Committee agreed that $20 000 be set aside to initiate the savings plan and also approved the formation of a trustee committee, which would continue the work begun by the Committee on Income Tax. Dr. Kelly visualized a small staff who would act in a new department of the CMA and be headed by an assistant secretary. On Sept. 1, 1957, Mr. Freamo joined the CMA and took that post.

Enrolment in the new CMRSP increased from 362 on Oct. 26 to 1762 by the last day of the year. It was expected that total contributions for 1957 would amount to $1.5 million, two-thirds of which would be invested in common stocks and the remaining one-third in the insured annuity. The publicizing of the plan had begun in the Aug. 1 issue of the *Canadian Medical Association Journal*, with information on its progress taking up about one-third of a page. In response to the many enquiries from members, the information occupied a whole page of the Dec. 1, 1957 issue.

The Trusteeship Committee was established with Dr. Gerald W. Halpenny of Montreal as chairman, and as members Drs. Elmer W. Mitchell and T. Tweed Samis from Toronto, Dr. Nat J. Blair from British Columbia, Dr. D.G. MacQueen from Alberta, Dr. John D. Leishman from Saskatchewan, Dr. Roy W. Richardson from Manitoba, Dr. Cyril Rotenberg from Ontario, Dr. Gibbon E. Craig from Quebec, Dr. H. Young from Nova Scotia and Dr. John H. Maloney from Prince Edward Island. The first three named formed the Nucleus Trusteeship Committee; the rest were divisional representatives.

On Feb. 15, 1958, the Executive Committee approved the recommendations of the Trusteeship Committee as they pertained to its proposed terms of reference:

> *Whereas it is considered desirable to delineate the responsibilities of the Nucleus Trusteeship Committee and the corresponding Divisional members of the Committee, be it resolved that the Nucleus Trusteeship Committee shall have the final responsibility with respect to investment decisions, but shall have no personal financial liability either individually or as a group.*
>
> *Be it further resolved that the representatives appointed by the Divisions to this Committee shall act only in an advisory capacity. They shall not be voting members nor shall they be held responsible for the actions of the Committee, unless they attend meetings of the Nucleus Trusteeship Committee at the request of the Chairman.*
>
> *And that this be adopted subject to the approval of the solicitor.*

Membership in the CMRSP continued to grow. At the May 1959 General Council meeting in Toronto, the honorary treasurer, Dr. Gerald W. Halpenny, reported that at the end of December 1958, enrolment in the plan was 2050 and total contributions up to that date exceeded $4 300 000 of which $2 700 000 had been invested in the Common Stock Fund (CSF) and the balance in the insured annuity fund (IAF). During 1958 and for the first 2 months of 1959 the interest rate in the IAF was 4.5%; this was 1% higher than the guaranteed rate. During the same period the value of the unit in the CSF increased from $10.00 to $12.63. By the end of 1959 participants had invested more that $7 100 000 in the plan since its inception.

In his report to General Council in Banff in June 1960, Dr. Halpenny brought forward a proposal for the establishment of a Canadian medical non-registered savings plan. The purpose of the proposed plan was to provide investment facilities currently available to participants in the CMRSP who wished to save, on a long-term basis, monies that were not registered and there-fore ineligible for income tax exemption.

It was further proposed that a non-registered trust agreement would be drawn up between the CMA and the Royal Trust Company; units in the fund would be the same whether they were in the registered part of the fund or not. Dividends would have to be retained and reinvested; participants would be notified as to their income-tax obligations. Costs to the participant would be similar to those assessed participants in the registered part of the fund, i.e., 0.5% yearly of the fund's current value.

The Trusteeship Committee had spent a lot of time debating the pros and cons of such a fund and decided to submit the following to the Executive Com-mittee for consideration: "That in order to improve the retirement position of members of the profession a companion non-registered fund be established."

The committee's report was approved by the Executive Committee and sub-sequently by General Council. On Nov. 30, 1960, the Canadian Medical Equity Fund (CMEF) was launched. By June 1961, there were 340 participants who had contributed more than $375 000.

Unit value in the CSF had risen to $14.17 by the end of February 1961 and the interest rate for the IAF was 5.13%. The honorary treasurer, Dr. George E. Wodehouse, reported to General Council in Winnipeg in June 1962 that $13 903 125 had been contributed by 2892 participants in the CMRSP and more than $1 000 000 by 306 participants in the CMEF. Out of the nearly $14 million contributed to the CMRSP over $9 million had been invested in the common stock portfolio.

The administration of the funds had reached such proportions that it could no longer be handled by the two or three people in the Department of Economics. Expert assistance was necessary, and Mr. J. Robert (Bob) Wright, an expert on annuities at the Standard Life Assurance Company was hired as an assistant in the operation of the CMRSP. Like Mr. Freamo, Mr. Wright would become well known to CMA members contributing to the CMA savings plans.

By Feb. 28, 1963, the number of CMRSP participants had climbed to 3257, with contributions totalling over $18 million. The interest rate rose to

5.33% in 1963 and 5.49% in 1964. CMEF investment was over $2.5 million. Total assets of CMRSP reached $28 241 081, and the unit value had risen to $17.81.

The Executive Committee approved a recommendation from the Trusteeship Committee to the effect that eligibility for participation in CMEF should be extended to members' spouses and children, and to lay members of the CMA and its divisions, and that members be allowed to set up accounts for children and grandchildren. Also approved was a second recommendation concerning an agreement reached with the Bank of Montreal whereby recent graduates who joined CMRSP would be able to borrow up to $7500 at favourable rates of interest in order to establish themselves in practice and be allowed a maximum period of 5 years to repay the loan.

The fiscal year ending Feb. 28, 1965, was deemed to be an outstanding one for both the CMRSP and CMEF. There were 632 new participants in the CMRSP, bringing the total to 4325; for the CMEF an additional 321 participants brought its total to 990 physicians and their spouses. Contributions in the same period were over $6 million to the CMRSP and more than $1.5 million to the CMEF. The interest rate for the IAF was 5.59% including dividends of 2.09%; for the CMRSP the unit value had risen to $20.94. CSFs were valued at $31 518 851.

In 1964, the Trusteeship Committee was asked by the Executive Committee to re-examine its terms of reference and to propose new ones that would more adequately reflect the work of the committee. Since its formation and approval of its terms of reference in February 1958, the Trusteeship Committee had operated as a special committee of the CMA. In September, the Executive Committee considered the results of the review and decided that the Trusteeship Committee should retain the status of a special committee and that provision should be made for its continuity as well as planned changes in its membership. It was held that the several areas of responsibility, viz., acting as the custodian of very large amounts of money, supervising loans to establish practice programs, and dealing with the requests of members, required a greater degree of autonomy than was usually afforded other special committees.

The new terms of reference were approved by the 1965 General Council:

> *A Special Committee, to be called the Trusteeship of the Canadian Medical Association, shall be appointed to act on behalf of the CMA in the operation and supervision of the Canadian Medical Retirement Savings Plan and the Canadian Medical Equity Fund and such other investments as may be designated from time to time.*

The Chairman shall be appointed by the Executive Committee. The Honorary Treasurer shall be a member ex-officio and may serve as Chairman if so desired. Personnel shall be appointed by the Executive Committee and shall include a nominee from each of the Divisions of the CMA, preferably a contributor to, or be a member of, one of the plans.

Persons so appointed should preferably have expressed their consent to serve for a minimum of three years. Where a Division fails to make a nomination, the Executive Committee may appoint a member from that Division.

A Nucleus Committee, consisting of the Chairman and not more than three other persons, shall be appointed by the Executive Committee. The Trusteeship Committee shall meet at quarterly intervals or as necessary, and be responsible for all investment decisions and recommendations concerning changes in policy, but shall have no personal financial liability, either individually or as a group. The Nucleus Committee shall have the authority to act for the Trusteeship Committee between meetings of the latter Committee and shall be responsible to that Committee, but shall have no person financial liability, either individually or as a group.

The Trusteeship Committee shall be responsible to, and report to, the Executive Committee and shall report annually to General Council.

The frequency of meetings of the whole Committee should be subject to periodic review in the light of experience as to the necessity of holding, and the benefits accruing from, such meetings.

The June 1966 General Council meeting in Edmonton heard the new chairman of the committee, Dr. Nat J. Blair, report that as of Feb. 28, 4866 doctors were using the CMRSP and 1224 doctors and their spouses were enrolled in the CMEF. From February 1965 to February 1966, $7 278 726 had been invested in the CMRSP and $1 820 056 in the CMEF. The IAF interest rate was 5.60%, including dividends of 2.10%, and the unit value had reached $21.14.

The trusteeship reviewed the agreements under which both funds operated and made changes in order to obtain the best legal methods of operating them to comply with changes in succession duty legislation, to more fairly allocate administration costs between the two funds and to make allowances for mortality changes for new participants in the plan.

Enquiries regarding loans to establish practice continued to increase, and Dr. Blair reported that loans to the tune of $899 040 had been made.

In 1967, the centenary of the CMA, delegates to the General Council Meeting in Montreal heard that the number of participants in the plan continued to grow and currently stood at 5264 in the CMRSP and 1322 in the Canadian Medical Insured Annuity Fund (CMIAF), formerly the common stock portion of the fund.

Changes in nomenclature were recommended by the Association's legal advisers. Henceforward the CMRSP would be known as the CMARSP. Other changes approved in 1966 necessitated new arrangements with Royal Trust and with the National Life Assurance Company of Canada, the CMIAF's underwriter. The latter agreed to improvements in the contract between itself and the CMA that would lead to a reduction in administrative costs as well as improvements in the formulae pertaining to dividends and administrative costs. Effective March 1967, the CMAIF was valued monthly, and participants were able to liquidate units on a monthly instead of a quarterly basis. Monies could be deposited in the registered plan quarterly, but non-registered contributions could be deposited on a monthly basis.

By June 1968, the number of doctors using the CMARSP was 5744; CMIAF enrolment was 1435. Total assets of the two funds exceeded $70.5 million. The CMARSP unit value was $21.79; net interest rate for the CMIAF was 5.70%. The gross value of loans taken out under the Loans to Establish Medical Practice Programme was $1 730 000. The collateral with the Bank of Montreal was increased to $62 500, but because of the increased demand, the maximum loan had been reduced from $7500 to $5000. A new agreement was reached with the bank whereby the rate of interest on loans was set at 0.25% above its prime rate of interest and made subject to change concomitant with changes in the prime rate.

The Trusteeship Committee had functioned for a decade as a special committee, albeit with a greater degree of autonomy than was usually given to special committees, and it was now of the opinion that its status should be changed to that of a standing committee.

A recommendation to that effect went to the Executive Committee for its consideration, but as a review of the CMA and its organizational structure was being considered at that time, the recommendation was put on hold.

Another recommendation from the Trusteeship Committee to the Executive Committee was that the CMA should establish a performance investment fund. This recommendation was approved by the Executive Committee, and in April 1969 it directed the Trusteeship Committee to proceed to write a prospectus and report back. Following the directive numerous discussions took place between the Trusteeship Committee, the CMA's legal advisers and the Ontario Securities Commission (OSC) and a preliminary prospectus was prepared. It was planned that this proposed new vehicle would protect the CMA pension funds and other members' benefits.

The OSC required that the CMA's CSF be registered, and at the same time a similar requirement came from the Quebec Securities Commission (QSC). The cost of such registration was about $5000. The Trusteeship Committee proceeded with the necessary audits of securities and records in order to comply with the necessary registration requirements. The OSC expressed its concern over the role of CMA staff who were promoting participation in both present and anticipated future funds, pointing out that any person on salary or commission whose income, in whole or in part, was derived from such activity must be licensed to sell securities. The CMA argued that its staff — Bernard E. Freamo, J. Robert Wright and Rod Macleod — was not actively selling but was merely the conduit through which information about CMA funds was provided to members.

A solution was arrived at whereby the plan would be promoted on a national basis and this would involve the creation of a corporation that would be a wholly owned subsidiary of the CMA. The corporation would act as a management company for CMA funds, present and proposed. This structure would be licensed in each province and legislation obtained to permit the officers of such a company to sell or promote its funds in all jurisdictions where such funds were registered. Officers would not be directors of the corporation and would be permitted legally to promote and give investment advice to members of the CMA.

Reorganization of the CMA committee structure had already taken place, and the numerous committees were scheduled to be coalesced into five councils. One was to be called the Council on Personal Services to Physicians, and included in its mandate were pensions and insurance, and the CMA savings plans.

In June 1969, Dr. Blair, chairman of the Trusteeship Committee, accompanied by committee members, Drs. John D. Leishman, Cyril Rotenberg and Jacques Sylvestre, presented the following report of the committee to the CMA Board of Directors:

1. *That the Council on Personal Services to Physicians be authorized to establish the necessary structures for CMARSP in order to comply with the requirements of the Securities Commission.*
2. *That the Board of Directors approve the establishment of a performance fund on the following basis:*
   (a) The fund will be tentatively named The Lancet Performance Fund Ltd. It will issue shares rather than units and will be registered with the ten provincial securities commissions.

(b) *The fund will be valued on a monthly basis.*

(c) *Contributions will be made through the Royal Bank who will act as custodian of the securities.*

(d) *There will be no front end load but there may be a charge on liquidation of shares.*

(e) *That the maximum fee for investment management and administration will be 1/12 of 1% monthly of the value of the fund.*

(f) *There will be a number of fund managers with a minimum of three.*

(g) *The Fund Board of Directors will be composed of the 11 members of the Council on Personal Services to Physicians, the three current members of the Nucleus Committee who will not normally sit on Council — Drs. Rotenberg, Leishman and Samis — The Honorary Treasurer and the Chairman of the Board of the CMA.*

(h) *All voting shares will be owned by the CMA.*

3. *That the Board of Directors approve the establishment of a further corporation to be called Lancet Management Ltd., to operate on the following basis:*

(a) *All shares would be owned by the CMA who therefore has control and any surplus profits of Lancet Management Ltd may be paid to the CMA through dividends.*

(b) *The CMA would invest the current Trusteeship Administrative reserve in this new company either as a loan or in redeemable preferred shares.*

(c) *Lancet Management Ltd., would execute management contracts with the Lancet Performance Fund and with the Royal Trust and National Life re. CMARSP and CMIAF. The contracts with Royal Trust and National Life would be substantially identical with present contracts.*

(d) *Because of the legal requirement, the staff of CMA who will be involved in the promotion of the Fund will be named as officers of the company.*

The changes in the CMA organization had included the creation of a board of directors, and it was that body that approved the report and its recommendations. At its meeting of Sept. 26 and 27, 1969, Dr. Blair told the Board of Directors that existing restrictions on investing in CMA funds would be maintained and that fund managers would not invest in the common stocks of companies having a major interest in pharmaceutical or tobacco products.

The matter of setting up an insurance agency to receive commissions on annuities, purchased for retiring members was discussed by the Board of Directors, but no decision was reached, pending the issuance of new governmental regulations with respect to the licensing of salespersons for insurance and mutual funds.

The Lancet Performance Fund (LPF) now joined the other two CMA-administered funds — the CMEF (later renamed the MD Equity Fund), and the Investment Fund (later renamed the Alta Vista Fund). Lancet Management Ltd. took over the operations of the three funds via four major brokerage houses and guaranteed "payment to the Bank of Montreal all old, present and future debts and liabilities now or at any time due or owing to said Bank by the CMA, up to a limit of $87,000 at any one time." This established a security deposit with the bank for the Loans to Establish Medical Practice Programme.

The officers of Lancet Management Ltd. were Dr. N.J. Blair, chairman of the board; Dr. John D. Leishman, president; Mr. Bernard E. Freamo, executive vice-president and Mr. J. Robert Wright, vice-president. At the meeting of the CMA Board of Directors on Nov. 27 to 29, Dr. Leishman reported that 50% of Mr. Freamo's salary would be paid by Lancet Management Ltd. and that there was the likelihood that the demands by Lancet on Mr. Freamo's time would increase. In retrospect, a most prescient remark!

Although the funds were attracting more participants and the assets were increasing, not all was plain sailing. Securities legislators received complaints, primarily from insurance companies, that the CMA, the "new kid on the block," was selling securities without being properly licensed to do so. To address this matter it was necessary to create and incorporate a company to be known as Lancet Management Ltd.; this was done without any change in the relationship between Lancet and the CMA. Lancet Management Ltd. Inc. was a wholly owned subsidiary of the CMA, beneficially owned all the voting shares, and its operation was reported to General Council through the Council on Personal Services to Physicians.

In 1970, the OSC ruled that registered retirement savings plan (RRSP) funds were not securities within the meaning of the act and could therefore be sold without a prospectus. This did not apply to the CMAIF, which was held to be a security and, as such, did require a prospectus. It was also the opinion of the OSC that the intermingling of RRSP and non-RRSP assets was not acceptable, and this led to the creation of a new mutual fund for CMAIF investments.

The General Council, meeting in Winnipeg in June 1970, was told that the initial response to the launching of the LPF was three times the expectation and that there were 1984 shareholders with contributions of $3 232 393.88. Because of the increased work load, Mr. Ronald Bannerman was hired in 1971, bringing the staff complement dealing with the savings plans to four.

Lancet Management Ltd., 1969.

L–R (back row): Dr. J. Sylvestre, Dr. C. Rotenberg, Dr. E.C. McCoy, Dr. J.D. Leishman (President, Lancet Management), Dr. C.L. Gosse, Mr. J. Scholes (Royal Trust Co.), Dr. L.E. Prowse, Dr. H.D. Roberts, Dr. J.S. McGoey, Dr. J.C. Day, Dr. B.L. Jewett, Mr. J. R. (Bob) Wright (Vice-President, Lancet Management)

L–R (front row): Mr. E. Rabin (Royal Trust Co.), Dr. J.H. Maloney, Dr. N.J. Blair (Chairman of the Board, Lancet Management), Dr. T.T. Samis, Mr. B.E. (Woody) Freamo (Executive Vice-President, Lancet Management).

Loans were still very popular with those members about to establish medical practice and nearly 900 had taken advantage of the program since its inception in 1964. Between March 1970, and February 1971, a further 357 loans totalling $1 521 300 were made.

The year 1970 was a very successful one for the CMARSP, with 1093 new participants. The total value had risen to $11 700 000, and the unit value had reached $26.47, an increase of 23.7% in 12 months. By mid-1972 the assets had passed the $19 million mark, and the unit value was $29.95 at the end of the year.

The Alta Vista Fund, successor to the CMIAF, began on Oct. 31, 1971, with its units being valued at $10. Six months later, the unit value was $11.86. The increasing activity in the administration of the various savings plans brought with it the need for improvement, and one area where this was achieved was in a new computer program enabling confirmation of contributors' payments. At the same time consideration was given to the possibility of making investments monthly as opposed to quarterly.

Although the LPF was deemed to be successful, it was believed that its performance could be improved, and to this end Mr. (later Sir) John Templeton of the Templeton Growth Fund was engaged to manage all the monies in the fund. Confusion existed in the minds of a number of participants due to the word "Lancet" appearing in different contexts, and on Mar. 24, 1972, Lancet Management Ltd. became MD Management Ltd. (MDM).

The Alta Vista Fund and the LPF had similar portfolios, and, because they were expensive to administer separately, they were amalgamated in 1972. The new fund was called MD Growth Investments Ltd. and was managed by Mr. Templeton.

Between Mar. 1, 1971, and Feb. 29, 1972, 446 doctors borrowed $2 125 000 from the loans program. Arrangements were made for other major banks to join in the program and the maximum amount of a loan was increased from $5000 to $7500.

In 1973, the name of the Council on Personal Services to Physicians was changed in 1973 to Council on Membership Services and its new terms of reference were as follows:

The Council on Membership Services shall be concerned with the services which are provided to Association members both collectively and individually. This shall include all activities affecting the recruitment of members and the maintenance of their memberships. Through the Secretariat or through corporate entities organized for specific purposes, the Council shall provide Association members with the broadest possible range of appropriate personal services.

The chairperson of the Council on Membership Services told the 1973 meeting of General Council of concerns over the perceived ill-defined relationship between council and MDM. Members of the council also made up the board of MDM, whereas the Executive Committee of MDM was appointed by the CMA Board of Directors from Association members not on the council. In a similar vein, the president of MDM was also appointed by the CMA Board of Directors. As a result of an apparent dichotomy, there was a lack of definition of the roles and duties of the various parties, particularly when applied to direction of performances in the investment programs. The CMA Executive Committee called for tenders from consulting firms to submit for its consideration proposals for a path that both council and MDM could follow.

The consulting firm of Kates, Peat, Marwick and Co. was selected from firms that had submitted tenders, and a blueprint was drawn up for future activity and relationships. The existing administrative processes and procedures were affirmed, and new criteria were offered for use in assessing and implementing membership services. Concurrent with this activity, the CMA had been reviewing the activities of all five councils and had found a great deal of overlap and duplication. This was evident in the way in which MDM reported its activities. The Council on Membership Services reported to General Council whereas MDM reported to the CMA Board of Directors, a shareholder in MDM, at each board meeting. As a result of the review, it was recommended that the Council on Membership Services be disbanded and that its functions be assumed by MDM, with special emphasis being placed on the development of new programs.

In 1974, General Council approved the following:

- *That the Bylaws of the CMA be amended to delete reference to the Council on Membership Services.*
- *That MD Management Ltd. assume the responsibilities of the Council on Membership Services.*
- *That the CMA Board of Directors will subsequently report on the activities of MD Management Ltd.*
- *That the Executive Committee of MD Management Ltd., together with the appropriate officials from the CMA Secretariat, form the committee responsible to the CMA Board of Directors for the organization of membership services through the related subsidiary companies.*

The federal budget, introduced in October 1974 and approved in March 1975, included the creation of a new before-tax savings plan designed to allow first-time home buyers to invest monies for such purposes. MDM introduced a CMA Registered Home Ownership Savings Plan (RHOSP) toward the end of March, and as of Apr. 1, 425 members joined the plan, contributing $410 500. The legislation permitted those who did not purchase a home to transfer accumulated savings under the plan to an RRSP. New legislation also permitted spousal accounts, and in a 3-month period 508 such accounts were opened in the CMARSP.

In the 12 months ending Feb. 28, 1975, unit value in the CSF declined from $27.98 to $24.34. The IAF's assets at the end of February were $61 500 000. MDM consultants considered it imprudent to allow the size of the fund to increase relative to the assets of the National Life Assurance Co. of Canada, so discussions were held with other insurance companies. Those discussions led to an agreement with the Manufacturers Life Assurance Company whereby a proportion of new monies contributed to the IAF would be invested and held by that company.

At this time MDM also introduced a new program designed to provide a temporary investment medium when stock markets and/or interest rates were volatile. The new fund was known as the CMA Short-term Deposit Fund, and $0.5 million were contributed to it in 2 months. It was anticipated that the monies in the fund would be transferred by the contributor to either the CSF or the IAF as economic conditions stabilized.

During 1975, a special committee on membership and promotional services devoted itself to a study of MDM's existing programs, assessing them objectively as to their usefulness to members and looking at ways in which they might be made more attractive. The committee found that the CMA RHOSP had turned out to be an attractive investment vehicle with over 800 participants contributing $560 950; the annualized rate of interest was 9.25%.

The number of contributors to the CMARSP continued to grow, and 907 new accounts were opened in 1975–76. Total accumulated value of all contributions within the CMARSP on Feb. 27, 1976, was $171 876 000.

In 1974, MDM had been giving seminars to doctors and their spouses on general business and income tax information. In January 1975 MDM held a special seminar in Toronto for doctors approaching retirement; emphasis was placed on the social and philosophical aspects of retirement. Other seminars on business matters and investment were provided during the rest of that year.

MDM had undertaken a major study to accumulate data to support the need for changes in income tax legislation and, in particular, legislative changes that would permit additional contributions to RRSPs. The CMA president, Dr. Lloyd C. Grisdale, was authorized to make a submission on behalf of the CMA. This took the form of a brief, "Comparison of Employee and Self-Employed Pension Benefits," accompanied by the following letter to the Minister of Finance, the Hon. Donald S. MacDonald.

The Canadian Medical Association wishes to draw to your attention certain anomalies in existing legislation and regulations which discriminate against self-employed persons endeavouring to provide an adequate retirement income. Since 1972 self-employed persons have been allowed to contribute a maximum of 20% of earned income or $4,000 to a registered savings plan. The value of these savings has, of course, been eroded by the high rates of inflation which we have experienced in recent years. In addition to this erosion from inflation, it has become obvious that existing rules and regulations have favoured employees and discriminated against self-employed persons. The attached brief analyses existing legislation and makes comparisons between benefits available to employees and self-employed persons. It provides the justification for the following recommendations which we would commend for your immediate action:

(i) The maximum contribution to a RRSP be increased to the lesser of 20% of earned income or $8,000;

(ii) The maximum contribution to a RRSP should be regularly increased according to the wage index used to determine increases in yearly maximum pension earnings in the Canada Pension Plan;

(iii) That a doctor be permitted to make additional future tax deductible contributions to bring up his aggregate contributions to an amount equal to the current annual maximum multiplied by the number of prior years during which contributions have been made;

(iv) That when changes are made in the permissible maximum contribution doctors be permitted to make additional future tax-deductible contributions to bring up their aggregate contributions in prior years to an amount equal to the new annual maximum multiplied by the number of prior years during which contributions have been made.

We would be pleased to meet with you at your convenience to discuss these recommendations which we believe are essential to a fair and adequate retirement program for self-employed persons. We would point out that these recommendations are not inconsistent with your policies to control inflation as they should result in an increase in long-term savings.

Yours sincerely,
The Canadian Medical Association
Signed by L.C. Grisdale, MD, President

The deputy president of the CMA, Dr. Estathios W. Barootes, wrote to the federal minister of finance on Feb. 14, 1977, expressing the Association's concerns over the changes proposed by the minister in respect to contributions to RRSPs and registered employee pension plans. Bill C-22 proposed an increase in the maximum annual contribution by an employed person by 40% to $3500 and of self-employed persons by 37.5% to $5500. In addition, as of Sept. 1, 1976, the maximum pension payment allowed under the legislation would rise to $60 000 per annum. Dr. Barootes pointed out that these changes were discriminatory against the self-employed contributor and also asked that the current legislation on the matter of life-annuity purchase requirements be changed.

The minister's reply on Apr. 12 was noncommittal, so the CMA wrote him a further letter on May 10, expressing criticism of the changes announced in the federal budget concerning the transfer of funds from an RHOSP to an RRSP and requesting that a special provision be introduced whereby monies invested before the Budget speech could be transferred. The minister's reply on June 10 stated that deletion of the allowability of the transfer of funds in an RHOSP to an RRSP removed a discrimination whereby a homeowner who could not participate in an RHOSP was restricted to saving for retirement within RRSP limits, whereas a non-homeowner, using an RHOSP could effectively exceed the limits by $1000 per annum and that he (the minister) would not accede to the CMA's request.

During 1976 and 1977 the board of MDM was concerned over the relatively poor performance of the CSF within the CMARSP. The LPF, under Mr. Templeton, achieved increases of 49% in 1975 and 43.3% in 1976, and it was noted that Mr. Templeton could invest worldwide whereas RRSPs were limited to a holding of 10% of investments outside Canada. As of Feb. 28, 1977, the value of the common stock was just under $82 million; the value of the IAF was $103.5 million.

MDM introduced a new fund called the Canadian Medical Annuity Plan, which provided for CMA members to invest after-tax monies in a long-term fixed-income fund that sheltered income until the funds were withdrawn. This plan was managed by the National Life Assurance Company of Canada and paid interest rates equivalent to those of the IAF. Legislative changes made RHOSPs much less attractive to older doctors, and many CMA RHOSP accounts were liquidated before the end of the year. Young doctors participating in the plan were encouraged to remain, and it was as a result of their response that the plan was named the best in Canada for 1977, according to the *Financial Post* rating. The rate of interest paid was 9.9%. The same accolade was given to the IAF whose performance was rated the best of all guaranteed savings funds in Canada.

Because the CSF continued to be below expectations, it was decided that its overseas component should be segregated, effective Jan. 1, 1978, and be managed by Mr. Templeton. The MDM Board of Directors transferred the management of the Canadian component of the CSF from the Royal Trust to the Mackenzie Financial Corporation in Toronto; Royal Trust continued as trustee.

Once again the CMA's ongoing concerns over the inequities and inadequacies in the income tax provisions for retirement planning were drawn to the attention of the Minister of Finance, the Hon. Jean Chrétien, in a letter dated Feb. 17, 1977, over the signature of Dr. Robert Gourdeau, CMA president. The response from the Minister was noncommittal.

The year 1978 was a good one for MDM as the new team of Templeton and Mackenzie, through their combined management talents and expertise, caused the unit value of the CSF to rise to $34.45, an increase of 30%. The interest rate for the IAF was 9.6%. As a result of these impressive figures, the number of new accounts increased markedly with direct contributions to the CMARSP exceeding $24 million. MD Growth Investment's share value rose to $23.61, an increase of 33.2% during the calendar year. The Canadian Medical Annuity Plan (CMAP) also attracted a large number of new contributors.

As of Feb. 28, 1979, the total funds under MDM were $291 830 000, an increase of $64 million over the previous year. Numerous changes were made in administrative practices, including the use of the CMA computer system to record MD Growth Investment Fund transactions and a new collection system whereby all incoming contributions were processed at CMA House.

On the principle that maintaining an attack would eventually lead to the enemy's capitulation, the president of the CMA, Dr. D. Laurence Wilson wrote to the minister of finance, the Hon. John Crosbie, on Nov. 13, 1979, expressing the Association's concerns over the discriminatory legislation pertaining to RRSPs. The minister replied on Nov. 26:

Dear Dr. Wilson:

Thank you once again for providing me with the views of the Canadian Medical Association on tax related matters. I have noted your suggestion that the deductible contributions to registered retirement savings plans be increased for self-employed individuals. As you will appreciate, proposals such as this are given consideration as part of the budgetary process. Therefore, although I am not at liberty to discuss this matter in detail at this time, I appreciated receiving your comments.

Yours sincerely,
Signed by John C. Crosbie, Minister of Finance

The MDM Board of Directors was not impressed by this reply and asked the CMA president to restate the frequently expressed concerns to the new minister of health, the Hon. A.J. MacEachen. His reply was as noncommittal and as unhelpful as those of his predecessors.

In September 1980, in Vancouver, the General Council was told that the CMARSP continued to grow in numbers of participants, assets and performance. The unit value of the CSF was $43.57 in February 1980, an increase of 26.1%; by August the value had risen to $47.46. An increase of $54 million raised the value of CMARSP funds to $315 million. Under Templeton guidance the share value in MD Growth Investments Ltd. rose to $30.05 at the end of 1979, an increase of 27.3%. In the 5-year period 1974 to 1979 share value had increased 394%. On March 1, 1980, shares of MD Growth were split 6.25:1.

MDM now set out on a new venture with an involvement in the Canadian oil and gas exploration industry. A contractual agreement was reached with National Resources Exploration Ltd. (NRE), under which MDM acted as an agent making units of NRE's 1980 drilling fund available to CMA members on favourable terms and conditions. Interest in this venture was so great that applications for units far exceeded the number of units available, so, in order to match supply and demand, only one unit was allotted to each applicant. This was followed by a similar offering in 1981; 1500 units were assigned to the CMA and allowed for up to three units per applicant on a first-come first-served basis. In fact only 550 units were purchased by CMA members.

During the year February 1981 to 1982, 2270 new participants joined the CMARSP. Unit value in the CSF continued to climb, reaching $49.07; the interest rate in the IAF averaged just over 13% during the same period. MD Growth Investments continued its good performance with its share value rising by 38.7%. The Canadian Medical Annuity Fund's assets increased to $21.9 million with the opening of 300 new accounts contributing $8.4 million.

Seminars for office assistants and other seminars on practice management, investment strategy and retirement continued to draw capacity audiences. The programs, begun a few years earlier, increased their content and were made available to more members. Special emphasis was placed on programs and seminars for interns and residents; in addition an intern and resident self-study program had been developed, using an audio-cassette workbook on how to plan and establish a successful medical practice.

By the end of 1981, some 20 000 CMA members and their families were participating in MDM's investment plans. In the 12 months ending Feb. 28, 1982, 1800 new members joined the CMARSP, contributing $30.5 million. The rollover period for the IAF was reduced from 15 years to 10 and was scheduled to be completed in 1983. During the period 1981 to 1982 interest rates on new contributions varied between 13.73% and 18.06%, averaging 16% over the year. Attractive rates of interest encouraged many members to use the Short-Term Deposit Fund, whose unit value on Feb. 28, 1982, was $20.45, an annual increase of 17.7%. Total CMARSP assets increased by $23 million to reach a total of $391.5 million.

In January, MD Growth Investments moved to a weekly valuation and participation was extended to medical office staff and related personnel.

The federal budget of Nov. 12, 1981, proposed changes affecting deferred annuities and all but eliminated the advantages of contributing to CMAP. This did not deter contributors who opened 170 new accounts and invested $5.9 million; interest rates averaged 16.5% over the year. The Loans to Establish Medical Practice remained popular, and 200 loans were approved during the year. The maximum loan was increased to $15 000; the interest rate for repayment was 0.25% above the prime rate of the five major banks participating in the program.

The budget also stimulated an extensive review by MDM of the proposals contained therein and the implications as they pertained to MDM's various investment programs. Following the review the CMA president, Dr. Léon Richard wrote a long letter to the minister of finance, the Hon. Allan J. MacEachen outlining once again the Association's concerns in a number of areas — RRSPs, tax treatment of retiring partners, interest deductibility and research foundations — and asked that the maximum contribution to RRSPs be increased to $9350 and that legislation be introduced making provision for automatic increases each year to offset inflation. A specific request was made for the discontinuance of the discrimination directed against self-employed persons that prevented them from making a contribution applicable to an earlier tax year in which maximum allowance had not been claimed. It was pointed out to the minister that employees in a registered pension plan were permitted to make contributions for the years in which they did not participate in their employers' pension plans. The response from the minister was that the government was unwilling to modify its position with respect to RRSPs but that it would be prepared to discuss changes once policy had been decided for other forms of pension plans.

Also in 1981, MDM approved in principle the introduction of a real estate investment fund with the idea that CMA members could invest in such a fund, designed for long term capital appreciation.

In 1982, a number of the provincial securities commissions required MDM to effect a number of changes in its operations. A prospectus had been issued for each of its investment funds with the exception of the IAF, which was under the governance of insurance law. MDM was also instructed that the practice of having divisional insurance representatives must be discontinued, pointing out that investment funds may only be sold by duly licensed securities representatives.

In 1982–83, the CMARSP had a banner year with the opening of 2600 new accounts and contributions of $40.5 million. The unit value of the CSF had soared to $65.01, an increase of nearly $18. Unit value of the Short-term Deposit Fund rose to $23.24. In the second half of the year, interest rates generally declined; new money interest rate for deposit in the IAF ranged between 16.5% and 11.9%. The pattern of investing appeared to be changing with an increase in the CSF from 27% to 36%, 42% to the IAF and 22% to the Short-term Deposit Fund. MD Growth's fund market value exceeded $100 million, and its share value rose to $6.88. With the decline in interest rates demand for loans to establish medical practice increased. Response to the 1982 NRE Fund was lower than expected and the board of MDM elected not to offer an oil and gas fund for 1983.

The federal government's regulations pertinent to non-registered deferred annuities, such as Canadian Medical Annuity Plan, remained in limbo and no apparent direction was forthcoming from governmental sources. During 1982, MDM expended considerable time and energy in the planning and introduction of a real-estate fund to be known as the MD Realty Fund. The idea was that such a fund would permit investors to participate in a wide range of industrial and commercial real estate property investments. At the launching of the fund more than $8 million were invested in it.

The OSC had granted MDM an exemption regarding aspects of the CSF and the Short-term Deposit Fund regulations, but this was rescinded and terminated on Mar. 31, 1983. The QSC would not give MDM a similar exemption and ruled that MDM must establish an office in the province, staffed by an appropriately licensed person. MDM made arrangements to establish an office in Montreal by Apr. 30, 1983. This was the first branch office of MDM; in 1984, offices were opened in Toronto and Vancouver.

In August 1984, General Council was told that the value of the assets in the Association's investment plans was $806 million, an increase of $200 million in one year. CMARSP contributions amounted to $52 million; new members numbered 4000 bringing the total membership in the plan to 21 000 and its total assets to $604 million. The CMARSP was made up of three funds: the IAF ($305 million), the Investment Fund, formerly the CSF ($255 million), and the CMA Short-term Investment Fund ($44 million). IAF interest averaged 11.6% and the unit value in the Short-term Investment Fund increased by 9% to $25.33. MD Growth investment unit value rose to $9.03, an increase of $2.15; at year-end the assets were $150 million.

MD Realty, which had begun operations in 1983, had assets of $20 million, and subscriptions plus reinvested earnings amounted to $17 million. There were 1900 accounts, of which 1200 were RRSPs. The CMA RHOSP had two investment funds: the CMA Investment Fund and the Short-term Deposit Fund; the CMAP was discontinued as an investment vehicle but its accumulated benefits remained in force until withdrawn by planholders; there were 870 participants with market assets of nearly $4 million. The delayed legislation on non-registered deferred annuities received Royal Assent on Mar. 31, 1983, and this had sounded the death knell for the CMAP. The plan's 88 members were provided with detailed information designed to assist participants in deciding the most appropriate time and method of liquidating their assets.

In keeping with the requirements of the various provincial securities commissions, MDM filed prospectuses for the CMA Investment Fund and the CMA Short-term Fund and as of Sept. 30, 1983, these funds were available to CMA members and their families by prospectus only. "Families" was defined as spouse, children of majority age, parents, brothers and sisters, as well as spouses of children, brothers and sisters.

A landmark was reached at the end of February 1984 when the Association's investment plans passed $1 billion. Total active accounts numbered 36 000, 17 000 of which were for CMA members. In the year 1984 to 1985, 3600 new accounts were opened and regular contributions totalled $58.5 million; in addition, $31 million were transferred from other RRSPs. Of those new accounts, 50% went to the Investment Fund, 36% to the IAF and the balance to the Short-term Deposit Fund. A 5:1 unit split took place in the Investment Fund on Aug. 30, 1985. The unit value of the Short-term Deposit Fund increased from $25.33 to $28.04; the rate of interest in the IAF averaged 12.7% on new deposits.

The board of MDM approved changes in the IAF, such changes being designed to respond to the special needs of members nearing retirement. A new short-term insured annuity fund (SIAF) was established on Mar. 1, 1984, to receive contributions from members aged 65 and older; for contributors aged 60 to 65 years an increasing proportion of their accumulated IAF benefits was transferred to the new fund on each plan anniversary date during those 5 years.

During the year MD Growth had 1450 new accounts, bringing the total number to 8000; total deposits were $49 million, bringing the total assets to $220 million. MD Realty Fund had purchased five properties, two in Vancouver and one each in Victoria, Toronto and Montreal. At the end of May, total MD Realty Fund assets were $36 million and unit-holders' equity was $30.2 million; there were 2600 active accounts distributed almost equally between the A and B units.

In 1984 and 1985, 370 loans were approved. There were 770 loan repayments outstanding, totalling $7.3 million. Bad debts were rare, and payments to satisfy loan defaults were, to some extent, partially offset by the one-time administrative charge of $6 per $1000 borrowed.

The federal budget, brought down by the Hon. Michael Wilson on May 23, 1985, effectively killed another savings plan. This time it was the RHOSP. Contributions to such a plan were not tax-deductible if made after May 22. Benefits in such a plan would have to be withdrawn before the last day of 1985 in order to receive them free of tax.

The emphasis in teaching new physicians how to establish a medical practice continued with the introduction of a booklet *Guide to Establishing a Medical Practice*, which replaced the earlier self-study kit. Seminars were held across the country for interns and residents; there were 350 attendees in the first 6 months of the year and 400 in the second half. More than 10 000 physicians received MDM's *Financial Planning for Physicians* and its update information as well as issues of the *Retirement Bulletin* and *The Investment Letter*.

Regional offices of MDM were opened in Halifax, Winnipeg, and Ste-Foy, Que. Two new programs were introduced in 1985. The first was a Registered Retirement Income Fund (RRIF) designed to provide additional flexibility to members retiring from the CMARSP; payments of benefits were, by choice, either monthly or annually. The second new program was an Employee Benefit Plan (EBP), which allowed employees to withhold a stipulated portion of an employee's salary to a maximum of 20%. The invested amount was not considered part of the salary and was free of tax. There were several formulae for withdrawing benefits. Discussions were entered into with the Citibank Canada and Crédit Suisse Canada to elicit their willingness to offer a high-interest banking facility to members.

In mid-August 1986, MDM moved out of the main part of CMA House and into the two-storey addition. Assets under MDM had reached $1.5 billion with the receipt of $250 million in deposits. Regular contributions to the CMARSP were $79 million and two lump-sum transfers from other RRSPs accounted for a further $40 million. The Investment Fund took 70% of monies invested, IAF took 20% and the balance of 10% went to the Short-term Deposit Fund. The value of the Investment Fund rose by 31%, the rate of interest in new monies invested in the IAF averaged 11% and 8.9% for the Short-term Deposit Fund. Like Topsy, MD Growth just "kept on growing," with total contributions during the year amounting to $115 million; at the end of February 1986, total CMARSP assets reached $988 million.

MD Realty Fund portfolio now held eight properties. During 1985 the Fund grew by $22 million in gross assets to reach $52 million. Income-producing properties increased to $35 million and mortgages increased to nearly $12 million. At the end of 1985 total equity was $40 million; units were almost equally divided between A and B units with A unit yield at 7.75% and the B unit yield at 6.38%.

During the latter half of 1985, MDM introduced the Physicians Premium Account in cooperation with Citibank Canada. That arrangement permitted CMA members to open a chequing/daily savings account, offering interest rates comparable to 180-day term deposit rates — the interest rate was 2.5% below Citibank's prime rate compounded daily on the account's daily balance.

The federal government continued to wield its broadsword against savings plans, this time demolishing the EBP it had approved in the recent past. Contributions made to the plan remained on deposit, but no further contributions were allowed.

Early in 1985, MDM considered investing in business ventures unrelated to CMA membership participation and decided that it would be prepared to examine opportunities, judging each case on its merits. The CMA Board of Directors approved the concept, and MDM purchased a 30% equity position in NIM Management Ltd., a mineral exploration venture. Although MDM did not actively sell the limited partnerships in the 1985 offering, 40% of all units were bought by physicians at a cost of $30 million. The flow-through shares of the various mineral, oil and gas companies purchased by the partnership were transferred in mid-1986 to a mutual fund called The Perpetual Growth Fund, managed by John Templeton and the Vancouver firm of Phillips, Hager and North. In 1986, MDM actively participated in selling the limited partnerships in the provinces, excluding Quebec; $6.5 million was subscribed as a result of its efforts and a commission accrued to MDM. It was determined that in future ventures of such nature, MDM would need to posses an unrestricted securities dealer's licence.

The lobbying efforts of the CMA finally paid off with the announcement by the minister of finance that the RRSP maximum contribution level had been raised to $7500. By the middle of 1987, total assets under MDM exceeded $2.5 billion. Total deposits during 1986–87 amounted to more than $490 million whereas redemptions amounted to $168 million. Contributions to the CMARSP were $120 million from direct sources and $80 million from transfers. The value of the Investment Fund increased by 18.7% and the Short-term Deposit Fund provided an 8.1% return.

The board of MDM authorized a major change to the operation of the IAF. In 1984 the SIAF had been established, but the board's review was that the investment period for the long-term portion of the fund should be shortened. This led to the liquidation of the IAF, and its assets were transferred to the SIAF where the average maturity of investments was 3 years.

MD Growth showed no signs of slowing down as 7000 new accounts were opened and contributions were $240 million, bringing total assets in the fund to $759 million. During 1986 the fund's unit value increased by 23.6%. Its portfolio had been realigned so that 45% of assets were invested in US securities, 8% in Canadian securities, 20% in European countries and the remaining 27% in other parts of the world.

In 1986, MD Realty Fund purchased three new properties bringing its total of properties owned up to 11. Income-producing property assets rose to $55 million and mortgages increased to $15 million. Deposits were $11 million, split almost evenly between A and B units.

The assets of NIM-1985 were transferred to the Perpetual Growth Fund; the transfer amounted to $16 million worth of Canadian mineral exploration flow-through shares. Subsequently, the portfolio was liquidated and the cash invested in a diversified portfolio of equity securities. Shares of the fund were then listed on the Montreal Stock Exchange. The assets of NIM-1986 were transferred to Perpetual Growth Fund II on Apr. 16, 1987, and shares of the fund were also listed on the Montreal Stock Exchange.

MDM opened branch offices in Edmonton and Saskatoon, bringing the total number of such offices to eight. As MDM expanded its horizons it had to be conscious of the requirements of securities commissions. The OSC had required that 60% of the company's directors successfully complete The Partners, Directors and Senior Officers Qualifying Examination. Legal counsel recommended that a new company be formed as a subsidiary of the CMA and parent of MDM. The new company, known as MD Investment Services Ltd. (MDIS), was incorporated in August 1986. New directors and officers of MDIS were elected by the CMA, the sole shareholder of MDIS, and were those individuals who had held similar positions in MDM.

MDIS purchased from the CMA 9 of the 16 issued and outstanding common shares in the capital of MDM. The price of $9 million was met by the issuing of 1000 common shares of MDIS valued at $6 million and a secured promissory note for $3 million bearing interest. MDM paid MDIS an advisory fee based on the market value of investment plans managed by MDM.

In December 1986, MDM purchased an additional one-sixth equity position in CMA House at a cost of $1 053 000; this gave MDM a 50% equity in CMA House, including the new addition. The purchase was secured by a 25-year subordinated note with interest paid to the CMA at prime rate plus 1%.

During 1987 and 1988, 5330 new accounts were opened in the CMARSP; total deposits were $130 million and a further $83 million came from transfer of RRSPs from other institutions. The Investment Fund had a 3.1% rate of return and the Short-term Deposit Fund a rate of 7.4%. The IAF had been renamed and was now called the MD Income Fund; its rate of return was 9.6%. MD Growth opened 8650 new accounts with associated deposits of $104.9 million. The MD Realty Fund now owned 14 properties and was engaged in the development of 3 others. New participants in the fund numbered more that 2000 and deposits were $50 million. During 1987 the fund earned $5.3 million, net income was $3.7 million and the fund's yield was 15.3%.

There were now five Perpetual Growth funds, arising from NIM: 1985, 1986, two in 1987 and one in 1988. It was proposed that funds I, II and III be amalgamated. It was anticipated that there would be one more fund, with the assets being received in 1989. The CMA RRIF (Registered Retirement Income Fund), introduced in 1985, had two new funds added to the existing Investment Fund and the Short-term Deposit Fund — the MD Income Fund (formerly the IAF) and the MD Realty Fund. In 1987 the RRIF opened 180 new accounts and deposits amounted to $25.6 million. The fund had a market value of $42.1 million, almost half of which was invested in the Investment Fund. In June 1988 the board of MDM approved the introduction of the MD Bond Fund. In this fund investment was primarily in Canadian government, corporate and municipal bonds and was available to both registered and non-registered investors.

In the year 1988–89, MDM's "stable" of Funds had an influx of 11 500 new accounts and deposits of $400 million. Total assets under MDM exceeded $3 billion, an increase of $500 million over the previous year. There were 115 000 active accounts in MDM investment programs. The poor growth in the economy affected MD Growth but it still managed to post a 13.2% return for 1988; assets in the fund were just over $750 million. In August 1988, MDM retained a second investment manager, Globe Finlay Inc., a company managed by four principals located in Geneva, London, New York and Tokyo. The board of MDM approved an allocation of $100 million of MD Growth to the new company and at the same time approved up to $50 million of MD Growth assets for investment by the Templeton Group in emerging markets overseas.

MD Realty Fund holdings had increased to 38 income-producing commercial properties, and 5 additional properties were being developed. Direct deposits to the fund were $66.6 million in the registered portion and $37.2 million in the non-registered portion. The MD Bond Fund, introduced in June 1988, attracted registered deposits of $15 million and non-registered deposits of $35 million. The fund had a market value of $125 million, and the rate of return for the year ending June 30, 1989, was 12.3%.

The Investment Fund (IF), a component of the CMARSP since 1957, was considered by the MDM Board of Directors to be an excellent mutual fund for non-registered deposits and so on Mar. 31, 1989, the CMAIF became eligible for investment in both registered and non-registered components. The OSC came up with yet another requirement — a valuation of all CMA Funds, except MD Realty Fund, on a weekly basis, effective January 1989. MD Realty continued to be valued on the last day of each calendar quarter.

A ninth office was opened; this one in London, Ont. The CMA Retirement Income Fund (CMARIF) introduced in 1984–85 was believed by the board of MDM to be a good retirement option for CMARSP participants, and arrangements were made with the Standard Life Assurance Company to provide two investment options within the fund. One option was a fixed income with a locked-in interest rate; the other was the provision of a deferred payment contract whereby a member could purchase an RIF at any age after 60 to obtain the current interest rate while deferring the initial payment until age 71 years or earlier, if so requested.

In the period 1989 and 1990, MDM became the third largest mutual fund manager in Canada with $3.5 billion in plan assets. During 1989 total deposits of $515 million were recorded. The two registered plans — the CMARSP and the CMARIF — remained very popular with members and other participants. The CMARSP had $2 billion in assets, 50% of which were in the Investment Fund, managed by the Mackenzie Group; the other half was distributed among the MD Bond Fund, the Short-term Deposit Fund, the MD Income Fund and the MD Realty Fund. The CMARIF was the preferred retirement option for those converting their retirement savings plan benefits; participants numbered 800 and assets were $100 million. Many RIF purchasers took advantage of the Standard Life Assurance Company option, which provided investors with a guaranteed rate of interest return. During 1989, 375 RIFs worth $35 million were purchased.

MD Growth opened 2600 new accounts in 1989, bringing the total of active accounts to 26 700; deposits during the year were $148 million. On June 28, 1989, MD Growth shares split 4.25:1, and a similar split took place on the same day in the Investment Fund. MD Realty had 1260 new accounts in 1989 and this brought the total up to 4 000 active accounts in the nonregistered portion of the Fund. Net deposits were $32 million. The board approved a unit split for both A and B units, effective June 30, 1990. The Investment Fund was made available for non-registered investments at the end of March 1989, and this led to deposits of $26 million. The MD Bond Fund had 1100 new accounts and deposits of $32 million.

Request for loans to establish medical practice continued to be received at CMA House. Since 1988 Citibank Canada had been the only bank participating in the program. Loan maximum was now $30 000; successful applicants had the choice of either a floating interest rate equivalent to Citibank's prime rate plus 3/8 of 1% or a fixed term equivalent to Citibank's 5-year residential mortgage rate plus 3/4 of 1%. In both instances the repayment period would be 5 years. In 1989, 240 new loans were approved; 700 loans totalling $9.2 million were outstanding. In 1989 MDM set up the MD Education Trust and very quickly 300 trusts had been established, primarily oriented towards children's education. The minimum initial deposit was a payment of $25 000 or a preauthorized payment plan deposit program of $200 per month.

In 1990, MDM was managing $3.6 billion in its investment programs. CMARSP and CMARIF investors had the choice of seven investment vehicles, and there were five non-registered plans for after-tax investments. The names of two funds were changed: the CMA Investment Fund was renamed the MD Equity Fund and the Short-term Deposit Fund became the MD Money Fund. The Short-term Deposit Fund had been a component of the CMARSP for many years, but in January 1991, it also became available as a non-registered fund.

There were changes at the top in July 1991. Mr. Freamo was appointed director and vice-president of MDIS and Mr. Roland Breton became the president and chief executive officer of MDM Ltd. Mr. Breton brought to MDM extensive experience in the banking, trust company and investment fields. Mr. Freamo had been the executive vice-president of MDM from 1969 to 1982, secretary general of the CMA from 1982 to 1986, president and chief executive officer of MDM, executive vice-president and chief executive officer of MDIS from 1986 to 1992, and chairman of MDM Ltd.

During 1990, the CMA reviewed the corporate relationship between itself and its financial subsidiaries and recommended that a detailed study be carried out. This was done by Arthur Andersen and Company. In its report the company included recommendations on strategy, structure and mandate of all organizational units and interrelationships between the various components. It was opined that objectives and effectiveness of the various components would be best served by a new permanent committee of the CMA, to be named the MD Advisory Board. The CMA Board of Directors approved the proposal in August 1990.

The mandate of the new body was to advise MDIS on the provision of investment services and programs of the Association. The MD Advisory Board was made up of one representative from each division and reported to the CMA Board of Directors on how it saw MDIS meeting its objectives. Appointment to the MD Advisory Board was made by the CMA Board of Directors, which also had the prerogative of nominating the chairperson. The study also had recommended that the mandate of MDIS be revised to include investment of the reserves of the Association and its subsidiary operations, should such need arise. MDIS continued to be responsible for the design and development of appropriate investment programs and financial services for CMA members and their families. The board of MDIS was reduced to 11 members and for the first time lay persons, two in number, were board members.

Some of MDM's investments were transferred to MDIS as part of the reorganization. A component of this transaction was that MDM sold its 50% interest in CMA House to the CMA at fair market value. CMA then owned all of CMA House. The final part of the transfer was scheduled for completion in 1991, at which time the CMA would exchange the seven MDM common shares that it owned for additional common shares of MDIS.

MDIS carried out a study, the result of which was the addition of a third investment manager to operate in the MD Growth Fund; Marvin and Palmer Associates Inc. were retained and given $100 million of the fund's assets on Jan. 14, 1991. This amount was invested in 12 countries.

The Association's newsletter *Net Worth*, providing topical comment on financial issues, was now replaced by a redesigned, updated financial newsletter titled *Strategy*. The publication is included with the *Canadian Medical Association Journal* mailed to members. The content of the newsletter had been the responsibility of MDM since 1989.

During 1991, net new contributions to the Association's savings plans totalled $285 million and by mid-1992 total assets exceeded $4 billion. MD Growth had a 20.3% increase in share value, the MD Bond Fund was up by 18.3%, MD Money Fund had a 9.4% return, MD Equity Fund was up 7.6% while MD Realty Fund declined by 4%. The MD Income Fund had a yield of 10.5%. MDIS approved the increase in foreign content of the MD Equity Fund. The changes had been made possible because of federal legislation that permitted an increase in foreign content from 10% to 12%. The eight Perpetual Growth funds were reviewed and the MDIS board recommended to the boards of directors of those funds that a special meeting of shareholders be held in June 1992, to consider amalgamation of the Funds with a closed-end investment corporation. The outcome of those meetings was that in December

1992 shareholders voted to wind up the funds. Redemption of shares was scheduled for February 1993.

Over 250 seminars either conducted or sponsored by MDM were held on a variety of subjects in the investment field; included were retirement and incorporation. MDM joined the Investment Fund Institute of Canada in late 1991. In February 1992 a third lay person became a director of the MDIS board.

By mid-1993, total assets under MDM had reached $4.6 billion. New contributions in 1992 were $140 million net and for the first 2 months they were $110 million. MD Equity Fund's performance had been disappointing but a marked improvement between Jan. 1 and Apr. 23, 1993, when unit value increased by 18%, mollified the somewhat discontented. The picture in real estate was anything but rosy. MD Realty Fund's board of trustees, in consultation with MDIS and with the consent of the regulator of securities, suspended redemptions from the fund, as well as not accepting any new subscriptions, both actions to be effective Dec. 29, 1992. It was held that there was a need for a comprehensive review of the fund and of the valuation methodology used to arrive at the asset figure.

In 1991, MDM had put forward a strategic plan for the period 1991 to 1995. The plan was approved by the MDIS board at that time. Five strategic issues had been identified: fund performance, CMA membership, information technology, quality and excellence of service and corporate financial objectives. In December 1992, the MDIS board approved an updated corporate financial plan, a 1993 marketing plan and a 1993 corporate budget.

Mr. Freamo retired in the summer of 1992 and planned to continue to do consulting work, primarily in the area of fund management performance.

In mid-1992, MD Money Fund had come under in-house management, and its performance improved to the extent that in the first 3 months of 1993 it ranked number one among similar funds of competitors. MD Growth Fund advisors were reduced to two from three. The Templeton organization continued to manage 75% of the fund's assets; the balance was managed by Marvin and Palmer Associates Inc. The fund's growth was marked in early 1993 by an increase in share value of 10.5%. Branch offices were opened in Ottawa and Calgary. In October 1992 MDM launched three new mutual funds: MD Balanced Fund, MD Dividend Fund and MD US Equity Fund. By the end of March 1993 these funds had attracted $60 million in new monies and $90 million for other funds as investors adjusted their mix of investments.

The work load of MDM had increased to such an extent that it had outgrown its new quarters in the addition to CMA House and the resulting congestion rendered operations less than ideal. In 1989 the Association had established a building committee, chaired by Dr. Athol L. Roberts, and its report was presented to the Board of Directors in 1991. The committee recommended that further additions be built on CMA House. The plan was the addition of three stories to the existing addition, two of the floors to be occupied by MDM. Building was begun in 1992 and completed in February 1993. MDM moved into its new quarters in August 1993.

During 1993, the share value of MD Growth Fund increased by 45% while the unit value of MD Equity Fund increased by 43.5%. In the first 6 months of 1994 these two funds took in deposits of $160 million. In November 1993, MDM launched a new fund — the MD Select Fund, managed by Guardian Capital — designed to meet member needs for higher returns and asset growth while stressing protection of capital. The restructuring of the MD Realty Fund was time consuming, but on June 29, 1993, a special meeting of unit holders accepted the restructuring plan.

A new program for interns and residents was introduced and a revised edition of the *Guide to Establishing a Medical Practice* was published. In the regional offices additional financial consultative services were introduced to provide greater accessibility and improved service for participants in CMA funds. Staff recruitment at the regional level was ongoing in development and training. A part-time branch office was opened in Hamilton, Ont.

In the fall of 1993, a state-of-the-art record-keeping system was put in place at CMA House. The operations of two funds in particular — MD Realty Fund and MD Income Fund — required special efforts by MDM staff during the initial stages of implementation, but once that phase was completed, the new system proved that it would provide improved and up-to-date reporting to participating investors.

The MD Advisory Board (MDAB), established in 1990 as an advisory body to the CMA and the MDIS, undertook a review of its mandate in August 1993. Six recommendations emanated from that review:

(i) *Amend the first article of MD's mandate to read: "Advise MDIS on the general provision by the CMA of investment services and financial programmes to its members and families in all respects";*

(ii) *MDIS to solicit input from the MDAB on a more timely basis concerning the introduction of a new product or service or a proposed enhancement of an existing product or service;*

(iii) *The MDAB Chairperson, or alternate, attend meetings of MDIS as an observer;*

> *(iv) The MDAB chairperson attend CMA Board meetings in a capacity similar to that of a Council chairperson;*
>
> *(v) The MDAB to report directly to General Council or at the time of the CMA Board of Director's Report to General Council;*
>
> *(vi) The MDAB to meet four times per annum and that the meeting format accommodate a full day for each session.*

The CMA Board of Directors, in addition to reviewing the recommendations, reviewed the role of the MDAB, and in May 1994 the MDAB was renamed the Advisory Committee on Benefits, Services and Membership with a mandate to advise the CMA Board of Directors on: "(i) all membership services benefits and services, including financial services, provided by the CMA and its subsidiaries; (ii) membership needs, promotion and retention programmes."

In December 1993, the federal government had put forward a number of proposed changes in matters of taxation and included in them was one that would change the maximum tax deductibility in respect of RRSP contributions. In response to the government's proposals, a CMA/MDM working group was formed to work with other interested groups of self-employed professionals to develop a strategy to oppose the proposed change. Before the February 1994 federal budget, the CMA mounted its own direct lobby and took the lead in organizing a coalition of 12 national organizations, all of which opposed the proposed change in legislation.

A 13-page brief — "RRSP's: An Asset, not a Liability" — was presented to the Hon. Paul Martin, minister of finance on Jan. 28, 1994. The brief stressed the principles of fairness and equality and the importance of treating RRSPs as assets and not liabilities. Meetings were held with key officials of the Department of Finance, members of parliament and the minister's political staff. A letter-writing campaign resulted in hundreds of letters from physicians being received by the minister's office.

In addition to its own brief, the Association contributed to briefs presented by the coalition and by the Health Action Lobby (HEAL). The recommendations of the coalition brief were:

- *That the federal government consider the total cost of the retirement savings system before making changes to the Income Tax Act.*
- *That the equity established during pension reform not be disturbed by discriminatory changes and that any fundamental changes to the system should involve a process of informed thoughtful enquiry and debate.*
- *That the federal government foster economic development by treating RRSP contributions as assets rather than liabilities and by exploring the regulatory*

changes necessary to ensure increased access to such funds by small and medium-sized businesses.

The Association's strategy paid dividends when the minister of finance announced that there would be no changes to the maximum tax-deductible RRSP contributions. The Association offered its assistance to the minister and his staff in any further discussions on RRSPs, registered pension plans and related matters. It was with concern that the Association heard the minister say at the end of 1994, that in the federal government's review of areas where cost-savings could be effected, "everything was on the table." Included in that menu were RRSPs, pensions, and savings plans. The federal Finance Committee heard from many presenters at its hearings and communications from other individuals, that RRSPs and employer-sponsored plans should not be the subject of any changes in tax-deductibility.

In keeping with its philosophy to provide CMA members and their families with further options in investment strategies, two new funds were introduced in late 1994: the MD Emerging Markets Fund and the MD Global Bond Fund. The former was designed to take advantage of the emerging-market countries whose economies have grown more rapidly than those of the industrialized world. The MD Global Fund was created to allow investment in about 20 established international markets with about 95% of its holdings being in high-quality government bonds.

At the end of 1994, member assets in CMA savings funds were just under $6 billion and there were 150 000 active accounts. The plan had come a long way from the 1957 "seed money" of $20 000!

Here is a list of the funds under MDM administration at the end of December 1994: MD Balanced; MD Dividend; MD Bond; MD Emerging Markets; MD Equity; MD Global Bond; MD Growth; MD Money; MD Realty; MD Select; MD US Equity; MD Income Fund.

Lancet Insurance Agency

The history of the CMA savings plans would not be complete without the story of the Lancet Insurance Agency and the integral part it played in the operations of MDM and its predecessors.

When the CMARSP was created in 1957, the initial stress was placed on getting contributions and on operating the plan in an efficient and effective manner. At the start not too much attention was paid to senior members, particularly those near retirement, but that soon changed. On Jan. 15, 1963,

Mr. J. Robert (Bob) Wright joined the CMA staff as an assistant in the operation of the CMARSP. His background with the Standard Life Assurance Company of Canada, where he had developed expertise in the matter of annuities, made him an ideal source of help to those members of the plan who were approaching retirement and were ready for advice on annuities.

The annual meetings of the Association were ideal places to meet members and discuss their retirement plans, and Mr. Wright soon found that he was spending more and more time at this task. He formed an "annuity shopping service" whereby the best available rate of return could be obtained. The Trusteeship Committee became concerned over the matter of commissions and began to consider the viability of its own insurance agency. Mr. Wright's advice and financial planning service were not, in themselves, generating any financial return for the Association because it was not legally empowered to sell annuities, and the commissions from the sale of annuities were going to agents who had provided little service to the annuitant.

As a result of the review by the Trusteeship Committee, Lancet Insurance Agency was born and became incorporated in the Province of Ontario in July 1970, becoming the agent of record for the CMARSP. Mr. Wright, then vice-president of Lancet Management Ltd., became president and a director of the agency. To maintain its licence, the agency had to be controlled by a licensed agent or agents. Three common shares were issued: one each to Mr. Wright, Mr. Freamo and Dr. John D. Leishman. This share structure was subsequently restructured to give MDM an increased financial position in the agency, but control remained in Mr. Wright's name.

In its early days the agency's revenue was very limited. The National Life Assurance Company of Canada made no payment of commissions when benefits were converted to annuities, even though its rates were lower than many of its competitors. MDM paid $20 000 to the agency as consulting fees to give it a fiscal base. Eventually National Life changed its policy and, effective September 1981, agreed to pay to the agency 1.4% commission fees on the amount used to purchase annuities from it.

Demands for counselling and advice continued to increase, and Mr. Wright spent a lot of time criss-crossing the country, meeting with CMA members in their own communities. In 1972, bilingual services were added to the agency with the hiring of Mr. Michael Landry. Because of the large number of demands, the concept of holding seminars was considered, and by late 1974 the financial status of the agency permitted the introduction of such a program. The first Lancet Retirement Planning Seminar took place in Toronto on Jan. 18, 1975, attended by 50 couples who heard presentations on finance, law and travel as well as the philosophical and social aspects of retirement. The venture was considered a success and the second seminar was held in Vancouver later in the year in conjunction with a British Columbia Medical Association meeting. Further seminars were then planned.

Between 1975 and 1979 the age level at which members could begin to take advantage of the services offered by the agency was lowered and the new level was set at 55 years of age. Agency records show that almost 500 members received one-on-one advice over the next 5 years.

The agency produced an audiovisual program on financial planning, which was shown at seminars and at annual meetings of divisions. This action became so popular that its further extension and development were called for, requiring an infusion of money and an increase of staff. On Jan. 1, 1976, MDM assumed responsibility for the program, and Mr. Landry was appointed to head a new MD Marketing Department with responsibility for marketing and for the seminar programs. This new department took over the publication of the *MD Retirement Bulletin*. This publication had been started by the agency in 1974 under the title *Lancet Retirement Planning Bulletin* and was available quarterly to members over 55 years of age who were participants in the CMARSP.

Reference has been made to the payment of commissions when benefits are converted into annuities. In the 1970s, the average front-end loading was in the 5% to 5.5% range. The agent was paid 2% to 3% with the balance going to the branch manager and head office for costs associated with promotion, and so on. To eliminate such charges the agency negotiated group annuity contracts with a number of major life assurance companies, and this produced an improvement in the rates of commissions.

The new commission scale for the agency for locked-in CMARSP benefits was 1% for the first $200 000 and 0% over that amount. For non-locked-in CMARSP benefits the commission was 2% on the first $50 000, 1% on the next $150 000 and 0% above $200 000. Between 1970 and 1980, agency annual revenue rose from $9187 to $161 416; over the same period the percentage of the agency's revenue out of the combined revenues of Lancet Management Ltd./MDM and the agency ranged from a low of 3.21% to a high of 21.6%. By the end of 1987 the agency's revenue had risen to $438 744 with expenses around $200 000.

In the late 1980s, the agency recognized that a significant portion of RRIF business was going to be underwritten on an investment certificate basis and, because MDM had a group life annuity contract with the Standard Life Assurance Company, the agency was able to negotiate a RRIF contract on behalf of MDM. During the first year of the contract the agency earned commissions on all of the business under $100 000 per contract and in return arranged all contracts and paid all penalties. MDM assumed administration of this contract as of July 1,1990.

The agency was concerned that, when the 1986 federal budget changed the rules pertaining to RRIFs, older planholders would need options other than annuities. Mr. Wright advocated the creation of a bond fund that would provide older, more conservative investors with a steady source of income from their RRIFs. In 1987 MDM introduced the MD Bond Fund, which by early 1994 had more than $350 million in member assets under management.

In the summer of 1994 Mr. Wright went into semi-retirement but agreed to undertake some limited consulting with MDM. To quote from the July 1994 issue of *Strategy*: "The legacy of Bob Wright's tireless efforts on behalf of CMA members will always remain at the core of MD Management's approach."

Chapter V

COUNCILS

THE CREATION of the five councils in 1969, resulting from the incorporation of many of the 44 committees of the Association into those bodies, brought a different approach to the way in which topics had been dealt with in the past. In the main, committees had been composed of a nucleus, with the rest of the members providing their input by correspondence. The nucleus usually consisted of doctors from the same area, and the committee as a whole met once a year before submitting its report to the General Council. Under the new structure, each council was made up of one representative from each of the 10 divisions plus a chairman appointed by the Board of Directors and would meet on a quarterly basis. Ongoing reports were to be made to the Executive Committee and the Board of Directors, and an annual report would be presented to the General Council.

As councils developed so did the departments that provided the administration and resources for them. The councils and their departments were described by a past president as "the engines which drive the CMA." When one looks at the number and range of subjects considered and dealt with by councils, it becomes obvious that a chapter alone would not do justice to them. Indeed, a separate book would be needed to cover the first quarter-century of their existence. The following describes some of the subjects that were dealt with by councils between 1969 and 1994.

Council on Medical Education
The 1969 terms of reference of the Council on Medical Education were:

> *Council shall be concerned with medical and allied health professional educational activities and without limiting its terms of reference, shall study and report on undergraduate, graduate and postgraduate medical education; continuing medical education; educational programmes of allied health personnel; provision of general guidelines or the Scientific Programme*

of the Association's Annual Meeting, including endowed and subsidized lectures,
and other such matters as may be referred to it by the General Council and/or
the Board of Directors.

The council took over the responsibilities of five standing committees: medical education, intern training, approval of training programs for medical laboratory technologists, approval of schools for radiology technicians and the central program committee. In addition it took over two special committees: audiovisual aids in medical education and approval of training programs for nuclear medical technologists. Other responsibilities of the new body included matters relating to the allied health profession in areas not covered by the special and standing committees.

Over the years, the terms of reference were modified a number of times, but the main foci have remained, viz., medical education in all its phases and the accreditation of allied health personnel training programs. In its first year of operation, the council looked at intern training programs (ITP) and what appeared to be some paradoxes that existed. ITPs not approved by the CMA were being offered to graduates of Canadian medical schools, whereas ITPs approved by the CMA were not accepted by some provincial licensing authorities. The General Council decided that there must be minimum standards that would be acceptable to all provincial licensing authorities and that would ensure the output of well-qualified medical practitioners with portability of licence between provinces.

By June 1970, the council was in a position to provide the General Council with recommendations on rotating and straight internship programs as well as recommending the criteria for approval of programs approved by the College of Family Practice of Canada (CFPC). The criteria for the three categories were:

Rotating Internship Programmes
◆ *The hospital must be fully accredited by the Canadian Council on Hospital Accreditation.*
◆ *The hospital must have a capacity of 33 beds excluding bassinets, or less if it is part of a university teaching programme for internships.*
◆ *The hospital must have an autopsy rate of thirty-five percent.*
◆ *The hospital must have a range of fifteen to thirty teaching patients per intern. (To qualify as a "teaching patient" requires that the intern is provided with both significant responsibility for the patient and supervision by the medical staff).*

- *The hospital must have Certificants or Fellows of the Royal College of Physicians and Surgeons of Canada (RCPSC) or hold other medical qualifications acceptable to the CMA.*
- *The head of the Department of Family Practice or General Practice should be a member of the CFPC.*
- *The hospital must be a general hospital with at least the services of Internal Medicine, and Surgery. Other services — Obstetrics and Gynaecology, Paediatrics, Psychiatry — must be provided within the hospital or by arrangement with other hospitals.*

Straight Internship Programmes

RCPSC and Quebec CPS approved straight internships will be recognized by the CMA. Straight internships not approved as above must be taken in a hospital approved for rotating internships; such hospitals must have a range of fifteen to thirty teaching patients per straight intern over and above those required for rotating internships. Approval would be considered in any medical discipline.

First Year Family Medicine Programmes

CFPC programmes will be recognized as approved by the CMA.

The programme must contain in its first year four months of General Medicine, or two months of General Medicine plus two months in an ambulatory service in which fifty percent of the patients being cared for are adults with medical problems.

A year later the council gave some thought as to why it was concerned with intern training programs and answered itself by pointing out to the General Council that one of the obligations of a profession is the duty to ensure adequate education, self-assessment, ongoing development of educational programs and setting standards for training. All of these fell within the council's mandate, and the approval of ITPs was seen as part of that mandate. It was noted that an ITP is but one part of a continuum of medical education. The council believed that a broader look should be taken at ITPs and therefore established a working group of representatives from the CMA, Royal College of Physicians and Surgeons of Canada (RCPSC), CFPC, Association of Canadian Medical Colleges (ACMC), the Federation of Provincial Medical Licensing Authorities of Canada (FPMLAC), and the Canadian Association of Internes and Residents (CAIR). In 1972, the working group was renamed The Joint Committee on Approval of Preregistration Physician Training Programmes.

The same year saw the General Council approve the council's recommendation that the CMA and ACMC join forces in order to carry out surveys and accreditation of Canadian medical schools. This led to the establishment of the Committee on Accreditation of Canadian Medical Schools (CACMS). The following year saw a lot of time and effort being applied to continuing medical education (CME) and its relationship to quality of care. Extensive discussions were held with other organizations on the question of "a licence to practise medicine" and whether or not undergraduate and intern training provided the scope and depth required for practice. The council brought its views to the 1973 General Council where they were discussed at length and resulted in the passing of a number of motions pertaining to medical education and competence to practise. The General Council also approved a number of recommendations on the subject of continuing medical education and on the importance of funding and of developing programs in family medicine.

An emotionally charged issue in 1975 was the training and licensure of graduates of foreign medical schools. A task force under the aegis of the council, chaired by Dr. Albert J. Davis from St. John's and with representation from the FPMLAC, had developed a green paper on the subject. Three main questions had been considered.

1. Are we adequately evaluating graduates of foreign medical schools who apply to this country for further medical training and practice?
2. Having accepted a graduate of a foreign medical school for training, do we not owe it to him or her to see that the training takes into account any basic deficiencies in his or her previous training in medicine, cultural differences and problems stemming from inadequate language training?
3. Should we not expect the graduate of a foreign medical school to undergo evaluations which place him or her on a par with our own Canadian-trained physicians before he/she is permitted to practise independently?

The debate on the green paper led to the passing of the following two recommendations:

That the Canadian Medical Association recommend to the Federation of Provincial Medical Licensing Authorities of Canada that all physicians wishing to enter independent or unsupervised practice in Canada, whether they be graduates of Canadian or foreign medical schools, be evaluated to fulfil uniform standards of competence before licensure including special evaluations as deemed necessary by the appropriate licensing body.

That the Canadian Medical Association receive for information the green paper 'The Graduate of the Foreign Medical School: Evaluation and Educational Requirements for Admission to Training Programmes and Medical Practice in Canada" as a document to be used in discussions with appropriate education, licensing and governmental agencies for further study and development.

Reaction to the green paper was generally favourable, both in Canada and in other countries, and the paper was summarized and reproduced in a number of overseas medical journals. Suggestions for amendments were received from many sources. These were incorporated into a revised edition of the green paper and the presentation of the revised edition at General Council in 1976 led to a repeat in length of the debate the previous year. By the time the matter left the floor of General Council, 10 recommendations had been approved, all designed to ensure the welfare of both the Canadian health care system and the graduate of a foreign medical school.

The council had spent a lot of time and energy on the question of continuing medical education and presented a recommendation to General Council that the CMA, along with the RCPSC, CFPC, FPMLAC and ACMC, should attempt to get federal legislation changed so as to allow CME expenses to be tax-deductible. The recommendation was approved.

In 1978 the council's terms of reference were amended and amplified to read:

The Council on Medical Education shall be concerned with medical and professional activities. It shall be primarily involved with the education, training and maintenance of the professional competence of physicians. A further objective shall be to encourage, through the educational system, the provision of an appropriate number and mix of well-prepared physicians to the health field to ensure the delivery of a good quality health care to the public. To this end it shall also concern itself in a similar manner with allied health personnel to assure the most effective use of educational facilities. It will attempt to correlate these activities with those of other organizations involved in the development and operation of educational programmes in medicine, as well as those in allied health professional and technological fields.

It appeared to the council that the next logical step in its involvement with CME was to set up a process of CME accreditation, and to this end it recommended setting up a provisional coordinating council on Canadian continuing medical education with representation from the CMA, RCPSC, CFPC,

ACMC and FPMLAC. The General Council agreed with the concept but demurred over cost implications and withheld funding until the other partners in the proposed coordinating council had indicated how much of the financial load they were prepared to bear. After a year of unsatisfactory negotiations, the council found that it was not possible to implement its plans for CME accreditation inasmuch as the proposed cosponsors had reservations about the usefulness of the exercise and the costs. The Council on Medical Education then turned to other medical organizations seeking their voluntary cooperation in setting up a project of testing national guidelines on CME accreditation.

In 1980 and 1981, the guidelines were tested under the auspices of the Committee on Accreditation of Canadian Medical Schools, at CME departments at the University of Saskatchewan and Memorial University of Newfoundland. The following year, the Council on Medical Education formed a subcommittee to review and make recommendations for improvement in various aspects of CME, including the possibility of a linkage with the American Accreditation Council for Continuing Medical Education (ACCME) and greater involvement with the CACMS. In February 1984, the ACCME agreed to grant reciprocity to Canadian-based CME programs accredited by CACMS; this decision applied to 7 of the 16 medical schools then accredited by CACMS.

The council recommended in 1986 that more specific attention be paid to geriatrics and gerontology in medical schools and in postgraduate training, and it developed a working group to examine the matter and prepare a discussion document. This document was presented to General Council in 1986 and after discussion, it was approved:

- *That Canadian Faculties of Medicine and Education Funding agencies be encouraged to recruit teachers of Geriatric Medicine as a high priority.*
- *That all Canadian Faculties of Medicine review their core curricula to ensure suitable content, including clinical and preclinical study of human development in aging in its physiological, pathological, clinical, epidemiological and sociological aspects.*

It was further agreed that residency training and CME programs should include teaching in geriatric medicine.

In 1989, the council moved once more to look at the various aspects of professional competence. The RCPSC had been studying ways in which competence could be maintained by specialists, and the council believed that more should be done by the profession as a whole to ensure competence in practice by stressing the importance of lifelong learning in all aspects of medical education. The council's concerns were shared by the General Council that approved: "That the CMA encourage strategies and opportunities in undergraduate, postgraduate and CME that will enable physicians to develop the knowledge, skills and commitment to maintain professional competence throughout their careers."

The council had also raised the matter of program funding for CME with the Board of Directors; after discussing it in December 1989, the board referred the question for joint discussions between the councils on medical education and on economics. Subsequently, the councils produced a joint paper titled "Positioning for the Future," in which there were suggested guidelines to assist CMA divisions in their negotiations with their respective provincial governments on funding of professional CME activities. The paper concluded that the CMA and the provincial/territorial medical associations had important roles to play in facilitating mechanisms to help their members to maintain their professional competence.

Resolutions from the 1990 General Council encouraged the divisions to provide maximum flexibility in the use of funds negotiated for use in CME and to seek new funds from a variety of sources. The position paper developed by the council and now titled "Maintenance of Competence" was approved by the 1991 General Council, together with a recommendation that the CMA facilitate a major review and report on the educational requirements of physicians throughout their practice lifetime. A small working group was set up to develop strategies whereby that recommendation could be implemented.

During 1991, the council undertook a strategic planning exercise in a review of the CMA's role in medical education. Since its establishment in 1969, the council had been very active in many aspects of medical education as evidenced by the number of initiatives reported to and acted upon by the General Council during the period under review. The outcome of the exercise was a paper — "Medical Education at CMA" — that included the mission statement, "To provide leadership at the interface between the practising physicians and the academic community to facilitate high standards of education for physicians and service for patients throughout the lifelong continuum of medical learning."

In response to the direction by the 1991 General Council that the CMA conduct a major review and report on the educational requirements of physicians throughout their practice lifetime, the CMA coordinated an invitational workshop, "Increasing the Effectiveness of Continuing Medical Education," in February 1992. In addition to members of the council, participants came from the RCPSC, CFPC and ACMC. An outcome of the workshop was a recommendation that a broad review of CME be carried out, and a project proposal for such a review was approved by the Board of Directors in May 1993. The council produced a discussion paper and plans were made to hold a series of stakeholders' workshops during 1993 and 1994.

The review was carried out by a task force made up of representatives from the CMA, RCPSC, CFPC, ACMC and the Corporation professionnelle des médecins du Québec. The paper put forward a method whereby a more comprehensive system of CME accreditation might be developed, as well as a suggested format for a new accreditation committee on CME.

At the 1994 General Council the following motion was approved: "That the CMA ask that the Conference of Deputy Ministers urgently identify and ensure appropriate funding for the national centres of postgraduate education in subspecialty medical programmes."

Allied Health Disciplines — Accreditation and Education

A survey of the records shows that the CMA had been involved in the accreditation process of allied health disciplines (AHDs) since the 1930s. When the Council on Medical Education was formed, its terms of reference included the responsibility for "educational programmes for allied health personnel." Two of the standing committees (Approval of Training Programmes for Medical Laboratory Technologists and Approval of Schools for Radiological Technicians)and one special committee (Approval of Training Programmes for Nuclear Medicine Technologists), incorporated into the new council, had been directly involved with the accreditation of AHDs, and the council, having assumed the responsibilities of those committees, laid out three guidelines for its dealings with AHDs:

1. *The CMA should continue its support of approval programs for AHDs.*
2. *There should be more direct involvement and increased participation of the individual AHDs in the administration of programs.*
3. *The AHD-approved programs should become financially self-supporting, either through fees for surveys or through governmental grants.*

The council set up a subcommittee, chaired by Dr. Daniel P. Snidal from Winnipeg, with the other members being the chairmen of the previous committees of the individual approval programs. To act on the second guideline, the CMA appointed three subcommittees, one for each of the approval programs, with each having a chairman along with three physicians from four different geographical regions of Canada. The AHDs themselves supplied representatives to the subcommittees of their respective disciplines.

Proliferation of AHDs were beginning to cause a problem for the CMA as more and more groups of technicians and technologists sought national recognition in their respective disciplines. There was the spectre of a large financial burden devolving upon the association if all those who applied to the CMA were accepted. At the time the cost for each accreditation program was about $4000, not taking into account secretarial time and the costs of support services. The CMA held the position that it should make known its willingness to continue the responsibility for the establishment of standards and a correlation of national programs for AHDs, but at the same time believed that programs should be self-supporting by fee-for-survey or other means.

The road ahead, although it may have been paved with good intentions, soon started to deteriorate when differences of opinion arose between radiology technicians and laboratory technologists. The former were agreeable to a fee-for-survey while the latter would have none of it. Many meetings were held to find a way to end the impasse but, in the end, the 1971 General Council approved the transfer of the operations of the CMA/Canadian Society of Laboratory Technologists' (CSLT) Committee on Approval of Training Programmes of Laboratory Technologists to the CSLT. It was further recommended that the CMA withdraw its financial support of the survey costs, but the General Council did not approve and referred the matter back to the Board of Directors for further consideration.

The Council on Medical Education was given the authority to make changes as it saw fit in the bases of approval of training programs. To ensure that this directive from General Council was followed, a Committee on the Accreditation of Training Programmes of Allied Health Professionals was established with the chairman and vice-chairman coming from the council and the committee members being the chairmen of the various approval program subcommittees, plus a representative from the Association of Community Colleges of Canada (ACCC). In 1972, General Council asked the council to formulate a policy on the matter of the teaching of allied health professionals by physicians.

Criticism of the creation of a greater number of committees than had been in existence before the creation of the council was answered by pointing out that the new structure enabled a greater degree of direction and control. Criticism was also forthcoming over the fact that no sooner had a new committee or subcommittee been given a name than the name was changed. An example of this was the Committee on the Accreditation of Training Programmes of Allied Health Professionals, which became the Committee on the Accreditation of Training Programmes of Allied Health Occupations.

It was the council's view that by 1974 the only direct costs to the CMA for the accreditation programs would be those incurred by representatives of the CMA on the approval committees.

By 1976, there were four training programs accredited by the CMA. These were: Medical Laboratory Technology, Radiological Technology (diagnostic and therapeutic), Nuclear Medicine Technology and Respiratory Technology. These four technologies represented 17 professional organizations. Both the council and the Conjoint Committee on Accreditation expressed their concerns over the increase in new allied health occupations, spawned to a large extent by advances in technology. Questions raised were: at what point should the CMA become involved; should it offer advice in the formative stages or should it wait until educational programs were established; what were the manpower and utilization of resources implications. The 1977 General Council directed the Council on Medical Education and the Council on Medical Services to establish a joint subcommittee and to make recommendations for an acceptable CMA policy on the matter of its involvement in allied health occupation accreditation programs.

The joint subcommittee reported to the General Council in 1978 through the report of the Council on Medical Services. Two recommendations were made: (1) the creation of a subcommittee on allied health manpower under the aegis of the Council on Medical Services and (2) the creation of an inter-council allied health committee. These recommendations were approved, as were the terms of reference of the two new bodies, and General Council directed that it was assigning a high priority to the early functioning of the new bodies. Just like the course of true love, things did not go smoothly, and at the 1979 General Council, the Council on Medical Services reported that there were difficulties, experienced and foreseeable, in the implementation of the workings of the new structure. After much debate, a recommendation was put forward from the Council on Medical Education's Committee on Allied Medical Education (CAME) for an amalgamation of the various committees and subcommittees concerned with allied health occupations and that the outcome be a council. The recommendation was later modified to the outcome being a committee of the Board of Directors. The final version approved by General Council was:

- *That a Committee of the CMA Board of Directors, to be titled "The Committee on Allied Health," be created to assume the responsibilities related to the rational utilization of allied health workers, namely manpower needs, identification of emerging disciplines and recognition of new ones.*
- *That representation on the new committee be regional.*

- *That the accreditation of Allied Medical Education Programmes remain the function of a distinct subcommittee under the responsibility of the Council on Medical Education.*
- *That the terms of reference of the committee shall be:*
  - *(i) liaison with allied health groups, medical specialties and other education facilities;*
  - *(ii) allied health manpower;*
  - *(iii) emerging disciplines;*
  - *(iv) legislation in the allied health field;*
  - *(v) relations with other independent health professions when assigned by the Board of Directors of the CMA.*

When this resolution was subsequently studied by the Board of Directors, concern was expressed over the interaction between the new committee and the subcommittee of the Council on Medical Education. Logistic and administrative difficulties were foreseen, and the Board of Directors concluded that a broader-based study of allied health was essential and that such a study must include reference to accreditation. The board also concluded that the study should be carried out by the existing board Committee on Allied Health (CAH) and that the membership of that committee should be increased to reflect the expanded workload. This new direction meant that some of the activities of the Council on Medical Education would be taken over by the committee. The committee was made up of Dr. Arthur A. Scott (chairman), and members Drs. Robert H. Elder, John I. Frid, J. Lucien Perrault, Donald B. Rix, Chester B. Stewart, with Dr. David W. Irving representing the Board of Directors. Its first meeting was held on Sept. 13, 1980.

Perusal of board and council documents of that time leads the reader to the conclusion that a great deal of confusion existed in many minds as to the delineation of spheres of responsibility within this structure. In 1981, the Board of Directors presented to the General Council its clarification, viz.:

> *The Council on Medical Education, as the former parent of the Conjoint Committee on Accreditation, had been delegated authority by General Council to oversee and administer conjoint accreditation processes. Accordingly, decisions on accreditation procedures and accreditation status (for approved disciplines) were made at the level of the Council on Medical Education. To clarify and place on record the transferral of this responsibility to the Board Committee on Allied Health, the CMA Board of Directors formally reiterates that the authority to oversee and administer conjoint accreditation policy and*

processes (for approved disciplines) has been granted to the Board Committee on Allied Health, as the current parent of the Subcommittee on Allied Medical Education and its conjoint committees on accreditation.

> The Board Committee on Allied Health then set out its objectives:
> 1. maintain conjoint accreditation processes through CAME;
> 2. establish a general statement on the role of the physician and considerations that touch definition of a medical act or the need for medical supervision;
> 3. establish a procedure for the determination of a medical perspective on specific allied health workers' roles in health care;
> 4. develop and maintain an information bank on health care workers;
> 5. identify issues in allied health requiring initiatives and develop implementation strategy;
> 6. examine CMA policy on Associate status;
> 7. consider means by which the medical profession can more effectively influence legislation pertaining to allied health;
> 8. establish and improve communications with national associations of allied health workers in order to promote inter-group understanding and cooperation.

In 1982, the General Council received the Board Committee on Allied Health's lengthy report, which included a statement that had been approved by the Board of Directors and was now being put forward for ratification as Association policy. Many views were expressed by members of the General Council before the document was approved in principle, with a number of recommended revisions and amendments, and the directive that the revised document be approved by the Board of Directors and resubmitted to the 1983 General Council for information. The title of the report was "The Practice of Medicine in Relation to Other Health Occupations."

In 1983, there were accredited educational programs for six allied health disciplines: radiography, radiotherapy, medical laboratory technology, cytotechnology, respiratory technology and nuclear medicine technology. Twenty-three organizations cooperated with the CMA in the accreditation process; a number of these had begun to send the CMA levies on a per capita basis — about $20 000 per annum — in recognition of the administrative functions (and associated costs) carried out by the CMA. The costs of surveys, excluding administrative and clerical costs, were met by survey fees.

Two years later ophthalmic technology and emergency technology were added to the six disciplines already being accredited. The Board Committee on

Allied Health aimed to produce a publication that would provide an overview of a number of health-related occupations. The primary purpose of the publication was to describe the role of allied health workers and their relationship to physicians most closely involved in areas of medical practice where there would be professional contact between the two groups. The Board of Directors approved the idea, and in 1985 seven sections were given the seal of approval; further chapters were planned. The publication was titled *Perspectives in Health Occupations*, and when the 11-chapter book was published in both official languages in 1986, it was widely acclaimed. An exception was the Canadian Nurses Association that stated that it was "inappropriate" for the medical profession to produce such a book.

The conjoint accreditation process continued to grow and in 1985 and 1986 there were 90 programs involving 464 accredited institutions. There were now 10 disciplines in the program, and 30 national organizations or groups cooperated with the CMA, either as members of a conjoint committee or as a resource.

In 1988, the Board of Directors approved that the name of the committee be changed to Committee on Health Disciplines (CHD) without any change in mandate or guidelines. At the time, Dr. Brian Lentle was chairman of CHD and Dr. Elder was the chairman of the CAME. In February 1991, the CHD was disbanded and the arrangement whereby the CAME reported to it came to an end. The CAME returned to the Council on Medical Education whose "child" it had been from 1969 to 1979. It would now report to the Board of Directors and to General Council through that council, rather than to the CHD. The CAME's structure was amended by the addition of council and board representatives to its membership.

Since 1969, much had been achieved by both the CAME and the CAH/CHD. A firm base for relationships between the CMA and allied health disciplines had been laid down, and thus had not only enhanced the CMA's credibility in the eyes of those disciplines but had also ensured a high quality of care in the various approved technologies. It was held that the CAME would continue its excellent track record in the conjoint accreditation process, defined as a peer review process that measured allied health educational programs against predetermined national standards.

In May 1992, the Board of Directors approved that the CAME be renamed the Committee on Conjoint Accreditation (CCA). A mission statement was developed: "Conjoint accreditation is a process designed to ensure national standards for educational programmes in designated health science professions, thereby contributing to the competency of graduates and the quality of patient care in Canada.

The board also approved statements of philosophy, values and operating principles for accreditation that the committee had developed. Dr. David Cane, representative of the Association of Canadian Community Colleges, became the chairman of the CCA. In 1993 and 1994, the CCA prepared a draft of new criteria for the inclusion of additional allied health disciplines (to the 10 already included) in the conjoint accreditation process, and it was planned that this exercise would be finalized by the end of 1994.

Physician Manager Institute

In 1981, the Board of Directors presented the General Council with a three-part recommendation on the subject of medical direction and administrative responsibility in service departments carrying out prescribed medical diagnostic tests and/or therapy in hospitals and clinics. It was the board's opinion that such departments must have a medical director, accountable to the board of the hospital or clinic and to the organized medical staff. It was believed that such a medical director should be a duly qualified and licensed physician. The recommendation was approved by the General Council but came back the following year with further recommendations qualifying some parts of the 1981 resolution. These, too, were approved by the General Council.

At its first meeting following the General Council, the CMA Board of Directors approved the creation of an Ad Hoc Committee on Hospitals and gave it the mandate to examine and report on responsibilities in hospital departments. The committee asked the Council on Medical Education to review the administrative training needed by physicians for the development of skills necessary for them to assume administrative responsibilities in a variety of health and medical settings. The council formed a joint committee with the Canadian College of Health Service Executives (CCHSE), and this joint committee, after a study of the matter, formulated plans to develop programs for physicians currently in administrative positions.

The first step was a survey of physicians to obtain their opinions on specific needs and content requirements in administrative management education. After the results had been studied, the joint committee developed two pilot courses. Both were held in 1984, one in Jasper, Alta., and the other in St. Andrew's, NB. Evaluation of these courses by the planners and participants was overwhelmingly favourable, and it was decided that five courses would be made available in 1985 on a cost-recovery basis. Programs for physician manager training were also set up in Quebec by the Fédération médicale des omnipracticiens de Québec and the Fédération des médecins spécialistes de Québec.

By 1986, about 350 physicians had participated in the Physician Manager Institute (PMI), as the CMA courses came to be called, and there was a demand for more courses of this kind plus a request for courses of a more advanced nature. The joint committee considered these requests and the following courses were made available: PMI-I — Foundations of Management, PMI-II — Leadership Skills Development.

As of April 1988, 700 physicians had participated in the courses. That year eight courses were presented. The demand for more advanced training continued, and the joint committee examined the possibility of adding a PMI-III — Negotiation, Conflict Management and Politics: Skills for Effective Managers. The first PMI-III course was made available in October 1988. Suggestions for content and more advanced training courses continued to reach the joint committee, and it was not long before a PMI-IV — The Challenge of Change: Managing the Shifting Medical Environment — became available. In 1989, the CMA Board of Directors approved the acceptance of corporate sponsorship of the PMI programs on the understanding that any such sponsorship by the pharmaceutical industry would not divert funding away from the *Canadian Medical Association Journal.*

In 1991 and 1992, the joint committee, now called the PMI Steering Committee, reviewed all its programs and goals, and particularly PMI-I. Effective Jan. 1, 1992, the CMA took over the administration of the PMI, and the CCHSE continued its sponsorship of, and involvement in, the development and promotion of the institute. Also in 1992, the PMI-I curriculum was completely revised and given a new title, "Leadership for Shaping the Future"; this course made its entry into the world in Quebec City in February 1993.

In the 10 years leading up to 1994, the institute had conducted over 70 courses, and demand for those courses showed no signs of decreasing. Because of this demand the institute was considering, in 1994, presenting the courses in institutions across the country rather than holding them in commercial meeting facilities.

Council on the Provision of Health Services
The terms of reference of the Council on the Provision of Health Services when it was formed in 1969 were as follows:

> *The Council shall study and report on all matters relating to the provision of health services and without limiting its terms of reference shall be concerned with the following areas: Employed physicians, General Practice, Group Practice, Hospitals, Manpower, Medical Care, Occupational Medicine, Pharmacy, and such other matters as may be referred to it by General Council and/or the CMA Board of Directors.*

Medical and Nonmedical Use of Drugs

One of the council's first tasks was to obtain information on the prescribing of certain drugs and to use that information to formulate recommendations to the Board of Directors for use by the CMA in its brief to the LeDain Commission of Inquiry into the Non-Medical Use of Drugs. The council set up a subcommittee with representation from the federal Food and Drug Directorate, the Pharmaceutical Manufacturers' Association of Canada (PMAC) and the Canadian Pharmaceutical Association, together with physicians and pharmacologists. With the assistance of a $15 280 National Health Grant, a questionnaire in the form of a diary was devised and the necessary arrangements made for computerization of the data. Twenty-four thousand questionnaires were sent out to practising physicians; the overall response was 21.2% that was considered a valid basis for meaningful conclusions.

The council and its subcommittee were surprised and concerned to learn that 32.9% of prescriptions were for "mood-modifying drugs." These concerns were passed on to the board and were reflected in the CMA's brief, viz.:

> *Stimulants, including amphetamines, their derivatives and like substances, are now suffering too-ready medical use and wide-spread non-medical use. The same is true with respect to hypnotics, sedatives such as barbiturates, and minor tranquillizers. The health professions, and in particular, medicine and pharmacy, must accept a significant share of the responsibility for this state of affairs. The prescribing habits of many physicians in this area must be described as questionable with respect to the provision of quality medical care. Too many pharmacists have contributed to the resultant problems by "filling prescriptions," rather than fulfilling their professional responsibilities in the dispensing of pharmaceutical products. The correction of these problems, where profession-initiated is, in our opinion, largely a responsibility of the professions concerned.*

In February 1972, the minister of national health and welfare introduced a new policy with respect to regulations concerning the use of amphetamines, and the council's subcommittee was directed by the Board of Directors "to continue discussions with government officials regarding the proposed regulations to control the prescribing of amphetamines, etc., with direction from the Board that the regulations should interfere as little as possible with the practising responsibilities and privileges of the physician, in keeping with a responsible profession that is subject to peer review." Meetings were held between the CMA and the Department of National Health and Welfare, and modifications and clarification of the regulations sought. The regulations announced in May indicated that all prescribing physicians were authorized to prescribe amphetamines but that medical indications would be established by a panel of experts nominated by the CMA and l'Association des médecins de langue française du Canada (AMLFC). In addition, the CMA nominated experts to each of the three advisory panels established by the minister.

The final version of the regulations became effective Jan. 1, 1973, and reflected the efforts of the council and its subcommittee in devising some acceptable, if not universally desirable, regulations affecting physicians prescribing amphetamines. It was proposed by the council that there be a further survey of physicians' prescribing habits at an unspecified date with the intent of seeing if changes for the better had occurred.

In 1972, the council's name was changed to Council on Medical Services and the new terms of reference were: "The Council on Medical Services shall be concerned with the provision of medical services as an integral part of the provision of health care to the people of Canada. It shall concern itself in particular with personal health care delivery and with matters involving the utilization of medical manpower in cooperation with other health professionals and technologists."

On the advice of the advisory panels established by the Department of National Health and Welfare, the number of recognized indications for the therapeutic use of amphetamines was increased from four to six, with special provision being made when the drug was used for research purposes. Toward the end of 1973, the department announced that two elements of the regulations were being removed, viz., notification and a requirement for consultation in cases in which amphetamines were to be prescribed for periods exceeding 30 days. By mid-February 1974, the Health Protection Branch of the Department of National Health and Welfare reported a 90% reduction in the prescribing of amphetamines since the regulations had been introduced. The advisory panels reviewed the regulations again and on the basis of that review, it was agreed, both by the panels and council, that there were no indications for any changes in the list of designated drugs and no grounds for adding newly recognized indications for their use.

The follow-up questionnaire on prescribing habits had been circulated, but a study by the council's subcommittee on pharmacy had found that statistics on prescribing could be obtained from the International Monitoring Services. These statistics were provided to the federal government and to provincial departments of health. The council recommended that attempts be made to obtain this information from the provinces.

Over the next 4 years the council studied many matters as they related to drugs, for example, the Canadian Drug Formulary System, the drug known as Laetrile, the misuse and abuse of mood-modifying drugs, child-proof packaging, prescription packaging and patient package inserts. The council represented the Association as member of the Project Committee on Supplementary Information, a committee of the Canadian Pharmaceutical Association and better known as the Nairn Committee. This committee's mandate was to produce a methodology for the development, production and distribution of supplementary information on medication by pharmacists providing prescription drugs to patients of physicians. In January 1979, the Nairn Committee presented its 50-page report plus seven appendices to the Canadian Pharmaceutical Association; the report was endorsed by the member organizations, including the CMA, represented on the committee.

One of the many subjects contained in the council's terms of reference was manpower. In January 1970, the council formed the Committee on the Delivery of Health Care. This committee included representatives from the RCPSC, CFPC, FMLAC, ACMC and the Canadian Nurses Association. The council represented the CMA in the planning of and participation in the First National Conference on Assistance to Physicians, held in Ottawa Apr. 6–8, 1971. Among other things, this conference studied the use of allied health personnel in those geographical areas where there were few physicians, as well as their use in institutional settings.

In 1971, the council reported on its study on the maldistribution of physicians and the family practitioner/specialist mix. The concerns elicited from its studies were taken to the Department of National Health and Welfare's Committee on Physician Manpower by the CMA representatives on that committee. Another matter with which the council had concerned itself was the regionalization of health services and, in view of the fact that nearly a quarter of a century later the question of regionalization is still a matter of study within the CMA, it is appropriate that the report of the council to General Council in 1972 be reprinted here.

Regionalization
Within provincial jurisdiction, discretionary powers have their widest base at ministerial and cabinet levels. In this highly centralized management of health care services, capricious use of such powers is likely to be the antithesis of planning for unmet needs and the conservation of energy required to meet these needs.

There is a growing concern about the failings of highly centralized planning and delivery of health services and related systems that have evolved up to the present time. It is becoming apparent that health care enumeration, evaluation and planning can best be undertaken on a geographic basis such as a region. In each province custom and usage has produced well defined regions which are provincially recognized and are presently used for a variety of economic or social functions. These regions, the definition of which is best applied on a provincial basis, can well be utilized for medical purposes, and indeed are so utilized in a number of provinces at the present time.

We are soon to observe the allocation of large sums of money geared to the development of new kinds of systems of delivery of health care services. While the intent is to meet and resolve impending crises in the spiralling cost of health services through our present system, the danger of developing new systems on a basis of politically inspired rather than regional or community inspired ideas is a serious one. The development of regional health councils and the sponsorship of regional boards of trustees might save the expenditure of trust funds such that new systems do relate to consumer needs. In the analysis of social organization and its systems it is possible to categorize three basic elements of power: government, professional and community. In many instances, it is the community which is most chaotic and disorganized and therefore weak and vulnerable. At the present time, it often appears that government is relating to community with words like "consumer" but may simply be paying lip service to a force that it poorly understands and underestimates. Power is not relinquished easily and it is unlikely that centralized managers of power such as government will readily transfer power from central authority to the community. However, it is possible that power be invested in the regional board of trustees such as is done in a crown corporation, with the balance struck between government, the providers and the community. In the operation of such regional boards, evaluation of service may logically be separated in three parts with government measuring cost effectiveness, with professional bodies measuring and controlling quality and the community itself measuring social effectiveness and consumer satisfaction.

RECOMMENDATION

a) THAT IN EACH PROVINCE WELL DEFINED GEOGRAPHIC REGIONS BE DEVELOPED WHICH ARE APPROPRIATE TO THE LOCAL GEOGRAPHY AND POPULATION.

b) THAT THERE BE REGIONAL BOARDS OF TRUSTEES WITH REPRESENTATION FROM LOCAL GOVERNMENT, PROVIDERS AND THE COMMUNITY AND THAT SUCH BOARDS HAVE POWER TO RESEARCH, PLAN AND PROGRAMME THE

DELIVERY OF HEALTH CARE SERVICES IN RELATION TO ITS REGIONAL NEEDS.

c) THAT REGIONAL BOARDS OF TRUSTEES REPORT VERTICALLY TO THE PROVINCIAL DEPARTMENTS RESPONSIBLE FOR HEALTH CARE AND SOCIAL DEVELOPMENT.

d) THAT SUCH REGIONAL BOARDS OF TRUSTEES BE RESPONSIBLE VERTICALLY TO A SUPRA-REGIONAL BOARD OF TRUSTEES IN EACH PROVINCE WITH REPRESEN-TATION FROM GOVERNMENT, THE PROVIDERS AND THE COMMUNITY. THE FUNCTION OF THIS BOARD WOULD BE TO:

i) PLAN, DEVELOP AND MAINTAIN INSTITUTIONS AND SERVICES SHARED BY ALL REGIONS.

ii) IDENTIFY REGIONAL DISPARITIES AND REALLOCATE RESOURCES TO DIMIN-ISH THESE DISPARITIES.

iii) THAT IF REGIONALIZATION IS TO FUNCTION EFFECTIVELY, FISCAL AUTHOR-ITY MUST BE DELEGATED BY THE CENTRAL AUTHORITY TO THE REGIONAL BOARD.

The General Council did not endorse the recommendation as presented but did approve section d). The matter was then referred back to the council "to obtain a clearer idea and a wider view from the various regions of the country and for clarification." On the matter of the regionalization of hospitals, the council's recommendation that the CMA work closely in liaison with the federal government and support the divisions in their dealings with provincial governments was approved.

In 1973, the National Committee on Physician Manpower set up a Committee on Requirements to estimate medical manpower needs in the year 1981. To this end, 30 different working parties, each representing a medical specialty, were established by the respective specialty organizations. After the committee received the reports of the working parties, it prepared its own report, which was reviewed by the council. The council strongly disagreed with some of the estimates in that it believed these estimates had been based on data recognized as being flawed. The General Council agreed with the council's assessment of the report and resolved that attempts should be made to remove the offending data from the final position to be issued by the National Committee on Physician Manpower.

In September 1976, the CMA sponsored a conference on manpower, and the opinions of representatives from the divisions and the specialist societies were incorporated into the CMA's official response to the report of the National Committee on Physician Manpower. It was the council's opinion that future medical manpower need be based on a 45-hour week and an annual output of 44 weeks.

The CMA Executive Committee prepared a statement on physician manpower requirements, and this was discussed at the conference. One of the main recommendations was "that a manpower data bank be maintained by the CMA and that it include an analysis of the clinical and non-clinical professional activities of medical students, Canadian medical graduates and registered physicians in Canada, and that these data be used by the National Committee to determine ongoing requirements for physician manpower."

The 1977 General Council discussed the council's report on medical manpower and eventually agreed that a select committee of experts be established to examine the subject of physician manpower, develop expertise in it and provide advice to the CMA Board of Directors on an ongoing basis. This select committee replaced the council's subcommittee.

In June 1978, the General Council approved the amalgamation of the Council on Medical Services and the Council on Community Health. During its 9 years of existence, the council studied many subjects, some of them of a highly contentious character, and the board recognized its contributions, particularly in providing resource documentation in the making of CMA policies.

Council on Community Health Care

The 1969 terms of reference of this council were:

> *The Council on Community Health Care shall be responsible for all matters affecting health and health care within the community itself, and without limiting its terms of reference, shall be responsible for the following specific areas: aging, cancer, child health, maternal welfare, medical aspects of traffic accidents, mental health, nutrition, physical education and recreation, public health and rehabilitation.*

Abortion

In 1965 and 1966, the CMA Committee on Maternal Welfare had addressed the matter of abortion and had submitted a number of recommendations for consideration at the 1966 General Council. The debate reflected the marked division in views that was to be present at every General Council for the next three decades. The only matter on which consensus was reached when abortion was debated in 1966 was the referral of the council's recommendations back to it for clarification. In 1967 the council brought back the following recommendation:

> *That the CMA recommend to the federal Minister of Justice that the Criminal Code of Canada be amended so as to provide that an operation for*

the termination of pregnancy shall be lawful: (a) if continuation of the pregnancy will endanger the life or health of the pregnant female or there is substantial risk that the child may be born with a grave mental or physical disability, and the operation is performed by a duly qualified and licensed medical practitioner, in a hospital accredited by the Canadian Council on Hospital Accreditation (CCHA) after approval by a Therapeutic Abortion Committee of such hospital, or (b) where there are reasonable grounds to believe that a sexual offence has been committed from which pregnancy has resulted.

After extended debate the General Council approved this recommendation.

In 1970, the council set up a study committee, with its members and representation from the Board of Directors, the Society of Obstetricians and Gynaecologists of Canada (SOGC) and the Canadian Psychiatric Association, to prepare a position paper on family planning, such paper to include abortion and sterilization. Implementation in August 1969 of changes in the *Criminal Code* had removed some of the difficulties faced by physicians, but there existed still a number of problem areas that had not been solved by the legislative changes.

The council presented the findings of its study committee to the General Council in 1971 in the form of a report containing nine recommendations. The Board of Directors opened debate by submitting a recommendation of its own:

It is the opinion of the Board of Directors that acceptance of these recommendations implies acceptance of the concept that abortion should be permitted for other than purely medical reasons. The Board believes that General Council should debate this specific issue prior to consideration of the nine Council recommendations. The recommendation is "That the CMA agrees there is justification on nonmedical social grounds for the deliberate termination of pregnancy."

The recommendation was amended by changing "agrees" to "recognizes" and approved as amended by 78 votes to 74 on a standing count.

The council unequivocally rejected any idea that abortion was an acceptable and desirable method of family planning but felt it necessary to point out to the General Council that "strictly medical reasons" for abortion had been declining over the previous quarter-century. It had also come to the view that the concept of hospital therapeutic abortion committees was not working out in practice and was proposing that the *Criminal Code*, Section 237, be further amended by deletion of all references to such committees. The General Council approved the following:

- *That advice and assistance on family planning be made readily available to all residents of this country.*
- *That provision of advice and information on family planning is a responsibility of the practising physicians of Canada. Within the community this responsibility should be shared with other educational and health agencies.*
- *That facilities in addition to physicians' offices for dissemination of advice on family planning be established throughout the country, and that these facilities be developed in consultation with and under supervision of the medical profession to assure adequate medical follow-up.*
- *That in the event of an unwanted pregnancy, the patient should be provided with the opportunity to have full immediate counselling services.*
- *That Section 237 of the Criminal Code of Canada be further amended by deletion of all reference to the Therapeutic Abortion Committee.*
- *That the appropriate sections of the Criminal Code of Canada apply only to the performance of abortions (a) by persons other than qualified licensed physicians, or (b) in facilities other than approved hospitals.*
- *That, faced with a request for an abortion, a physician whose moral or religious beliefs prevent him from recommending and/or performing this procedure should so inform the patient so that she may consult another physician.*
- *If society should dictate that the indications for the performance of abortion should include others than those involving a medical opinion, society should be responsible for providing special facilities and staff for carrying out the procedure when it follows from these further indications.*
- *That in view of the significant hazards (both of morbidity and mortality) from induced abortion, the Council wishes to recommend in the strongest possible terms that induced abortion should not be considered as an alternative to contraception as a method of family planning.*

Three other resolutions relating to the subject of abortion came from the floor of General Council during the council's report.

- *That the profession make every effort to document and study the effects of abortion upon the health and social welfare of the people of the community.*
- *Physicians or other health personnel should not be required to participate in the termination of a pregnancy and a patient should not be forced to have a pregnancy terminated.*
- *That abortion be defined as the termination of a pregnancy before 20 weeks of gestation.*

In its 1972 report to General Council, the council stated that it had no reason to amend the resolutions approved the previous year but did express its concern and disappointment that the federal government had not even debated the matter in the House of Commons, let alone considered changing the relevant sections of the *Criminal Code*. In 1973 the council reported that it had not been able to provide an answer to the 1971 resolution whereby it was asked to study and document the effects of abortion on the health and social welfare of the community, because no single study appeared to provide answers to all the questions raised in a multifacetted subject. It did suggest that monitoring systems be established in all hospitals where abortions were performed, and this was approved by General Council.

By 1975 it was very obvious that there were marked regional disparities in the provision of abortion services, including counselling services, and it appeared to the council that the major cause was either the absence or the deliberate nonfunctioning of therapeutic abortion committees. Once again its recommendation that references to therapeutic abortion committees be removed from the relevant sections of the *Criminal Code* was approved by the General Council. A recommendation asking the federal government to form a special commission to study all the medical, psychological and social implications related to abortion, including patient profiles and guidelines for facilities, procedures and personnel, was approved, and the council was gratified when the Privy Council appointed the Committee on the Operation of the Abortion Law in September 1975.

The council's name was changed to the Council on Health Care in 1980, and its new terms of reference were: "Council shall be concerned with the provision of comprehensive health care in the protection and promotion of the health of the individual, the family and the community. Within this framework Council shall concern itself with the role and scope of activities of physicians and other providers of health care."

One year later the General Council approved a recommendation by the Council on Health Care that the CMA review the situation with respect to therapeutic abortions in Canada. Following a number of consultations with the Executive Committee and the Board of Directors, the council undertook the following tasks.

1. The assessment of available statistics and surveys on numbers of abortions being done, the manner of operation of therapeutic abortion committees and society's attitude towards the problem.

2. The obtention from affiliate societies, especially the SOGC and the Federation of Medical Women of Canada, opinions on the procedure and operation of the abortion law.
3. The conducting of a statistically valid survey of CMA membership for its views on abortion and the relevant laws.

In its review of statistics, the council found that, although the number of abortions had increased, the maternal death rate in the procedure had fallen to such a low level that a rate could not be computed. On the matter of therapeutic abortion committees, the federal government's study reinforced the council's findings and recommendations on the ineffectiveness of therapeutic abortion committees, and the council indicated it would be sending out a questionnaire to CMA members with the intention of using the information obtained in a draft Association policy statement that would be presented to the 1983 General Council.

The information from replies to the questionnaire was reviewed by outside consultants who expressed the opinion that the results presented a reasonably accurate picture of the views of the CMA membership. The council reviewed the data from the membership and the affiliate societies and submitted its report to the Board of Directors who, after discussing the report, saw no reason to change CMA policy on the matter. It was recommended that the council should conduct a further analysis of the responses as they pertained to therapeutic abortion committees and to suggested changes in the *Criminal Code*. This was done in 1983 and 1984 with no indication of any changes in CMA policy. In January 1988, the Supreme Court of Canada struck down Section 251 (pertaining to therapeutic abortion committees) of the *Criminal Code*, and later in the year the General Council approved the establishment of an ad hoc committee to review abortion policy.

Traffic Safety
Another area of interest for the council from 1969 onward was that of safety factors associated with various methods of travel. Its very first three recommendations to the General Council were related to the medical aspects of traffic accidents, viz., blood alcohol and breathalyzer tests, restraint systems and emergency department facilities. By 1973, the council had produced the first edition of a booklet entitled *Guidelines for Physicians in Determining Fitness to Drive a Motor Vehicle*, which was sent to every member of the Association as well as federal and provincial agencies. The following year the council reviewed seat-belt usage and, finding that it was not being improved much

by educational means, recommended that the CMA strongly support mandatory restraint legislation for all highway motor vehicles and that mandatory standards be established for children's safety seats.

In 1976, the council's attention had been drawn to the emergency medical kits in commercial aircraft and, after review, gave its opinion that these kits were inadequate. It recommended to General Council that steps be taken to require commercial aircraft to carry an acceptable minimum of equipment and therapeutic agents for in-flight medical and surgical emergencies. The council had also been asked by the 1975 General Council to review the operation of air ambulances, and this led to the recommendation that the CMA cooperate with federal and provincial departments to develop minimum standards for equipment, training of personnel and organizational policy for Canadian air ambulance services. Both recommendations were approved by the General Council.

During the following year the council worked on developing the basic requirements for a portable medical kit to be carried on emergency medical flights. Meetings between the council and officials of the federal ministries of transport and national health and welfare led to the installation of major resuscitation equipment and appropriately trained staff in airport terminals in Toronto, Montreal and Vancouver. The council recommended that the emergency medical kits, which it had recommended for commercial aircraft, be installed on major public ferries.

The problems associated with alcohol and the operation of motor vehicles, boats and aircraft continued to cause the council concern, and after a study of the accident figures, morbidity and mortality where alcohol was involved, it recommended that "the federal government be requested to form a commission with representation from the CMA, Canadian Bar Association, law enforcement agencies and the public, such a commission to study and advise on all aspects of the legislative attempts to control the problem of alcohol use related to the operation of vehicles, and to suggest legislative and/or other methods of reducing this serious public health hazard."

By 1979, the fitness to drive guide was receiving commendation from national and international sources. Permission had been sought by agencies outside Canada to reprint it for use in their countries. The second edition was prepared and published after input from a number of areas, including some of the Association's affiliate societies. The council did not take kindly to a proposal by one provincial motor vehicle licensing authority to introduce a waiver in the matter of the issuance of a restricted licence, based on the criteria in the guide, where the applicant had appealed the decision of the authority to issue a restricted licence. This led to a recommendation from the council, approved by General Council:

> *That the CMA strongly oppose efforts by any motor vehicle licensing agency to request individual physicians to issue medical certificates contrary to the principles outlined in the Guide for Physicians in Determining Fitness to Drive a Motor Vehicle, with the implied assumption of legal responsibility for the consequences of such action, and that such decisions should be made by provincial motor vehicle licensing authorities in consultation with duly established medical review committees.*

The third edition of the guide was published in 1982, and work was begun on a fourth edition to be published in 1984.

During 1985, the council spent a lot of time on Bill C-18, a federal government bill that proposed a number of amendments to the *Criminal Code.* The amendments included making compulsory the withdrawal of a blood sample for determination of blood-alcohol level from people involved in an automobile accident. The Association pointed out that in the 15 years of the council's existence, it had submitted and had had approved by general councils, more than 30 recommendations on the subject of alcohol and driving. The council agreed with the intent of the proposed legislation but was concerned over the lack of protection from litigation that might be instituted against the physician taking the blood sample. The council therefore recommended that the CMA divisions press for legislation to protect physicians from civil liability when taking blood for the determination of blood-alcohol content in accordance with the *Criminal Code.*

A number of national jurisdictions, particularly in Europe, held that the legal limit for blood alcohol when driving should be 50 mg%. The council was in agreement with this level and the General Council in 1986 endorsed council's recommendation. Council had reviewed the morbidity and mortality figures in motorcycle and all-terrain vehicle accidents and stated that it could find no medical reasons for the issuance of a certificate of exemption from approved helmet use to operators of such vehicles. By 1991, the council was tackling the matter of helmets for cyclists, and this led to the approval by the 1992 General Council of a recommendation that provincial and territorial governments be urged to enact legislation mandating compulsory use of helmets.

In 1992 and 1993, the council reviewed the concept of a graduated licensing system for new drivers and proposed to General Council that such a system be adopted in all areas of Canada. In 1993, the General Council approved the appropriate recommendation.

Swine Influenza

In 1976, the council found itself in a situation in which its credibility was challenged, not from outside the CMA, but from within the Association itself. This situation arose from the swine influenza vaccination program proposed by the federal government. Prior to the 1976 General Council, the CMA had announced that it would support the program, based on the expert advice provided by the National Committee on Immunization. Subsequent to the announcement, the council spent a lot of time reviewing events and many scientific reports pertaining to the outbreak of influenza in a military establishment in the United States. Council members sought out information and opinions from many sources and came to the conclusion that the proposed program of mass immunization appeared to be based on nonmedical reasoning and, in their opinion, the likelihood of a major epidemic was not borne out by their studies. In October 1986, Council recommended to the CMA Board of Directors that the proposed mass vaccination program not be carried out but that immunization be offered to high-risk individuals, as had been done in previous years during the "influenza season."

The council's recommendation placed the board in a difficult position inasmuch as the CMA was already on public record as supporting the mass immunization program. The chairman of the Board of Directors was invited to attend a meeting of the National Committee on Immunization, where he heard discussions on the rationale for the committee's decision, which was based on intervention rather than prevention. Large stocks of vaccine had been prepared, and although there was no epidemiologic evidence to support the program, the board believed that it should accept the advice of the federal committee and maintain its position.

In April 1977, the council asked the Board of Directors to recommend to the minister of national health and welfare that the swine influenza vaccination program be discontinued. The board agreed. The proceedings of the 1977 General Council recorded: "It is interesting to note that subsequent events have vindicated the conclusions and recommendations of your Council of Community Health."

Health Hazards of Tobacco Products

For many years prior to the establishment of the council, the CMA's Committee on Cancer had been drawing attention to the health hazards associated with the use of tobacco products, and the council carried on the same campaign. On its recommendation, a multi-organizational National Committee on the Health Hazards of Smoking was formed to serve as a central clearing house for all educational materials on the matter to be distributed to health professionals and the general public. The council was pleased to know that the CMA's 1969 brief to the House of Commons Standing Committee on Health, Welfare and Social Affairs had been very favourably received and given prominence in that committee's report. The minister of national health and welfare had written to the CMA indicating his department's cooperation with the Association in attempts to reduce or eliminate the dangers of cigarette smoking.

In 1973, the Association, through the council, was involved in the establishment of a coordinated interagency called the Canadian Council on Smoking and Health (CCSH). In the same year, for the first time in the CMA's 106-year history, smoking was banned at General Council and all of the concomitant scientific meetings. This did not sit well with everyone, particularly some members of the Fourth Estate, who complained bitterly that they had to miss parts of the proceedings when the need for a cigarette became paramount. In 1974, the General Council regularized the ban with the following resolution:

> *Whereas smoking is widely recognized as a contributing factor to poor health, and whereas physicians should set examples of lifestyles promoting good health, and whereas other national and international medical associations do not permit smoking at their meetings, be it recommended that the CMA prohibit smoking by participants during meetings of General Council and during scientific sessions of its Annual Meeting.*

The council, through the CMA representative on the CCSH, Dr. Norman C. Delarue, was kept apprised of actions being taken in the area of information on the health hazards of smoking. In 1975, the CMA president, Dr. Lloyd C. Grisdale, jointly signed a letter with the minister of health; the letter and a "prescription card" were sent to all physicians asking them to refrain from smoking during their professional duties and to display the "card" in their waiting rooms to discourage patients from smoking. Bill C-242, *An Act respecting relief to nonsmokers in transit*, was reviewed by the council and then by the Board of Directors. The intent of the legislation was

> *to give relief to travelling nonsmokers by requiring that railways, planes and buses under federal jurisdiction be required to provide them with separate seating accommodation, since there is medical evidence to the effect that secondary smoke inhalation not only causes distress to the nonsmoker but could jeopardize that person's health, particularly if suffering from a respiratory ailment.*

In April 1980, the council invited the executive director of the CCSH to present a summary of its aims, activities and concerns. The main contributors to the CCSH were the Canadian Heart Foundation, the Canadian Cancer Society and the Canadian Lung Association, with supplementary funding coming from grants from National Health and Welfare, donations from private industry and individuals, plus annual membership fees of $100 from each member organization. It was the council's opinion that the CMA should increase its support of the CCSH.

The council made the following recommendation to the 1984 General Council:

> *That the Council on Health Care direct its attention to the enormous health cost to Canadians caused by cigarette smoking by promoting initiatives such as:*
>
> (i) *Government incentives in the development of educational programmes directed at smoking prevention in schools, and smoking cessation in general;*
>
> (ii) *legislation to prevent smoking in government buildings, including in particular, hospitals and other buildings where health services are provided;*
>
> (iii) *incentives to control smoking in private buildings, and in particular, places of work;*
>
> (iv) *taxation of tobacco products at a level which will discourage their purchase and which will produce tax revenues, earmarked for health budgets, commensurate with the social cost of tobacco-related illness;*
>
> (v) *legislation to prevent tobacco advertising in conjunction with athletic events;*
>
> (vi) *government incentives which would encourage tobacco farmers to change to alternate crops, or would assist them in retraining for new jobs.*

The recommendation was approved by the General Council.

In February 1985, the executive director of the Canadian Pharmaceutical Association presented the council with a program designed to discourage the sale of cigarettes in retail pharmacies. The CMA Board of Directors approved the council's recommendation that a congratulatory message be sent to the Canadian Pharmaceutical Association. At General Council in that year, a recommendation expressing approval and appreciation of those pharmacies that had discontinued the sale of tobacco products and/or rejected the promotion of tobacco products was approved.

The council's Subcommittee on Environmental and Occupational Health reviewed the scientific literature on the subject of secondhand or sidestream smoke in the workplace and recommended to the council that regulations be developed to provide protection consistent with protection from other hazardous products. A council recommendation to that effect was approved by the 1986 General Council, as were other recommendations: (1) no smoking to be permitted in public gathering-places; (2) all packaging of tobacco products to be of a plain nature and with the wording "This product is injurious to your health" printed in the same size as the brand name; (3) smoking be banned at all official functions of the CMA, including social functions.

In 1987, the federal government invited the Association to present its views on Bill C-51, *The Tobacco Products Control Act*, and Bill C-204, *The Nonsmokers Health Act*. The council was given the task of reviewing the proposed legislation and drafting the Association's response. Bill C-51 proposed a ban on all advertising of tobacco products; Bill C-204, a private member's bill, proposed a smoking ban in all government buildings and in commercial aircraft, and the designation of tobacco as a hazardous product. The council recommended to the Board of Directors "That the CMA alert the public to the serious health hazards associated with the use of smokeless tobacco, and that the CMA approach the federal government to request that mandatory health warnings and the advertising restrictions proposed for other products apply equally to smokeless tobacco products."

On Oct. 27, 1987, representatives appeared before the House of Commons Legislative Committee with the CMA's response to Bill C-204 and on Dec. 10, with its response to Bill C-51. In January 1988 the Association was one of 12 organizations that presented a joint brief on the matter of tobacco tax policy to the federal minister of finance. In March 1989, the CMA's Political Action Committee submitted six recommendations pertaining to smoking and tobacco use to the Board of Directors for consideration; two of those recommendations were referred to the council. After review by the council, the recommendations were presented to the General Council, which approved the following:

- *That the CMA recommend that its members initiate a nonsmoking policy in their offices and clinics, and that physicians serve as role models by avoiding the personal use of tobacco.*
- *That the CMA recommend to hospitals and other health care institutions that there be a prohibition on smoking by staff and visitors while on the premises and that smoking by patients be discouraged, but nevertheless permitted only in designated areas.*

In each of the years 1989 and 1990, the CMA contributed $10 000 to the establishment and operation of a national clearing house on tobacco information and programs, to be operated by CCSH. During 1990 and 1991, the council reviewed the scientific literature on the health hazards associated with radon, a naturally occurring radioactive gas produced during the decay of radium. It was reported that levels of radon in basements could reach hazardous levels through leakage from the surrounding soil, and it was postulated that the inhalation of radon, combined with the ill effects of smoking, could hasten the onset of lung cancer. The General Council approved a recommendation "That the CMA continue to prevail on Canadians to abandon or reject smoking as the activity involving the greatest risk of lung cancer, bearing in mind that smoking increases a person's risk of lung cancer due to radon."

In 1993 and 1994, the council spent considerable time drawing up the Association's response to Health Canada's national strategy to reduce tobacco use. For years the CMA had stressed the health hazards of tobacco products, pointing out that not only were they addictive but also that they were one of the leading causes of preventable death. The council was of the opinion that it had often been the animateur with many of its recommendations becoming the law but that much stronger regulations were necessary to combat the health hazards of tobacco products. It therefore recommended to the General Council "That the manufacture, advertising, packaging, sale and use of tobacco be strictly regulated, as they are for other dangerous products." General Council approved the recommendation.

Family Violence

The council began its involvement in this area in 1971 with its study of the "battered child syndrome." It was held that there was a large number of unreported and under-investigated cases. In the majority of the provinces, reporting of child abuse was obligatory, but not all provinces carried a penalty for failure to report. The council believed that each province should have a central registry for the recording of cases and that physicians should become more aware of the syndrome. This view was taken to the General Council in 1973 and a motion made, calling for the establishment of such registries, backed by legislation, which required the reporting of proven and suspected cases of the battered child. A motion to have the word "battered" replaced by "abused" was defeated, but it was not long before the standard nomenclature was "the abused child."

In 1976, the CMA, through the council, was expressing its views on child abuse and neglect to the parliamentary Standing Committee on Health, Welfare and Social Affairs, which had been directed to study and report back to the House of Commons on appropriate measures for the prevention, identification and treatment of such conditions. In 1980, a federal conference on legislation on child abuse and neglect was held, the CMA being represented by the chairman of the council, Dr. John R. Brummit. Later, the council considered a recommendation that the Ontario Medical Association (OMA) had made to the CCHA on the reporting and management of child abuse cases being incorporated into the *CCHA Procedures Manual for Hospitals.* The recommendation was strongly endorsed both by the council and the General Council.

The OMA's Committee on Child Welfare sent the council a recommendation, endorsed by the OMA Council, pertaining to child pornography. The recommendation was in turn endorsed by the council and forwarded to the CMA Board of Directors. From there it went to the federal minister of justice in this form: "The CMA recognizes child pornography as a form of sexual abuse and urges the Minister of Justice to give a high priority to the implementation of a legislative solution to the problem." In his letter of acknowledgement, the minister thanked the CMA for its recommendation and support and pointed out that the strong measures proposed to deal with the problem introduced in the last session of Parliament had not met with the approval of all members of the standing committee. He further stated that public support for the proposed legislation was increasing and that he would be in a better position to introduce appropriate legislative action when he received the report of the Committee on Social Offences against Children and Youth.

Following a February 1983 address to the council by Ms. Lucie Pépin, president of the Canadian Advisory Council on the Status of Women, on the subject of "battered women," the council decided to approach the issue of violence from a broader viewpoint, including abuse of the elderly, women and children. Council support staff prepared a long document, "Family Violence Information Package," designed to provide a general overview, to alert physicians and other health care providers to the signs and symptoms of family violence and to provide information on treatment modalities. The document was approved by General Council, following which it received wide acceptance and approval from health care organizations and the general public. The council's recommendations were:

♦ *That Health and Welfare Canada and provincial Ministries of Health and Education alert the Canadian public to the existence of family violence, including wife assault, child abuse, and abuse of elders, and to the services available which respond to these problems.*

- ◆ *That organized medicine (through such vehicles as professional journals, newsletters, conferences and formal medical education), alert the physicians of Canada to the problem.*
- ◆ *That all physicians learn to recognize the signs of family violence in their daily contact with patients and undertake the care and management of victims, using available community resources.*
- ◆ *That the CMA provide the necessary resources to publish the Family Violence Information Package for distribution to all members of the CMA.*
- ◆ *That the CMA recommend the enactment of legislation which, in situations of family violence, places the onus for leaving the family home on the perpetrator rather than on the victim.*

The resolutions were widely distributed and actions were implemented in a number of areas by provincial governments and others. A project in which the council, representing the CMA, was involved was the Interdisciplinary Project on Domestic Violence. Nine professional associations, with financial support from the Donner Foundation and the federal government, worked to create guidelines and practical resource materials that could be used in cooperative approaches to dealing with domestic violence. The third and final phase of the project was begun in 1992. This phase concentrated on the production of a resource kit for use by professionals, which included information and a video on ways and means of achieving interdisciplinary cooperation in the recognition and management of domestic violence and its outcome. Distribution was begun in late 1992, and participating organizations were given the responsibility of ensuring receipt by their respective memberships.

Human Immunodeficiency Virus (HIV) and Acquired Immunodeficiency Syndrome (AIDS)

In 1983, the council noted the increase in the incidence of HIV and AIDS and recognized that it had a role to play in monitoring of this matter. In 1985 it prepared a document, which it presented to the Board of Directors, on the question of a national policy for blood and blood products for Canada. Its recommendation to the General Council was approved: "That all blood and blood products to be administered be tested, prior to their use, for antibodies to the virus believed to be responsible for AIDS in humans." By the time the General Council met in 1987, the council had done a lot of work in collecting and collating information and presented nine recommendations, seven of which were approved and two of which were referred back to the council.

That the CMA :

(i) urges the federal and provincial governments to continue to increase financial support for research into the prevention and treatment of AIDS and to provide adequate funding so as to inform and educate health professionals regarding these diseases;

(ii) encourage health authorities to maintain an active public education programme that will include school populations;

(iii) insists that educational messages state that sexual activity is not rendered totally safe by the use of a condom;

(iv) proposes that individuals suffering from AIDS or who have confirmed antibody seropositivity to HIV be subject to mandatory non-nominal reporting;

(v) stresses the need to respect patient confidentiality and, where necessary, the need for legal and regulatory safeguards for such confidentiality;

(vi) urges health care institutions to recognize the need of health care professionals directly involved in patient care to be made aware of the potential risks of infection;

(vii) urges that all hospitals implement appropriate safety measures for the handling of body fluids and tissues.

Referred back to the council were:

(a) That the CMA propose that individuals suffering from AIDS or who have confirmed antibody seropositivity be subject to mandatory contact tracing.

(b) That the CMA support the routine serological testing for AIDS in all patients admitted to a public hospital either as an outpatient or inpatient for either a medical or surgical procedure.

In 1994, the council's name was changed to the Council on Health Care and Promotion and its new terms of reference were: "The Council on Health Care and Promotion shall be concerned with enhancing the provision of clinical care and the promotion of health for the individual, the family and the community through the activities of physicians working with other health care providers and through the implementation of healthy public policies and public education."

Council on Economics

At its first meeting the council considered the terms of reference that had been approved for it, viz.:

The Council on Economics shall study developments in medical services, plans for the provision costs of health services from a national viewpoint, and shall coordinate insofar as possible the provincial application of such developments. It shall provide an information service for the Divisions in the field of medical economics. The provision for physicians' services through agencies of the federal government shall be kept under review.

The council interpreted this as permission to study, *inter alia*, total costs of medical care, fee schedules, medical incomes and expenses of practice at both national and provincial levels. Some members of the Board of Directors did not share this interpretation, and the board changed the terms of reference to read:

This Council shall study and report on developments in health insurance programmes. The Council shall provide a forum for the study of economic data and make this information available to the Divisions through a data or information centre. Without limiting its terms of reference, the Council shall be responsible for the study and provision of information on the cost of health programmes, and shall consider such other matters as shall be referred to it by General Council or the Board of Directors.

The council was unhappy with these new terms and sought guidance from the 1970 General Council as to the range of matters that it should study.

The General Council heard a recommendation from the Committee on Finance that an amalgamation between the Council on the Provision of Health Services and the Council on Economics should be approved. After discussion a recommendation to the effect that there be no such amalgamation was approved. On the matter of the terms of reference it was approved that the following be added: "That one point of interpretation of the Council on Economics be studies of gross and professional income on a national and divisional level and include those factors which influence changes in either gross or net income."

Between 1970 and 1972, the main focus of the council's activities was on physician remuneration, and a number of meetings were held with officials of the Department of National Health and Welfare who were responsible for the collection and publication of data on physicians' incomes. The council was consistently critical of the data being published by the department, but the response was that if the profession wanted the validity of the data to be acceptable, the profession would have to be more cooperative in providing information requested from it, rather than either not providing the information when requested or by providing information that was suspect.

In 1972, the council presented a recommendation to General Council, asking the profession to participate in studies that would lead to meaningful and reliable data. The General Council approved this and another recommendation from the council in which it requested that a department of economic affairs be established, staffed by highly qualified, technically competent professionals to advise the Association in its formulation of economic policy and to act as resource people for the divisions.

One of the first tasks delegated to the new department by the council was to set up a program whereby reliable data on physician remuneration could be obtained. In 1974, the council proposed:

Whereas the parameters of the available physician-income studies have not been designed by practising physicians to accurately reflect the effects of fee-for-service, be it recommended that:

(i) *The CMA Department of Research and Development carry out an independent study of physicians' incomes;*

(ii) *that a subcommittee of Council be appointed to work with the Department of Research and Development to delineate the correct methodological and data source parameters necessary for such a study;*

(iii) *that this be considered as an item of high priority by the Department of Research and Development.*

The Board of Directors directed the council in 1976 to enlarge the Subcommittee on Physician Remuneration by including in its membership two salaried physicians and to modify the subcommittee's terms of reference so as to embrace a study of all aspects related to the work of salaried physicians, with particular emphasis on negotiations, salaries, fringe benefits and contracts.

During the subcommittee's studies it became obvious that any analysis of physician remuneration methodology required a knowledge of income and overheads and, as physicians appeared unwilling to provide these data, the work of the subcommittee and council was stymied. The council asked the Board of Directors to institute a nationwide survey, but this request was denied by both the board and the General Council. The General Council did approve a recommendation that the Statistics, Systems and Economic Research (SSER) Unit, a support unit of the Department of Economics, develop guidelines and criteria for gathering income and information on overheads that could be used by the divisions, and for the making of comparisons on a national basis.

A matter of concern in many quarters was the portability of medicare benefits, and the council had explored a number of ways in which the problem might be solved. It did not appear that governments were willing or able to address the problem, and appeals to the federal government fell on deaf ears. The matter was the subject of extensive discussion at the 1977 General Council and led to the adoption of the following: "That the CMA, with the help of the Divisions, enjoin the provincial paying agencies to issue benefit cheques payable to the physician for services rendered to out-of-province patients, and that a universal form, based on existing forms, be developed and accepted by all provincial paying agencies for out-of-province patients."

Over the next 3 years the council spent a lot of time on matters related to medicare and, in particular, to the refutation of the frequently heard pronouncements, especially from governments, that health care costs in Canada were escalating out of control and that physicians were to blame. Dr. Marc Baltzan of Saskatoon, chairman of the council, demonstrated time and time again that this was not the case. On the contrary, restraints imposed by governments had caused the cost of services provided by physicians to decline as a percentage of the gross national product. These costs, or "prices" as they were frequently called, were determined by negotiations between the body representing physicians and respective provincial governments. It was the council's view that prices were out of date, lagging behind increases in costs in other sectors.

Questions were frequently raised over the effectiveness of the negotiating process as it was practised between the profession and the paying agencies. Provincial governments brought to the negotiating table a leverage not available to physicians, with the end result that, in general, the profession did not get the best of the bargain. In July 1978, the CMA had sponsored a Conference on Techniques of Negotiation, an exercise deemed by the divisions to be of great value and one that should be repeated on an annual basis under the auspices of the CMA Board of Directors, with budgeting and organization to be the responsibility of the council.

The CMA presented a brief to the Hall Review in Saskatoon on Feb. 27, 1980. Much of the content of the brief had come from the council; similarly the Association's brief to the Parliamentary Task Force on Fiscal Arrangements contained much information emanating from the council. In the same year the council studied collective bargaining, sanctions and unionization as possible methods whereby the bargaining powers of the profession might be enhanced during negotiations and came to the conclusion that there were only two socially acceptable mechanisms in arriving at the price of physicians' services. The first was to have the price determined between "buyers" and "sellers" directly. The second was collective negotiations between buyer and seller through representative agents or agencies. The council presented a report of its studies to General Council, outlining in detail the differences between the two mechanisms. A third potential factor — binding arbitration — did not appear to be on the agenda of any government. General Council directed the council to draw up a contingency plan for legal status collective bargaining.

The council continued to stress that paying agencies (i.e., the provincial governments) held a monopolistic position in the purchase of the services of physicians and that success in any negotiations would depend on factors such as opting out and/or balance billing. The debate on this at General Council demonstrated clearly the frustrations being felt by many in the profession and led to a resolution directing the CMA to promote in an active manner the demonopolization of medicare and to urge that funding from the private sector be permitted. The council was directed to consider establishing a task force to implement the resolution.

In August 1981, the report of the Parliamentary Task Force on Federal-Provincial Fiscal Arrangements, titled *Fiscal Federalism in Canada*, was reviewed by the council. Particular attention was given to the chapter titled "The national commitment to health care." The council reported to the General Council that it found the chapter to be "an incorporation of assumptions and hypotheses, clearly coloured by ideology." It was conceded that cost controls in health care in Canada were effective, but the council added that the controls were of such a nature as to lead to underfunding.

In its response to a directive from an earlier General Council meeting on the subject of collective bargaining, the council presented a multipage document outlining the difficulties inherent in the differences between provinces in matters relating to negotiations and collective bargaining, and outlining actions that might be taken at the divisional level to effect the implementation of methods to offset such difficulties. It was the council's recommendation that divisions seek recognition as the sole bargaining agent for fee-for-service physicians and when so requested, for non fee-for-service physicians, and that protocols be established for the process of negotiation. This was approved by the General Council.

Pursuant to the resolution on the establishment of a task force to study and encourage sources of private sector funding, the Board of Directors appointed Dr. Baltzan chairman of a six-person committee called the Committee on Rational Medicare. The committee met in January and April 1982, and reviewed the current state of health care funding in Canada. Governments were seen to be facing demands for new programs and services while they were looking for ways and means to reduce their financial obligations in the health care field. This dichotomy led to a level of available resources that was acceptable politically but was not necessarily the optimum for patient care. When the committee presented its report to General Council, the debate was hot and heavy with amendments to amendments to amendments flying around like autumn leaves in a wind storm. After the discussion had run its protracted course, the General Council approved a list of patient goals.

(i) *Patients have the right to seek care from the physicians of their choice, without impediment by the insurer.*

(ii) *Physicians to be under contract to the patient and not to the insurer.*

(iii) *Patients to have the right of ready access to the physician of their choice.*

(iv) *The physician workload to be such as to allow sufficient time to provide patient care.*

(v) *Patients to have access to health-care facilities that are competently and sufficiently staffed, and equipped and available when needed.*

(vi) *Health-care facilities should be under contract to patients, not an insurer.*

(vii) *Patients not be deprived of the basic insurance scheme if they opt for additional coverage.*

(viii) *In general, patients should have the right to buy insurance for any service from any insurer.*

(ix) *Patients should have the right to know how much services cost and how much they are paying for services (dollar costs and dollar benefits).*

(x) *Patients to have methods of registering dissatisfaction with any part of the health-care system.*

The council was directed to develop the means whereby the private sector could be induced to participate in the delivery of health care so that the best available quality of health care would be accessible, without financial hardship, to all Canadians. During 1982 and 1983, the council studied various ways in which medicare, including hospitals, might be funded; options reviewed included single-source public financing, combinations of public and private funding, and purely private funding. The council looked at areas where savings might be achieved without detriment to the availability and quality of health care and picked three areas where shortcomings or "inefficiencies" might be corrected: structural, organizational and procedural.

The first area of this trinity was defined as legal and/or conventional structures associated with the interaction among major resource groups with the intent of producing the least costly "acceptable quality product." These structures do not lend themselves to easily obtained changes. The second area — organizational — referred to the way resources were organized and the relationship within and between them. The third area — procedural — also described as "process," referred to the number, location and time involved in the production of services. In studying these areas, the council took into account a number of other factors: cost-effectiveness of nurse-practitioners, the funding of Canadian medical schools, comparison of provincial benefits paid for a range of common medical procedures, alternative delivery systems and international health care systems. In so far as the latter was concerned, various methods of reimbursing physicians in other countries were compared and their merits and disadvantages noted. The council was of the opinion that no one system was superior and that all systems would benefit from having guidelines and incentives to keep them cost-effective.

Cost-containment practices by governments continued to be a major subject of study by the council, and in 1985, it presented its views to the General Council, stating that there appeared to be meagre evidence to support global budgeting and capping, when taken in isolation, as effective cost-saving measures without causing deleterious effects, in the long term, on the health care of patients. The council approved a recommendation calling on governments to apply a moratorium on global budgeting and capping until studies of health manpower and patient access to health care demonstrated that such actions would not affect adversely the quality of care.

The council continued its studies on the benefits and disadvantages of privatization of the health care system, and in particular reviewed the experience of a hospital in eastern Ontario that, since 1983, had been managed by a US organization. One outcome of the review was a recommendation, approved by the General Council, to the effect that the CMA supported the option of private management and/or ownership of health care institutions, including hospitals, provided that the same well-defined standards of quality of care and costs applied as in publicly owned facilities.

Reliability of data published by governments continued to be viewed as suspect by the council, and it therefore recommended that the CMA develop a sound national health care database, accessible to health care professionals' associations and those involved in legitimate research. By 1987, there was a plethora of data being collected by numerous federal and provincial governmental departments and agencies, but there was a notable omission among the collectors, viz., the medical profession, one of the major users of data. General Council approved the council's recommendation that the CMA and the divisions establish a joint working group to study and identify the medical profession's health care data needs so that they could be included in governmental databases and so give a reliability, then lacking, to the published data.

In 1986, the council was directed to examine and report on the long-term funding of the health care system. This work was done through a council sub-committee, and its report, after consideration by the council in April 1988, was presented to the Board of Directors in May. It was the council's opinion that the federal deficit was of such magnitude as to have overall detrimental effects on the national economy and would require increasing fiscal restraints in a number of sectors, including health care. Federal funding through EPF (Established Programs Financing) grants was decreasing, and this made it very difficult for health care planners to design short-term and long-term plans for the system. The council recognized that funding allocation for health care had to take into account the variations in provincial fiscal capacity and that it would be necessary, therefore, to devise a formula for the distribution of monies coming from the federal coffers. In the absence of adequate federal funding, and to maintain acceptable standards of health care, the council believed there was room for greater involvement by the private sector in the delivery, management and organization of health care in Canada. This view was endorsed by the General Council.

The council went on to lay out what it believed to be the essential characteristics of a well-managed health care system, viz., one that:

1. develops goals and objectives;
2. creates reasonable expectations for the realization of stated goals and objectives;
3. insulates the health care system from use and abuse for political purposes;
4. creates stability and streamlines funding (at least in terms of minimum levels), while addressing issues of regional equity with respect to the accessibility to health services by Canadians;
5. provides health care administrators and physicians with the necessary tools and incentives to investigate and make decisions leading to effective and efficient use of health care resources, and provides for a more efficient delivery of quality health care services.

In the mid-1980s, the council continued to monitor the growth in interest in alternative health care delivery systems, shown by a number of provincial governments looking for ways to control costs. Greater emphasis was placed on the advocacy of health promotion and ill-health prevention. There was no lack of advocates for replacing the physician with other health professionals, even though no unbiased evidence was available to prove this would lead to savings in expenditure on health care. Often, and perhaps conveniently, overlooked in many of the arguments were the rapid technologic advances. One eminent clinician was heard to remark that governments wanted to keep paying horse and buggy rates for medical services in the space age.

The council noted with concern that there was no national body monitoring the introduction of new technologies and the General Council agreed with the council's recommendation in 1988, viz.,

> *That the CMA urge the federal government to support the CMA in an initiative for the development of a national medical technology assessment committee, such committee to have among its responsibilities:*
> (i) *the monitoring of new technologies;*
> (ii) *the identification of new medical technology that should be evaluated;*
> (iii) *support and coordination of the evaluation, where necessary (such support could be financial and/or technical);*
> (iv) *collection, assessment and dissemination of the results of these studies and/or studies from other jurisdictions.*

In the months following the General Council meeting, and most likely sparked by the resolution, greater interest was expressed in medical technology assessment. The council believed that, although the Association was being more frequently asked for guidance in technologic advances, particularly by some of the affiliate societies, it had not defined the role that it should play in the matter. On that basis the council recommended to the Board of Directors that a board subcommittee be formed with representation from all three CMA councils and the Committee on Ethics, and that such a subcommittee have terms of reference clearly defining the CMA's role vis-à-vis governments, physicians, and medical and nonmedical organizations. This recommendation was approved by the Board of Directors.

In 1990, the name of the council was changed to Council on Health Policy and Economics. The new terms of reference were:

> *The Council on Health Policy and Economics will be concerned with assessing and formulating policy options to the economics, organization and management of the health-care delivery system. Council will work with other Councils and Committees of the CMA and with other internal and external bodies to ensure that proposed policy options are consistent with the findings of Council and with the strategic directions of the CMA.*

As a result of the 1991 federal act known as *The Government Expenditure*

Act, EPF health and postsecondary education entitlements to the provinces were frozen for 2 years, later extended to 1994–95. The council was concerned over the impact that would have on programs, particularly in provinces that did not have strong economies. The council participated in CMA presentations to the federal government on the matter and had considerable input into the CMA brief to the Interprovincial Conference of Health Ministers, held in Charlottetown in 1991. The CMA Executive Committee directed the council to undertake a detailed review of the then-current CMA policies on health care funding. It was proposed that in the review, the council would make a detailed assessment of the sources and uses of health care funding, with the intent to identify more effective means of delivering and paying for medically required health care services.

The council drafted a policy statement that was approved by the Board of Directors after some amendments had been made; it was published in the *Canadian Medical Association Journal* in July of that year. The statement read:

> *The CMA believes that financial support from the federal government for health care should provide for the following:*
> ◆ *The maintenance and improvement of standards of health care services across Canada.*
> ◆ *The financial stability necessary to effectively plan health care delivery and the flexibility in spending across Canada to respond to local health care needs.*
> ◆ *A greater equity across the provinces and territories in the ability to finance necessary healthcare programs.*
> ◆ *The joint policy discussions necessary to address health issues of national importance.*
>
> *The CMA is committed to preserving the right of reasonable access to high-quality health care regardless of ability to pay. It is also committed to maintaining the national health care standards (accessibility, universality, portability, comprehensiveness and public administration), and developing health goals to ensure that all Canadians receive the best possible care when required. The CMA supports the goal of maintaining the national integrity of the health care system. It encourages the federal government to be sensitive to the concerns of equity and to ensure that provinces and territories that have not attained a level of health care services and facilities equivalent to those of other provinces and territories, because of fiscal incapacities, have access to additional funding requirements to reduce the gap. The CMA views stability in funding as essential to effective health*

care planning and believes that unplanned and unilateral federal reductions may compromise accessibility and quality of patient care.

A revision of policy on the matter of physician remuneration was requested from the council. The General Council suggested that the following factors be included in the new policy:

(i) *Medical practitioners must receive fair and reasonable remuneration for the full spectrum of their professional activities.*

(ii) *Individual medical practitioners have the liberty to choose among payment modalities.*

(iii) *Paying agencies must fulfil the terms of agreements negotiated with legitimate agents of the medical profession, and be obliged to honour a mutually agreed-upon and established process of negotiations with legitimate agents of the medical profession.*

(iv) *In the event of failure of negotiations relating to physician compensation, such disagreement be resolved by a mutually agreed-upon timely dispute mechanism.*

(v) *The Minister of National Health and Welfare must enforce the provisions of the Canada Health Act relevant to physician compensation (Section 122).*

Most of the deliberations on the council's report to the 1992 General Council reflected the ongoing concern about the financial sustainability of Canada's system of universal, publicly financed health care, particularly in view of the diminishing federal financial support of provincial and territorial health programs. The Board of Directors once again asked the council to study the current state of health care financing in Canada and to formulate a policy position for consideration by the Board of Directors.

To meet the board's directive, the council formed an ad hoc working group. The work was divided into three stages, the first being to define the dimensions of the funding problem and, as part of that stage, a 1-day consultation session was held in early March 1993. Participants came from the media, organized labour, financial and business organizations, consumer groups and government. The second stage was the development of a discussion paper, which critiqued the experiences of Canada and other countries and put forward options that could put Canada's health care system on a sustainable financial footing. The third stage was the development of draft policy for consideration by the Board of Directors.

The council submitted its report on the recommendations of the working group to General Council in 1993. One of the major recommendations requested that the CMA endorse the following primary principles as the basis for developing a new consensus on health care system financing:

Sustainability: That the methods and level of support for universal health benefits for all bona fide residents of Canada be commensurate with collective and individual ability to pay.

Accessibility: That access to health-care services be governed by relative medical necessity as determined, whenever possible and practicable, by a qualified medical practitioner.

Universal Coverage: That all residents of Canada be entitled to publicly-financed health-insurance benefits according to uniform terms and conditions.

Reasonable Uniformity of Benefits: That all residents of Canada be entitled to reasonably comparable levels of health-care benefits at reasonably comparable levels of taxation.

Choice: That all Canadian consumers and providers of health care can have freedom of choice as to health-care settings and/or modes of service delivery.

These five principles were incorporated into a draft policy paper presented to General Council in 1994 by Dr. Hugh Scully, chairman of the council. The report and the outcome are recorded in the chapter on medical insurance.

Throughout the 25 years of its existence, the Council on Health Policy and Economics has played a leading role in the development of CMA positions and policies in the following areas: physician resource planning, health financing, physician remuneration, tax reform and regionalization.

Chapter VI

ETHICS

ONE OF THE FIRST committees formed on Oct. 10, 1867, the second day of the newly formed Canadian Medical Association, was the Committee on the Code of Medical Ethics. The first *Code of Ethics* was written in 1868. Throughout the formative years of the Association, the main task of the committee was to refine and update the code. This endeavour was well described in the report of the Committee on Ethics to General Council in 1963 when there was criticism of the code:

> *The medical profession does not now subscribe to all that was laid down in the original Oath of Hippocrates. Our own* Code of Ethics *was first written out in 1868, just ninety-five years ago, and in the interval many changes have been made — changes that are attempts to place it in harmony with the "changing sentiments of the world" and the resulting changes in the conditions surrounding practice and the relations that exist between the profession, its patients and society.*

In 1965, the committee's agenda included a number of matters other than amendments to the code, and it was discussing topics such as group and clinic practice, sterilization and types of advertising that might be used by physicians. In 1968, the code was rewritten and split into two sections. The committee recommended that the first section consist of terse statements of direction to members on the basic principles of medical ethics by which the profession governed itself. The second section should consist of details and guides for the ethical behaviour of physicians in Canada in their relationships with patients, colleagues and society. This was approved by the General Council.

In the same year, the committee discussed the probable restructuring of the Association's committee format and asked the General Council for permission to explore the advantages and disadvantages of changing from a standing committee to a statutory committee. In 1969, the Committee on Organization brought forward its report that, in part, recommended that, with some exceptions, the 44 committees then extant be coalesced into five councils. In 1970 this change of status was effected and the Committee on Ethics became a statutory committee, with terms of reference being "the elaboration and interpretation of the Code, and the dealing with problems on the matter of ethics referred to the Association."

The next 5 years brought an increasing number of questions from members, arising out of the complex medico-socio-economic systems in which they practised medicine. Some of the subjects reviewed by the committee were: artificial insemination, human experimentation, genetic engineering, organ transplantation, euthanasia, abortion, the "right to die" and the "living will." In 1977, the committee presented to General Council a document titled *Guidelines for the Care of Prisoners in Canadian Penitentiaries.* In pointing out that the CMA was not attempting to interfere with the policies of the federal Department of the Solicitor-General, the committee believed that the expanding role of that department's health care division in the care of prisoners needed to be clarified and guidelines developed to prevent unethical practices.

From the ensuing debate, a number of recommendations were approved; these pertained to medical qualifications, accountability to the professional licensing body, the operation of regional psychiatric centres, the operation of such centres to follow the rules and regulations laid down by the Canadian Council on Hospital Accreditation and the need for provincial medical associations to monitor medical services delivered in prisons in the respective provinces.

There was a lot of discussion on the ethics involved in the transfer of patient care in circumstances where a physician does not wish to provide such care. In the end, the following recommendation was approved: "An ethical physician, when his personal ethic prevents him from recommending some form of therapy, he will so acquaint his patient and will advise the patient of other sources of assistance." When the General Council convened the following year, it was apparent that interpretations, never intended when the resolution was finally recorded, were being made and these, in the main, were that the resolution gave carte blanche to direct a patient seeking an abortion to a physician and/or a facility where the abortion could be carried out. The debate followed very closely the one of the year before, but was eventually approved as: "An ethical physician, when his morality or religious conscience alone prevents him from recommending some form of therapy, he will so acquaint the patient."

By 1979, the Committee on Ethics was being frequently asked to expound on bioethical matters and so its terms of reference were expanded to enable it to study and report on subjects of bioethical concern. In 1980, the committee came to the General Council with the recommendation: "That an advisory committee to the Committee on Ethics be formed, consisting of one expert specialist in bioethics; one member-at-large, interested in bioethical research, chosen from the CMA membership; one member of the Committee on Ethics; and that this committee be appointed by the Committee on Ethics for a two-year period, at the end of which the concept be reviewed." The General Council approved. David Roy, PhD, director of the Center for Bioethics, Clinical Research Institute of Montreal, was invited to meet with the Committee on Ethics and discuss with it how the proposed committee might function.

The advisory committee became a task force in early 1982 and its members were Dr. Roy, Professor Bernard Dickens from the Faculty of Law, University of Toronto, Dr. John Crookston, chairman of the Committee on Research, Faculty of Medicine, University of Toronto, and Dr. John Herbert O'Hanley, a member of the CMA Committee on Ethics. The task force submitted a report to the Committee on Ethics, listing the problems and issues illustrating the existence of a large core of bioethical concerns, and expressing the opinion that the magnitude of the numerous problems would require initiatives for their solution far beyond the medical profession.

As a result of that report, the 1982 General Council was presented with a recommendation asking medical schools in Canada to increase the teaching of medical ethics in their respective curricula, and requested provincial medical associations to assist in the creation of ethics rounds in hospitals in their respective provinces. It was further recommended that there be increased coverage of ethical issues in the *Canadian Medical Association Journal* and increased awareness and coverage of ethical and bioethical issues at meetings of affiliate societies. In approving these recommendations, the General Council also extended the life of the task force for a further year, but directed that it fall under the Council on Health Care and that a member of that council be a member of the task force. One of the first areas addressed by the task force was the question of surrogate motherhood, and this led to the 1983 General Council advising those physicians involved in the medical aspects of the procedure to act with great caution until the legal, social and psychological implications had been clarified.

The Committee on Ethics now consisted of a chairperson and four members, and the Board of Directors was of the opinion that the subcommittee should be returned to the Committee on Ethics. New appointees to the committee were experts in bioethical matters and would retain consultant status. The committee's mandate was enlarged by adding that its role was "to advise the

Association in matters pertaining to ethical issues that arise from scientific and technological progress in the health sciences and ethical issues of interest or concern to the medical profession."

In 1984 and 1985, the Committee on Ethics spent some time discussing the involuntary feeding of detainees and then presented to the General Council a statement to the effect that, when a prisoner refuses nourishment and is considered by the physician to be capable of forming an unimpaired, rational judgement about the consequences of such a refusal, the prisoner shall not be fed artificially. The consequences of refusing nourishment must be explained to the prisoner by the physician. The statement was endorsed by General Council.

The human immunodeficiency virus (HIV) and the acquired immunodeficiency syndrome (AIDS) brought ethical principles and their application into sharp focus in 1985 and 1986. The principle of confidentiality was being challenged by a society demanding to be told of the risks of contagion and of counteractive measures of protection. On the recommendation of the Committee on Ethics, the General Council adjured physicians to care for their patients with HIV or AIDS or to refer them to where treatment was available and to keep themselves current on treatment modalities. Physicians were to comply with legal requirements, bearing in mind confidentiality. In 1987 the Association approved the committee's recommendation that it support the Canadian Public Health Association's public service messages on HIV and AIDS.

Dr. Arthur H. Parsons, who had been chairman of the Committee on Ethics for nearly a decade, stepped down and was replaced by Dr. J. Noel Doig.

During 1987 and 1988, the committee revised and updated the CMA *Code of Ethics*. The committee's workload had increased to the extent that the Board of Directors considered the establishment of a department of ethics and legal affairs. The Board of Directors believed that medical ethics and law were becoming more interrelated, and if the CMA was to remain in the forefront in dealing with ethical issues, such a department would be essential. A grant of seed money was provided by the Department of National Health and Welfare and suitable candidates for the position of director of the Department of Ethics and Legal Affairs were interviewed. The successful candidate was Dr. Eike-Henner W. Kluge from the Department of Philosophy, University of Victoria.

Much of the committee's time was taken up with the role of the physician in dealing with HIV/AIDS. The CMA had commissioned a publication titled *Physicians, Ethics and AIDS* written by Drs. Norbert Gilmore and Margaret Somerville of the McGill Centre for Medicine, Ethics and Law in Montreal. From the review of that booklet came the recommendation "That the CMA condemn the principle that a physician may not refuse to treat a patient whose condition falls within his/her general area of competence, solely on the grounds of any condition that the patient may have (including AIDS or HIV seropositivity) except when such refusal can be ethically or legally justified." The General Council did not pass the recommendation, but went on to approve that the CMA endorse the principle that physicians have an ethical responsibility to take appropriate action when acts or omissions of a colleague imperil the health of his/her co-workers.

The Committee on Ethics was directed by the Executive Committee to prepare a document to serve as the Association's response to the federal government's Bill C-43, *An Act respecting abortion.* The bill had been introduced to replace Section 251 of the *Criminal Code* of Canada, that section having been declared unconstitutional by the Supreme Court of Canada in the Morgenthaler case. The paper, produced by the Department of Ethics and Legal Affairs and the committee, recommended that the CMA reject Bill C-43 in its entirety. The basis of the rejection was that abortion was going to be the only medical act in the code to draw criminal sanction. In the presentation of its brief to the House of Commons Legislation Committee on Abortion on Feb. 6, 1990, the Association stressed that, in its opinion, not only was the singling-out of the procedure for inclusion in the code discriminatory, but that the legislation proposed was also detrimental to the practice of responsible medicine and jeopardized the fiduciary nature of the patient–physician relationship. The Association was pleased that its arguments had contributed to the defeat of the bill.

On Oct. 25, 1989, the federal government established a Royal Commission on New Reproductive Technologies. Its mandate was "to inquire into and report on current and potential medical and scientific developments related to new reproductive technologies, considering in particular their social, ethical, health, research, legal and economic implications and the public interest, recommending what policies and safeguards should be applied." The Department of Ethics and Legal Affairs prepared a long document, designed to serve as the basis of the CMA's presentation to the Royal Commission. Input was sought from the divisions, the affiliate societies and other organizations that had interests in the matter. On Nov. 2, 1990, in London, Ont., a delegation led by Dr. Judith C. Kazimirski, chairperson of the CMA Board of Directors, presented the CMA's position to the Royal Commission.

In keeping with current day usage, the *Code of Ethics* was made gender-neutral. A number of revisions had already been made, and it was anticipated that a major revision would be required in the near future to take into account changes in the patient–physician relationship. The Committee on Ethics membership make-up was changed to reflect representation on a regional basis.

The status of the human fetus had been under discussion for more than 2 years in meetings of the Committee on Ethics, but because of the complexity of the issue and other factors related to human reproduction, it had not been possible for a consensus to be reached by 1990 as had been planned. It was on May 24, 1991, that the committee was in the position to present its report, *The Status of the Human Foetus*, to the Board of Directors. The report had benefitted from input from the Royal College of Physicians and Surgeons of Canada, College of Family Physicians of Canada, Society of Obstetricians and Gynaecologists of Canada, the Canadian Paediatric Society, the Federation of Medical Women of Canada and the Canadian Nurses Association. In the same year, the committee presented, for discussion purposes only, a paper on anencephalic donation.

In 1991, Dr. Kluge left the CMA to return to the University of Victoria and his place was taken by Dr. John R. Williams, principal research associate at the Center for Bioethics, Clinical Research Institute of Montreal. The committee adopted five topics for study: euthanasia; confidentiality of medical records; advance directives and resuscitation of the terminally ill; proxy decision making; and the relationship between physicians and the pharmaceutical industry. By the beginning of 1993, four out of the five planned background papers on euthanasia, prepared by the Department of Ethics and Legal Affairs, were completed. When the fifth paper became available, all five papers appeared in issues of the *Canadian Medical Association Journal* between Apr. 15 and June 15, 1993, under the title "Canadian physicians and euthanasia." Subsequently, the five papers were collated into a booklet. At the General Council meeting in 1993, the Committee on Ethics held an educational session on euthanasia, followed the next day by a strategic issue session on the subject. The views coming from the General Council meeting were taken under advisement by the committee, to be included in the preparation of a draft CMA policy paper for consideration by the 1994 General Council meeting.

The relationship between the medical profession and the pharmaceutical industry, one of the five priority areas of study by the committee and the department, led to the revision of an earlier Association policy on the matter, and a draft policy was prepared for consideration by the 1993 General Council meeting. Input was received from individuals and organizations for inclusion in the paper, titled *Physicians and the Pharmaceutical Industry (Update 1993)*. The paper was presented to the General Council in August 1993, and as is so often the case at General Council meetings when there are wide divergences of opinion, there was a plethora of amendments and subamendments before the document received final approval. The approved version contained 34 guidelines to help physicians recognize their individual and collective responsibilities in ensuring that their participation in collaborative efforts, such as research and education, would be in keeping with their duties toward their patients and to society.

The matter of confidentiality of medical records was addressed by the Committee on Ethics, and following the *McInerney v. MacDonald* case in which the Supreme Court of Canada ruled that a medical record belongs to the physician or health care institution that compiled it, a draft policy was prepared for consideration. The court ruled also that the patient had the right to examine the record and to copy all information contained therein, including consultation and other reports obtained from physicians. It was the Association's opinion that physicians should be prepared to explain, on request, the information contained in the medical record. Unless the law requires otherwise, patient authorization is necessary for the disclosure of information contained in medical records to third parties. In the matter of transfer of medical records to another physician for the purposes of patient care, it was recommended that the physician who compiled the medical record retain the original documents and that copies or abstracts be forwarded. The recommendations by the Committee on Ethics on confidentiality, access and disclosure of information were incorporated into Association policy.

In March 1992, the federal government established a subcommittee of the Standing Committee of Justice and of the solicitor-general of Canada to study proposals for changes in the *Criminal Code*, and an invitation was extended to the CMA to provide the subcommittee with the Association's views. A lengthy document was prepared by the Department of Ethics and Legal Affairs for consideration by the Committee on Ethics. After approval by the committee, the document was ratified by the Board of Directors and the CMA brief was submitted to the subcommittee on Oct. 19, 1992. This was followed by the appearance of a CMA delegation before the subcommittee on Nov. 24.

The brief, titled "Recodification of the *Criminal Code* of Canada: General Part, Issues for Canadian Physicians," focused on three issues: (1) the need to recognize explicitly, medical practice as a legitimate sphere of activity, distinct from the wrongs that criminal law seeks to address; (2) the ambiguities in the current law, particularly with respect to the obligations of physicians in initiating and stopping treatment; and (3) the need for an explicit definition of death in terms of the irreversible cessation of brain function or the prolonged absence of cardiac and respiratory functions, or both.

The report of the federal subcommittee in 1993 recommended that the *Criminal Code* be amended to state clearly that there is no offence of assault or assault causing bodily harm where a patient consents to medical treatment, and that physicians administering palliative care are not criminally responsible for accelerating the patient's death unless the patient refuses such care.

As had been directed by the 1993 General Council, the Committee on Ethics prepared a draft policy on physician-assisted death (euthanasia and assisted suicide). In the preparation of this paper, input came from a number of sources: a mail survey of Canadian physicians, as well as opinions from the General Council; discussions with the appropriate committees of the Royal College of Physicians and Surgeons of Canada and the College of Family Physicians of Canada; review of literature; a recent judgement by the Supreme Court of Canada; and the many unsolicited letters and position papers received from physicians and other interested parties. Prior to being presented to the 1994 General Council, the paper had been reviewed by the Board of Directors; some amendments were made, and the board recommended that it go to the General Council and be approved as CMA policy.

For the purposes of discussion, the following were defined:

Euthanasia to include the following components: the subject is a competent, informed person with an incurable illness, who has voluntarily asked that his/her life be terminated; the agent knows the person's condition and desire to die, and commits an act with the primary intention of ending that person's life; the act is undertaken with empathy and compassion and without personal gain.

Assistance in suicide means knowingly and intentionally providing a person with the knowledge and/or means of committing suicide, including counselling a person about lethal dosages of drugs, providing the prescription for such lethal dosages, and supplying the drugs to the person.

In the context of the proposed policy, physician-assisted death applies to competent persons only and does not include the withholding or withdrawal of inappropriate medical treatment or the provision of compassionate palliative care, even when life is shortened by such measures.

The draft policy paper recorded the relevant sections of the CMA *Code of Ethics* and questioned the law as stated in the *Criminal Code* and whether the legal status of physician-assisted death should be codified. The balance of the paper was taken up with defining safeguards, should physician-assisted death be legalized.

Just as in the case of other emotional and contentious issues that had come before general councils, the debate on the issue was wide-ranging. To facilitate the debate, the General Council moved into a Committee of the Whole. The chairman of the Committee on Ethics, Dr. Douglas M. Sawyer, stated that three levels of policy options had been identified — public policy (possibly legislation), professional ethics and clinical decision making — and recommended that the discussion should focus on the first level.

When the General Council resumed in regular session, a number of recommendations were placed before it. Discussion was prolonged once more, but the following recommendations were eventually approved.

That the CMA declare that its members adhere to the principles of palliative care. (The record shows that the vote for this was unanimous.)

That the CMA declare that its members specifically exclude participation in euthanasia and physician-assisted suicide. (This was approved by 93 votes to 74.)

On Nov. 23, 1994, the CMA made a presentation on physician-assisted death to the Special Senate Committee on Euthanasia and Assisted Suicide. It was the intention of the Association that the recommendations, in the form of a statement of policy, would help physicians, the public and the law makers participate in any re-examination of the then legal prohibition of physician-assisted death, and to arrive at a solution that would be in the best interest of Canadians. Members of the Senate Committee expressed appreciation to the CMA for helping them deal with the many complex issues they had to address, not just euthanasia and assisted suicide but also resuscitation, advance directives and termination of treatment.

The CMA's position on physician-assisted death was best summed up in a public statement made by the president of the CMA, Dr. Bruno L'Heureux, on Nov. 23, 1994:

Physician-assisted death is opposed by the vast majority of national medical associations and by the law codes of almost all countries. A change in the legal status of these practices in Canada would represent a major shift in social values and behaviour. For the medical profession to support such a change and participate in physician-assisted death would require a fundamental reconsideration of traditional medical ethics.

There is a great diversity of opinions within the medical profession as well as throughout society on almost every aspect of euthanasia and assisted suicide. Whatever public policy is chosen, there are likely to remain deep and sharp divisions within all sectors of society, including the medical profession.

Chapter VII

INTERNATIONAL HEALTH

FROM ITS VERY BEGINNINGS, the CMA has been active in the international health field, not only through its close ties with national medical associations and its membership in international medical bodies, but also through its direct involvement in the provision of health care in developing countries. There have been a number of instances where other national medical organizations have shared their meetings in Canada with the CMA's annual meeting; on the other side of the coin, the CMA has held annual meetings with other medical associations in their respective countries. Good examples of the interface between the CMA and other national medical associations can be seen in shared presidencies. A precedent was established when the CMA and the British Medical Association (BMA) held their joint annual meetings in Winnipeg in August 1930, presided over by the joint-president, Dr. W. Harvey Smith of Winnipeg. In 1955–56, Dr. T. Clarence Routley, long-time general secretary of the CMA, was president of both the CMA and the BMA. His Royal Highness, Prince Philip, Duke of Edinburgh, held both presidencies in 1959–60. Dr. Peter J. Banks of Victoria, BC, held both presidencies 1973–74, and Mr. Barry O'Donnell of Dublin was president of the CMA, the BMA and the Irish Medical Association in 1976–77.

The Commonwealth Medical Association
In 1947, the BMA proposed the formation of a British Commonwealth Council for the purposes of "developing and maintaining closer contact between medical practitioners in the United Kingdom and the Dominions; for advancing the status of British Medicine; for the discussion and interchange of views on matters of common interest; and for the promotion of interchange of professional facilities." Invitations went to the national medical associations in Canada, South Africa, New Zealand, Southern Rhodesia, Eire and Newfoundland. The first meeting of representatives of the medical associations was held in London in June 1948. The CMA representatives were Dr. Jack F.C.

Anderson, president, Dr. Wallace Wilson and Dr. Routley, general secretary.

The first full meeting of the British Commonwealth Medical Conference (BCMC) was held in Saskatoon in June 1949 at the time of the CMA annual meeting. Delegates came from Britain, Eire, India, Pakistan, New Zealand, Ceylon, Newfoundland, Australia, South Africa and Southern Rhodesia. The CMA was represented by Drs. Anderson, T. Clarence Routley, William Magner, George Ferguson, Harris McPhedran and Arthur D. Kelly. Dr. Anderson was elected president of the new organization.

Following that meeting, the conference met in 1952, 1955 and 1959. In 1959, the CMA delegates, Dr. E. Kirk Lyon and Dr. Kelly, told the CMA Executive Committee and General Council that "the CMA should continue to support this international organization which, in many respects, resembles a family gathering. The diversities of language which handicap communication in larger international bodies were not present, though the medical problems of the nations represented are sufficiently varied to make the Conference a very representative one."

The sixth meeting of the BCMC was held in Auckland, New Zealand, in February 1961, and was attended by Drs. T. James Quintin and Edwin C. McCoy, representing the CMA. At that meeting, it was the view of the majority that a Commonwealth Medical Association be formed, replacing the BCMC, and that the CMA be a founding member of that association. The CMA Executive Committee studied the matter after receiving the written and verbal reports of the CMA delegates, and expressed reservations, believing that the new organization might affect membership in the World Medical Association. It was decided that the CMA did not support the idea of a Commonwealth Medical Association. At the next meeting of the BCMC in Ceylon in 1962, the matter was again on the agenda and the CMA delegates were instructed to reiterate its opposition to the proposal.

The CMA, as a result of travel difficulties, was not represented at the meeting, and the nine countries that were, voted in favour of the formation of a Commonwealth Medical Association. The CMA was invited to become a member, but the Executive Committee recommended to the General Council that the invitation not be accepted. A motion from the floor to the contrary was defeated, but it was resolved that the CMA send its representatives as observers to the meetings of the Commonwealth Medical Association. In 1964, CMA president Dr. Frank A. Turnbull and Dr. Kelly attended the Association's meeting in London as observers and, on their return, advised the Executive Committee that the CMA should apply for membership. Following a study of the implications, the Executive Committee recommended to General Council that the CMA join the Commonwealth Medical Association. The recommendation was approved by General Council.

Application was made by the CMA and was accepted; the annual membership fee for the CMA was £400. CMA delegates attended the 1966 meeting in Karachi and the 1970 meetings in Kuala Lumpur and Singapore. In 1972, Dr. Duncan L. Kippen represented the CMA at the meeting in Ghana, where he, along with Dr. Matthew Beaubrun of Jamaica, was responsible for the drafting and presentation of a constitution for the organization. By 1976, there was concern over the viability of the association, as a number of its member national medical associations were becoming more and more involved in other, newer medical bodies, such as the BMA becoming a member of the European Economic Community Medical Committee, and with these obligations, national medical organizations were finding that time, personnel and finances militated against maintaining memberships in multiple international medical organizations.

In 1977, the CMA Board of Directors reviewed its membership in the Commonwealth Medical Association and discussed its future with the chairman of the BMA council, Mr. Walpole Lewin, and BMA secretary, Dr. Derek Stevenson. It was conceded by the BMA that the Commonwealth Medical Association could not point to any major accomplishments of a practical nature, but it did point out that the provision of such a forum for exchange of information and ideas was, in itself, of inestimable value. Their arguments did not convince the CMA Board of Directors and, before making a final decision, the opinions of the Australian and New Zealand medical associations were sought. The latter informed the CMA that it had already decided to withdraw from membership; the former was in the process of conducting a study of the merits of membership.

Mr. Barry O'Donnell, president of the CMA, attended the meeting of the Commonwealth Medical Association in New Delhi in December 1976, where he advised the meeting that the CMA had decided to terminate its membership. In his report to the General Council, Mr. O'Donnell stated that there was displeasure when this announcement was made, but that the CMA had been commended for attending the meeting to present its decision in person.

For the next 10 years, the Commonwealth Medical Association's activities were scaled down, mostly due to lack of funds. In the main, it was kept alive through the good offices of the BMA. However, because a number of national medical associations withdrew from the World Medical Association, there was increased interest in the Commonwealth Medical Association. In 1986, at the meeting of the Commonwealth Medical Association Council in Cyprus, the

BMA's offer to take over the Association's administration and provide funding for a 2-year period was accepted. There was a proviso that the situation would be assessed at the end of the 2 years and a decision made as to the future of the organization.

A number of aims and objectives were spelled out:

(i) *Exchange of information on a wide range of health issues via a quarterly publication.*

(ii) *Coordination of continuing medical education programmes.*

(iii) *Development of health education/promotion programmes.*

(iv) *Assistance and advice on ethical matters to national medical associations.*

(v) *Acceptance by WHO and by Commonwealth Ministers of Health as a credible and viable nongovernmental organization (NGO), capable of valuable input.*

(vi) *Assistance to national medical associations in organizational and related matters.*

In December 1988, the CMA Board of Directors agreed, in principle, to support the Commonwealth Medical Association and make a contribution of £1000 for the calendar year 1989. It was decided that this gesture was not be seen as establishing a precedent and that there would be an assessment of financial and other implications before any further contributions or commitment to join would be made. The Commonwealth Medical Association had become a much stronger organization, thanks to the support of the BMA, particularly by its secretary, Dr. John D.J. Havard. An example of its credibility was its cosponsorship in London in July 1989, with the American Society of Law and Medicine and the Commonwealth Legal Association, of the International Symposium of Health Law and Ethics, following its annual meeting at which the CMA was represented by Dr. John S. Bennett, associate secretary general, and Dr. Normand P. DaSylva, director of health services.

The status of the Commonwealth Medical Association was a subject of discussion at the 1990 General Council, which was told that it had been the recipient of a grant from the Commonwealth Foundation and that further funding was being obtained through a new structure of membership dues. It had been represented at the triennial meeting of the Commonwealth ministers of health in Melbourne, Australia, and had provided input to a number of discussed topics. It was one of five professional organizations that had joined together to set up a Commonwealth human-rights initiative, with the intent of submitting a report with recommendations on priority issues for presentation to the 1991 meeting of the Commonwealth heads of government in Harare, Zimbabwe.

In 1991, the CMA and the Commonwealth Medical Association entered into an agreement whereby the CMA's recently retired associate secretary general would serve as honorary assistant secretary, having special responsibilities for the Canada–Caribbean region. The CMA undertook the running costs, on the understanding that these would not exceed $5000 per annum and that specific projects would be funded separately. Other costs, including travel, were not to exceed $5000 per annum. The arrangement was for 2 years, and the monies involved would be in lieu of the CMA's annual dues to the Commonwealth Medical Association. CMA House would make space available for use as the regional office.

In July 1992, a workshop on medical ethics and human rights was held in London. It was attended by representatives from member medical associations and others from Canada and elsewhere who had expertise in the subject.

The first project carried out under the agreement between the two associations was an international symposium on reproductive health in developing countries of the commonwealth, held in Kingston, Jamaica, from Oct. 30 to Nov. 3, 1992. The president of the CMA, Dr. Richard J. Kennedy, attended the symposium and the triennial meeting of the Commonwealth Medical Association, and Dr. Bennett was responsible for much of the planning and administration of the symposium's actual proceedings. Out of the symposium came a training manual for national medical associations; this was used in workshops in St. Vincent, West Indies, and in Accra, Ghana.

In 1993, a working group on medical ethics and human rights was held at BMA House in London. Eleven briefing papers, including one from the CMA, had been commissioned by the 1992 workshop. Out of the 22 delegates who attended, 3 were from the CMA. The outcome of the deliberations was a document that could be used by national medical associations in developing countries to set up the appropriate machinery for the investigation of unethical conduct and to promote legislation for establishing a national independent statutory disciplinary body to enforce ethical standards.

The 2-year agreement expired in 1993 and was not renewed, the Commonwealth Medical Association believing that a better arrangement was to use the expertise, particularly in medical ethics, which was in CMA House, and for the CMA to pay its required annual dues.

The World Medical Association

During World War II, BMA House in London was where doctors from the allied nations met informally to talk about medical practice in wartime and to compare and contrast the practice of medicine and medical education in their respective countries. In July 1945, a number of physicians held an informal conference in London to initiate plans for an international medical organization to replace l'Association professionelle internationale des médecins. That 20-year-old organization had 23 member countries but had ceased operation when hostilities began in 1939. Out of the informal gathering came an invitation to a number of national medical associations to attend a conference, organized by the BMA and l'Association, in London from Sept. 25 to 27, 1946.

The general secretary of the CMA, Dr. Routley, was instructed by the Executive Committee to represent the CMA at the conference. Dr. Routley had played a major role in the creation of the World Health Organization, and from the knowledge and experience so gained, he suggested, in the form of a memorandum, his perception of the structure and objectives of an international medical organization. This memorandum formed the basis of discussion at the conference that nominated Dr. Routley as the chairman of the nine-person committee responsible for the drafting of the constitution of the new body, to be known as The World Medical Association (WMA).

On Sept. 18, 1947, delegates from 27 national medical associations met in Paris. This was the WMA's first General Assembly, at which the constitution and bylaws were adopted. In recognition of his valuable contributions, Dr. Routley was elected chairman of the WMA Council, a post he held for 4 years. When he stepped down from that office, he was named consultant-general. The editor of the *Canadian Medical Association Journal*, Dr. H.E. MacDermot, was a member of the first WMA editorial board. In 1948, the council, as the executive board of the WMA was called, established the Association's headquarters in the city of New York, so that it could be close to the United Nations and its various agencies.

Between 1947 and 1952, the American Medical Association (AMA) contributed $50 000 per annum to fund the WMA's operations. In 1954, collection of annual dues from member associations was begun. The CMA's annual contribution from 1954 to 1960 was $1000; a similar sum was paid by the Pharmaceutical Manufacturers Association of Canada (PMAC). One of the first important documents produced by the WMA was the 1948 *International Code of Ethics* and the *Declaration of Geneva*. This statement was approved by the CMA, and its endorsement has appeared on all subsequent printings of the CMA *Code of Ethics*. The CMA Committee on Medical Education was involved in the construction of the program for the First WMA World Conference on Medical Education, held in London in August 1953, attended by more than 700 delegates from 58 countries.

In Rome, in October 1954, the WMA General Assembly discussed such diverse matters as international medical law, maldistribution of physicians, occupational health services and bacteriologic warfare. As a result of the report to the Executive Committee by the CMA delegates to that assembly, a Special Committee on International Relations, chaired by Dr. Margaret Gosse, was formed. The CMA Committee on Medical Education undertook a detailed study of the findings and recommendations of the First WMA Conference on Medical Education, bearing in mind that the purpose of the conference had been to formulate plans and stimulate thought, with the aim of helping those responsible for medical education in developing countries.

In the same year, the CMA formed another committee, known as The Canadian Supporting Committee to the WMA. The aim of the committee was to solicit donations from individual physicians and organizations. The monies collected were used to defray the expenses incurred by the CMA in having Dr. Routley attend the WMA Council meeting in Dublin in 1955. The 1955 General Council was told of the generosity of Dr. John D. Hamilton, professor of pathology, University of Toronto, that enabled the supporting committee to present a complete set of pathology teaching slides to the University of Kabul, Afghanistan.

The two delegates to the Ninth General Assembly of the WMA, held in Vienna, were Drs. E. Kirk Lyon and Arthur D. Kelly. On their return to Canada, they reported that the major topic of discussion at the meeting was "social security" and the multifarious problems that were created by governments when they became involved in the practice of medicine. It was their opinion that, although the Canadian experience in that area left much to be desired, the CMA's problems paled into insignificance when compared to the happenings in some member countries.

The CMA and PMAC annual contributions were bolstered in 1957 by $1430 coming from $10 individual memberships; from this total, the CMA paid the WMA $2628.09, the equivalent of one Swiss franc per CMA member. Canada was designated as the host country for the 1959 General Assembly, with the venue being Montreal, immediately following the Second World Conference on Medical Education set for Chicago, from Aug. 30 to Sept. 4, 1959.

Questions had been raised by some members of the Association as to the effectiveness of the WMA and whether or not the CMA should continue to support it. To answer these questions the Executive Committee formed a small subcommittee in 1957 to examine the relationship between the CMA and the WMA and to review the WMA's achievements since its inception 10 years earlier. In February 1958, the subcommittee reported to the Executive

Committee, recommending that the CMA continue to support the WMA and be represented at general assemblies by two delegates, appointed in such a manner as to maintain continuity, who would be prepared to accept office and/or membership of WMA committees. At the 1958 assembly, the CMA, as host national medical association for the 1959 General Assembly, had the privilege of nominating the president of the WMA for the year 1959 and put forward the name of Dr. L. Gérin-Lajoie for that office. The assembly confirmed Dr. Gérin-Lajoie as president-elect for the association year 1958–59. It was a great loss to Canadian and international medicine when he died in February 1959, 7 months before his WMA presidency was to begin. The CMA submitted the name of Dr. Renaud Lemieux as president-elect and this was approved by the council of the WMA.

The CMA played an active part in the affairs of the WMA during 1959. The Committee on Medical Education had considerable input into the planning of the Second WMA World Conference on Medical Education, and the CMA delegates contributed in no small measure to its deliberations. The keynote address at the WMA General Assembly in Montreal was given by Dr. Norman H. Gosse, a past president of the CMA and chairman of General Council. In his speech Dr. Gosse urged that a reconsideration of the functions of the WMA be undertaken, that the financial structure be examined to find more satisfactory methods of funding the activities, and that more practical aid be provided to developing countries. His words brought mixed reaction from his audience, some of whom approved his thoughtful critique, whereas others saw it as an unwarranted attack upon the WMA Council and administration. The BMA delegation presented a recommendation that a five-person committee be established to study the points raised by Dr. Gosse and prepare a report for consideration at the 1960 General Assembly. After a long debate, the recommendation was approved. Subsequent to the Montreal meeting, the WMA Planning and Finance Committee, under the chairmanship of Dr. Routley, began a study of the relationship between WMA headquarters and the USA Supporting Committee.

In 1960, the CMA increased its contribution to the WMA to $10 000. At the General Assembly in Berlin, Dr. Routley's committee was not in a position to issue a final report on its findings but it did give a brief interim report. The Cuban delegation presented a number of recommendations to the assembly but only one was accepted and, after debate, it was defeated. The Cuban delegation expressed its displeasure by walking out.

The XV WMA General Assembly was held in Rio de Janeiro in 1961, and in his report to the CMA Executive Committee, Dr. Morley A.R. Young said that one of the main topics discussed was an article published in the *Tribuna Medica de Cuba* on the recommendations presented by the Cubans at the 1960 General Assembly. The article was highly critical of the actions and attitude of the assembly members, singling out the senior officers of the WMA and accusing them of dishonesty and prevarication. After much political posturing, a compromise was reached and the Cuban delegation apologized for its actions.

Dr. Young's report also commented on the question of social security, a matter that was of great interest to a number of South American countries. He said that they wanted

> *...to create social security immediately, and government is inevitably drawn into the picture. One of the fundamental requirements of social security is health, and in the health field, the need for hospitals is obvious. In most cases, hospitals are produced by government. Since the hospital is the "doctor's workshop," the medical man can very easily become a part of the social security organization. Is this story entirely strange to members of this Executive Committee?*

Drs. George E. Wodehouse and Kelly represented the CMA at the General Assembly in September 1962. The long-awaited report of the Finance and Planning Committee, put before the meeting, concentrated on the fiscal operations, and the subsequent discussions led to the acceptance of the view that a greater dependency be placed on dues coming from member associations and that the recruiting of new members was a priority. On the matter of tax-deductibility of donations, the committee had learned that it was very doubtful that donations to the USA Supporting Committee would be given tax-exempt status. Tax authorities in the US had concluded that the WMA was a "trade association." This decision, if allowed to stand, would be disastrous as far as the funds of the supporting committee were concerned; delegates were reminded that those funds had been the main source of the WMA's funding since the Association's inception. At this point, it was proposed that the objects of the WMA be examined and be restated in such a manner as to negate the conclusion put forward by the tax authorities. The representatives of the CMA, having had much experience in this area with the recent amending of the CMA's *Act of Incorporation*, played a large part in the acceptance of this proposal by an overwhelming majority.

On the matter of social security, the CMA delegates strongly opposed the proposal of the WMA Committee on Social Security that the Twelve Principles of Provision of Health Care in any National Health Care System, enunciated in 1948 and reaffirmed a number of times since then, be replaced by a new statement. The CMA had examined the proposed statement and found it unsuitable for application in Canada. Other delegates supported the views of the CMA and the matter was referred back to the committee, with the direction that written objections to the proposed changes be filed by February 1963.

The WMA's financial picture indicated a bleak future unless some corrective measures were taken. The revenues from the USA Supporting Committee were declining and many member associations were either tardy or delinquent in paying their annual dues. The CMA believed that the enforced economies at WMA headquarters were impairing the work of the association. Although it was unlikely that the CMA's contribution of $10 000 per annum would be increased in the foreseeable future, the CMA would try to have any remaining funds of the Canadian supporting committee ($845.17) turned over to the WMA.

The 1963 General Assembly meeting site was changed from Mexico City to New York. At the meeting, a number of delegates expressed dissatisfaction with the operations of the WMA. La Confédération des syndicats médicaux français proposed that a major reorganization be carried out, that the WMA headquarters be moved to Europe, and that members of council be elected from regions rather than from individual countries. The Finnish Medical Association submitted a proposal to streamline WMA operation and organization, including the recommendation that the General Assembly be held biennially instead of annually. By the time of the next General Assembly in Helsinki in 1964, a plan for reorganization had been drawn up by the WMA and approved at that meeting. In July 1964, the WMA was incorporated as a nonprofit educational and scientific organization under the laws of the State of New York. This incorporation established the legal and financial status of the WMA in the US, with the elected members of council becoming the equivalent of a board of directors. The process did not rule out locating the headquarters in another part of the world, should this be decided by the WMA. The meeting in Finland approved the outcome of a 5-year study of medical research guidelines; the document, which outlined the necessary protocols in clinical research, came to be known as the WMA *Declaration of Helsinki*.

The Executive Committee told the WMA that the PMAC was funding the distribution of the *World Medical Journal* to all CMA members and that this had prompted the BMA, the Australian Medical Association and the Medical Association of South Africa (MASA) to begin circulating it to their members.

The WMA asked its members to consider and submit their views on a definition of death. The Executive Committee of the CMA established a committee, made up of pathologists, lawyers and other experts in medicolegal matters, to study the matter and report back, so that the CMA could provide input when the matter was discussed at a future general assembly. On another matter, the WMA accepted the CMA's invitation to hold the 1971 General Assembly in Canada.

Since 1960, the CMA had contributed $10 000 per annum as its membership fee, but decided, after reviewing the matter and taking into account the methods used by some national medical associations in calculating their respective annual contributions, that the sum was in excess of what was required on a membership per capita basis and that the figure of $6700 was the correct one. The Executive Committee decided that the 1969 payment would be less than the $10 000, and that each annual payment would be less than its predecessor until the correct figure had been reached. The difference between the $10 000 and the actual amount paid was put into a reserve account to offset the expenses the CMA would incur when hosting a WMA General Assembly. In 1970, the CMA paid WMA dues of $7685.

Dr. Arthur F.W. Peart, general secretary of the CMA, resigned effective Mar. 31, 1970. The CMA had submitted his name for the position of president-elect for 1970 and this was approved by the General Assembly in Oslo in August. Ottawa was approved as the venue for the 1971 General Assembly.

The planning of the 1971 General Assembly occupied a great deal of work for the CMA secretariat and a local planning committee. Duties were allocated to senior staff. The CMA Executive Committee was given official delegate status, and the venerable Château Laurier hotel was chosen as the meeting site. Prior to the opening of the assembly, the CMA Executive Committee met with the official delegates of the AMA to discuss the future of the WMA.

Dr. Peart was duly elected president of the WMA. Neither the business part of the meeting nor the quality of most of the reports got very high marks from the CMA delegates. The words "travel club" were heard frequently when assessing the WMA's activities. Those who had never attended a general assembly before were amazed at the amount of politicking and wheeling and dealing that went on. The assembly was of the general opinion that the national medical association dues be increased, a view not shared by the CMA delegates who declared that, based on the quality and content of the reports presented, no increase could possibly be justified. The CMA delegates held a caucus, following which Dr. Lloyd C. Grisdale, chairman of the CMA Board of Directors, announced that the CMA would refrain from voting on agenda items pertaining to annual dues and other fiscal matters, and that the CMA would have to consider seriously the value of remaining a member of the WMA. This would be done by the CMA after the conclusion of the General Assembly.

In meetings of this nature where there are participants from many countries, there are always incidents that go under the heading of "memorable moments." For one member of the CMA senior secretariat, there were two such moments. He had been given the responsibility of being the liaison for the delegation from the USSR and was told to get the delegates to their places in good time for the opening of the assembly. Thirty-five minutes before the hour scheduled for the official opening, he telephoned the chief of the USSR delegation's room and was invited to come up. On entering the room he was handed a large glass of neat vodka and several cubes of black bread (brought from Moscow). Protocol demanded that a number of toasts be drunk, each one requiring a fresh supply of vodka and bread. He managed to get the delegation to their designated places on time, but had a somewhat dimmed appreciation of the rest of the day's activities. Needless to say, on subsequent days, the invitation to "come up" in response to his morning phone calls from the hotel lobby was respectfully declined!

His second memorable moment was at a dinner party held at his home for a dozen or so delegates and their spouses. Late in the evening there was a singsong around the grand piano. The accompanist was Dr. John Budd, president of the AMA, who had qualified at Dalhousie University and who confessed that his piano-playing at various "establishments" in Halifax had contributed in no small measure to helping him pay his way through medical school. On this particular evening he was ably assisted by a cardiac surgeon from Moscow who accompanied him on the balalaika. The chief of the USSR delegation enthralled everyone with her wonderful contralto; the baritones of the West African and Jamaican delegates, supplemented by the voices of a CMA past president, a CMA president-elect, the CMA general secretary and members of the CMA senior secretariat, spouses and others, made the rafters ring in a demonstration of harmony and fellowship that had been markedly absent in some of the business sessions earlier in the day.

Between the end of the General Assembly and the June 1982 meeting of the General Council in Montreal, there were many discussions on the WMA by the Executive Committee, the Board of Directors and the senior secretariat of the CMA. An in-depth study led to the decision that the CMA should withdraw from membership in the WMA, and the following recommendation was placed before General Council:

Whereas the Canadian Medical Association recognizes its responsibility to international health, especially within the developing nations, and whereas it is obvious that membership in the WMA has failed to provide the CMA with the means of fulfilling that responsibility; be it resolved that the CMA increase its participation in other programmes directed towards improvement of international health services and withdraw its support of the WMA at the end of the 1971–72 WMA year.

A lively discussion followed, with proponents and opponents vigorously arguing their cases. A motion to refer the matter back to the Board of Directors was defeated. A motion to defer further discussion until next year and that the Board of Directors (i) consider the discussions that had just taken place and (ii) undertake consultations with other organizations, was approved.

Immediately following the General Council, the CMA Board of Directors appointed Dr. Harry D. Roberts of St. John's to represent the CMA at the WMA General Assembly, scheduled for September in Amsterdam. He was provided with a list of principles that had been developed by the Executive Committee and approved by the Board of Directors.

(i)   *There should be an active international organization of physicians and the Canadian Medical Association should participate in it on the basis that, as we represent a "have" nation, we have something that we could, and should, contribute to nations that are less fortunate than ourselves.*

(ii)   *To meet the conditions considered to be desirable in such an international organization, the World Medical Association should broaden its aims and objectives by developing worthwhile programmes to assist developing nations that would welcome such assistance in the improvement of the standards of health care provided to their people. This would include assistance from member associations in the development within such nations of new and improved educational facilities for medical and allied health personnel as well as in the upgrading of the health services generally.*

(iii) *If the aims and objectives of the WMA are broadened in this manner, it will necessitate an increase in the activities of the Association and the members of its Secretariat in the areas of the world in which the majority of the emerging nations are located. The centre of activity of the Association, the Secretariat, should be geographically located in an area that is readily accessible to those nations. On this basis, the CMA has strong reservations about having it located in North America.*

(iv)   *It is essential that the Secretariat of the WMA be provided with strong leadership through the selection and appointment of a full-time Secretary-General. The future location of the headquarters might well be influenced by the country of residence of this individual, or by his judgment as to the most desirable site.*

(v)   *The efficiency of the organization would be greatly improved if the Treasurer resided in the same country in which the Secretariat is located. He should be required to have prepared an audited financial statement for submission to all Member Associations.*

(vi) *General Meetings of the WMA should be held less frequently than at present. The CMA recommends that a three-year interval be considered.*

(vii) *As a reduced frequency of meetings will place more responsibility on the Governing Council, it is recommended that broad representation on that body be ensured by limiting the number of representatives from any one nation holding office on the Council at any time, to two. This would require changes in the present method of nominating and electing members to Council.*

In response to comments and criticisms by the CMA delegates at the 1971 General Assembly, a WMA Ad Hoc Committee on Organization, Function and Objectives was established; this committee presented an interim report to the General Assembly. During 1972, the AMA withdrew from membership in the WMA, a new secretary general, Sir William Refshauge, was appointed, and a decision was taken to move the WMA Secretariat from New York to Ferney-Voltaire in France, a short distance from Geneva. During 1973, the ad hoc committee worked hard in its review of the WMA, and Dr. Roberts reported that a number of the CMA principles, outlined above, had been incorporated into the committee's report. The CMA welcomed this news and, on the understanding that the WMA should demonstrate whether or not the perceived shortcomings had been effectively addressed and appropriate corrective steps taken, the CMA General Council approved in 1973 that the CMA continue its membership in the WMA for the year 1974.

At the 1973 General Assembly, Dr. Roberts had been elected to the WMA Council; in this capacity he had been able to stimulate discussions on changes to improve the organization, and was in a position to report on the inner workings of the organization. The new secretary general was given credit for much of the reorganization. The 1974 General Council approved CMA membership in the WMA for a further year.

In 1975, Dr. Bette Stephenson submitted the following report to General Council:

The recommendations of CMA submitted to the WMA Ad Hoc Committee on Organization, Function and Objectives have been almost fully implemented. The new Secretary-General, Sir William Refshauge, has introduced renewed vitality and direction into the Association. The headquarters office has been moved to Ferney-Voltaire, France — 12 miles from Geneva — to facilitate communication and a cooperative effort with other international health organizations such as WHO, CIOMS, IOF and ICN. The complement of headquarters staff has been decreased from 13 to 8 and the staff organized to increase efficiency and productivity. A small New York office with a staff of two has been established to develop an enlarged associate membership campaign, and to provide service for the approximately 1000 USA associate members already recruited. This office operates with a separate budget funded by the associate membership fee.

The groundwork has been completed for close collaboration with the University of Illinois Medical Center for Educational Development (under Dr. George Miller) for :

1. a project for continuing medical education in developing countries; and

2. a series of educational workshop seminars. Dr Miller will in fact be working at least one half of each year from an office in WMA headquarters.

The MARIA (Medical Aid to Rural Indigent Areas) project in the Philippines and the MARINDA project in Indonesia (established by WMA in the late 1960s), have now become self-sustaining and are providing direct patient care, well baby and family planning care to several thousand patients in relatively remote rural areas where previously there was no access to scientific medical services.

Current activities in the area of health care include:

1. A worldwide study of methods of prevention of accidents during medical and surgical procedures;

2. A study of safeguards of electronically stored and retrieved medical data to assist in the development of methods of ensuring patient privacy;

3. A study of the preparedness and adequacy of first-aid equipment and personnel within international airports and the passenger airplanes used by international carrier companies.

The 1974 Annual Assembly in Stockholm included a conference on the role of the physician in population change, jointly sponsored by WMA, CFME, WHO, and IPPF, and attended by more than 400 participants from more than 70 countries.

The Conference resulted in the unanimous adoption by the participants of a statement, Strategy for Action for the Physician in Population Change, as a guide for the practising physician to assist him/her to undertake responsible action related to the worldwide population challenge and local circumstances and needs. This document has been submitted to all national members for consideration and action.

The subject of the 1975 Annual Assembly in Tokyo is The Development and Allocation of Medical Care Resources, to be explored by physicians, medical economists and medical educators. In 1976 the Annual Meeting will be held in Sao Paolo, Brazil, in conjunction with the 25th anniversary of the founding of the Medical Association of Brazil, the theme being Environmental Pollution and Human Health.

At the Council meeting held in Paris in March 1975, the following topics were considered:

1. Preliminary reports from the expert committee charged with redrafting the "Oslo Declaration on Therapeutic Abortion".

2. The report of the expert committee revising the Helsinki Declaration on Biomedical Research was received and the revised draft submitted by the Medical Ethics Committee was approved for editing, distribution for comment to member associations, and presentation to the Tokyo Assembly.

3. The submission of the joint BMA/IMA Committee and of La Confédération des Syndicats Médicaux Français on guidelines for physicians concerning torture and other cruel, inhuman or degrading treatment or punishment in relation to detention or imprisonment, were studied by the Medical Ethics Committee. A Declaration was drafted and accepted by Council for submission to member associations. This draft will be presented to the General Assembly in Tokyo for approval as the Declaration of Tokyo. In the meantime, however, it will be used as the WMA position paper for the International Conference on Detention, Incarceration and the Treatment of Prisoners to be held in Toronto in September of this year.

4. A brief statement on the use and misuse of psychotropic drugs submitted by the CMA was approved by the Medical Ethics Committee and Council for distribution to member organizations.

The Secretariat has continued to provide information on professional liability programmes and the WMA sponsored a visit of Dr. N.F. Brown of the Canadian Medical Protective Association to assist the Ghana Medical Association establish a programme based on the CMPA format which they had decided was the best one for their profession.

The Secretary-General has been actively involved in investigating charges of detention and imprisonment of physicians in Russia, Uruguay, Chile, Mali, Indonesia, Turkey and Sudan. In several instances, the action has brought swift release of the physicians concerned.

The Council received interim or progress reports which are at present being explored by the several committees of the Council. The CMA staff has been aware of increased activity at the WMA. We have been providing infor-

mation on a variety of medical subjects and in many instances, CMA input has influenced WMA policy statements.

The WMA Journal, while in precarious financial state, has been published regularly. The generous offer of the West German Medical Association to print the Journal and provide funding for staff and distribution was accepted by the Publications Committee and Council. With the new arrangement and improved advertising sales, there is a good prospect of a self-sustaining publication in the near future.

The financial position of WMA has stabilized as a result of regular payment of dues by many more members, the economies effected by the Secretariat and the constant critical vigilance of the Chairman of the Finance Committee, Dr. H.D. Roberts of the CMA. The WMA is certainly not suffering an embarrassment of funding, but it is expending available funds prudently and accounting for them accurately.

Compliance with the recommendations of the CMA and the appointment of Sir William Refshauge as Secretary-General have, within the brief space of two years, demonstrably changed the character and function of WMA. The Association, for the first time in many years, now shows real promise of the capability required to fully meet the aims and objectives established by its founders in 1947.

On the basis of that report, the General Council approved that the CMA retain membership and support the WMA.

At the Tokyo General Assembly in October 1975, the WMA issued "Guidelines for Medical Doctors Concerning Torture and Other Cruel, Inhuman and Degrading Treatment or Punishment in Relation to Detention and Imprisonment." These guidelines were called *The Declaration of Tokyo*. The General Assembly was attended by Dr. Lloyd C. Grisdale, and his report of the meeting to the Executive Committee and the Board of Directors was not one of approbation. Dr. Roberts, who had been renominated by the CMA for his seat on the council, was defeated by one vote. It was held that his defeat was the result of his toughness in council and on the Finance Committee that was not welcomed by a number of national medical associations, which apparently wished the WMA to be "an old boys' travel club." Dr. Roberts was given the task of looking after the affairs of the New York office, which continued to show a profit from the sale of individual memberships to US physicians, and was also given the privilege of attending council meetings and the general assemblies.

All was not sweetness and light at the WMA meeting. Against the advice of the Japanese Medical Association, the host for the 1975 General Assembly, the Government of Japan refused to issue visitor visas to the delegation from the Medical Association of South Africa, basing its decision on its disapproval of the apartheid practices in that country. The WMA secretary general, Sir William Refshauge was extremely upset by this decision and requested a 3-month leave of absence. This was granted, and he did not attend the 1975 General Assembly. There was speculation that Sir William might not return to the WMA and this possibility could lead to a number of member associations also leaving the association.

The matter continued to be troublesome and unresolved over the next 6 months, and on Apr. 7, 1976, Dr. Justus Imfeld, chairman of WMA Council, sent the following letter to all member national medical associations:

> *Dear Colleagues,*
> *I wish to inform you today that I resigned as Chairman of Council and as a member of the Council of the WMA, and that the Secretary-General terminated his appointment as Secretary-General of the WMA yesterday. My letter to the Vice-Chairman of Council reads as follows:*
> *Dear Dr. Bohene,*
> *In reviewing the march of events of the WMA through the last months and last days, I find myself compelled to hand in my immediate resignation both as Chairman of Council and as a Councillor of the WMA.*
> *Yours sincerely,*
Justus Imfeld

Sir William Refshauge wrote to Dr. Imfeld:

> *In view of the events leading up to and of today, the situation for me within the Council of the WMA has become quite intolerable. I personally do not want my name to be associated with the WMA. I therefore wish to inform you that I am terminating my appointment as Secretary-General as of today, April 6, 1976. I intend, of course, to inform the various agencies of the reasons leading up to this decision.*

After considering this correspondence, the CMA Board of Directors believed that the WMA was no longer a credible organization, and determined that CMA membership would cease immediately. The board's decision was ratified by the General Council in June 1976. It was not until 1990 that the CMA decided to rejoin the WMA, and the story of how that came about is related later in this chapter.

In 1991 the WMA invited the CMA to join a task force established to develop a strategic plan for the WMA over the following decade. The first meeting of the task force was in France, at Divonne-les Bains, located near Ferney-Voltaire, and was attended by Dr. John S. Bennett. In November, at the General Assembly in Malta, the CMA was represented by Dr. Carole Guzmán, CMA president, Dr. Léo-Paul Landry, CMA secretary general and Dr. Bennett. At that meeting, the CMA and the national medical associations of Bulgaria, Denmark, Finland, Iceland, Sweden, The Netherlands and Norway, were granted membership in the WMA.

CMA delegates attended the 1992 WMA Council meeting in Santiago, Chile, in May, and in September Dr. Ronald F. Whelan, CMA president, along with Dr. Landry and Dr. John R. Williams, director of the Department of Ethics and Legal Affairs, attended the WMA Council meeting and General Assembly in Marbella, Spain. At that meeting, statements on the following were approved: medical malpractice, alcoholism and road safety, hunger strikers, HIV and AIDS, child abuse and neglect, home medical monitoring, telemedicine, physician-assisted suicide, the WMA Human Genome Project and noise pollution.

In April 1993, at the council meeting in Istanbul, Dr. Landry was elected a member of council and chairman of the Medical Ethics Committee. Once again the council was to become embroiled in a controversial matter, viz., allegations over the conduct of the WMA president-elect, Dr. Hans Joachim Sewering of Germany, during World War II. For some years, a number of members of the Norwegian Medical Association had been concerned over the participation of Dr. Sewering in the affairs of the WMA, and this concern became focused when he became president-elect. A number of member national medical associations, including the CMA, demanded that the appointment be overturned, basing their objections on allegations that Dr. Sewering had belonged to the Schutzstaffel, the Nazi élite guard and that he had acted in an unethical manner in patient care. An earlier investigation had cleared Dr. Sewering of the allegations, but when new allegations were brought forward, the CMA and other associations initiated a further investigation. In late January 1993, Dr. Sewering stated that he would not assume the presidency of the WMA.

The Toronto Group

During the period 1976 to 1983, a number of national medical associations had resigned their memberships in the WMA and some of these, led by the Nordic countries, had set up a mechanism whereby meetings were held between them to discuss matters of mutual interest. The group consisted of the national medical associations of Britain, Denmark, Finland, Iceland, Ireland, The Netherlands, New Zealand, Norway and Sweden, although part of the group — the medical associations of New Zealand and Ireland — were still members of the WMA.

The CMA had been present by invitation at the group's meetings in 1984 and 1985 and had been afforded observer status. In 1986 it was invited to be a full member, and in 1987 the CMA hosted the group's meeting in Toronto. At that meeting it was agreed that the group would be known as the Toronto Group and that the Medical Association of Jamaica, which had been invited to the meeting by the BMA and given observer status, would become a full member. At the meeting, discussion covered a wide range of subjects, including patterns of practice, quality of care, governmental involvement in health care, litigation and the WMA.

The discussion on the WMA led to a position paper being drafted, outlining a number of conditions that would have to be met before those members of the group who did not belong to the WMA would consider joining or rejoining the association. The position paper, when approved, was sent to the secretary general of the WMA and to the director general of WHO. Four principles were laid out in the position paper:

1. *Medical associations in membership with the WMA must be truly representative of the medical profession within their respective countries.*
2. *Medical associations in membership with WMA must be politically independent of their respective governments.*
3. *The WMA must introduce a more democratic system of voting, which is no longer weighted in favour of the larger medical associations.*
4. *There must be no constitutional barriers to WMA adopting and publishing declarations or other pronouncements on issues of concern to the medical profession in general.*

The Toronto Group established a three-person committee to represent it in discussions with the WMA. The three people elected were Dr. Léo-Paul Landry, secretary general of the CMA, Dr. John D.J. Havard, secretary of the BMA and Dr. Bo Hjern from the Swedish Medical Association. In October 1987 the WMA Council, meeting in Madrid, discussed the letter from the Toronto Group and directed that WMA representatives meet with the group in early 1988. The meeting took place in July. Representatives of the group met in Norwich, England, at the time of the annual meeting of the BMA in that city, to discuss strategy to be followed for the meeting with the WMA representatives, scheduled to be held in London at BMA House on July 8.

At the meeting at BMA House, the following were present:

Representing the CMA: Dr. Athol L. Roberts, CMA president, and Dr. John S. Bennett.

Representing the BMA: Dr. John Marks, chairman of council, Dr. Vivienne Nathanson and Ms. J. Carmine.

Representing the Toronto Group: Drs. Landry, Havard and Hjern.

Representing the WMA: Dr. H. Lindsay Thompson, president, Dr. Tai-Joon Moon, immediate past president, Dr. André Wynen, secretary general, and Mme. La Forte.

Representing the AMA: Dr. Alan Nelson, Dr. James Sammons, Ms. Pat Hutar and Ms. Robin J. Menes.

Discussion centred on the four principles outlined in the Toronto Group's letter of June 1987. It was pointed out to the WMA that a number of its members did not truly represent the countries claimed, and several examples were given. The Colegio Medico Cubano Libre (CMCL) is located in Miami and cannot be said to represent Cuba. Transkei is a homeland in South Africa. The claim that Taiwan represents the Chinese Medical Association is not accepted by some countries. The WMA responded by saying that the CMCL had been accepted as a member in 1978 but that it had considered creating an "affiliate membership" with no voting rights to be given to those whose full membership in the WMA was perceived to be a contentious issue.

On the matter of political independence, and in particular as it applied to the membership of the MASA, Dr. Thompson reported on his recent visit to South Africa and recommended that the Toronto Group send its representatives to that country so that they could see at first-hand the situation and the relationship between MASA and the Government of South Africa.

The WMA representatives rejected any change in voting privileges. On the question of barriers to discussions on medical matters, the WMA and the AMA representatives explained that the anti-trust laws of the US applied to the WMA, inasmuch as the WMA was registered in that country and that those laws precluded discussion of certain topics of interest to the medical profession, such as manpower. On the other hand, the WMA registration in the State of New York gave it tax benefits, such as tax-free status recognition on funds donated to the WMA. These advantages would be lost if such registration was cancelled.

At the end of the day, the Toronto Group agreed that the sum and substance of the discussions would be distributed to all its member associations. Its next meeting was planned for Utrecht in February 1989. The WHO's response to the group's letter was to indicate that it did not consider the WMA as an officially recognized nongovernmental organization — despite having done so in

1982 — based on the fact that the WMA membership included MASA and the Transkei Medical Association. Prior to 1982, there had been a good working relationship between WHO and WMA.

The Toronto Group met in Utrecht from Feb. 9 to 11, 1989, and in addition to discussion about the WMA, it looked at physician prescribing habits, HIV and AIDS, medical ethics, torture and degrading punishment, and medical manpower. The CMA was represented by its president, Dr. John O'Brien-Bell and Drs. Roberts, Landry and Bennett. The following resolutions were adopted unanimously:

(i)   *That the Toronto Group underline the need for an acceptable world forum and take the necessary steps to explore possible alternatives to the WMA.*

(ii) *That the Toronto Group respond to the request of the Uruguayan Medical Association that a meeting be held with representatives of five South American national medical associations to discuss alternatives to the WMA.*

(iii) *That the Toronto Group explore the feasibility of its obtaining consultative status with WHO.*

(iv) *That the Toronto Group remain ready to continue discussions with the WMA on the four principles laid down and discussed at the meeting between the two parties at their meeting in London.*

In Miami in May 1989, Drs. O'Brien-Bell, Marcien Fournier, CMA president-elect, and Landry attended a meeting of the WMA Council. Drs. John D.J. Havard and Bo Hjern were present also. The Toronto Group's meeting was discussed, but no concessions were offered by the WMA. In 1990 the Toronto Group met in January in Kingston, Jamaica, where, in addition to the topic of the WMA, discussions were held on medical manpower, hours of work, particularly as it applied to doctors working in hospitals, national and international codes of ethics, structure and operation of an ideal international medical association, human rights, torture and drug abuse. It was believed that the WMA was prepared to accept and implement some of the group's recommendations.

The WMA Council met next in Jerusalem and was attended by the three-person committee of the Toronto Group. At that time all the recommendations made by the Toronto Group were discussed at great length. Following those discussions, the council agreed to recommend to its next World Medical Assembly:

(i)   *That there be a change in the voting structure to 1 vote per 10,000 declared members or part thereof.*

(ii) *That a vote on ethical issues should require a majority of at least three-quarters of those present and entitled to vote. Abstentions would count as votes against the motion.*

(iii) *That the membership of the Medical Association of Transkei be discontinued.*

(iv) *That the changes in the health care provision in South Africa and the passing of a series of anti-apartheid resolutions by MASA be considered in a favourable light, and that support be given by the WMA to MASA and other health organizations to uphold human rights and to provide a better quality of health care to the disadvantaged people of that country.*

(v) *That a recommendation go to the World Medical Assembly urging it to issue a strongly worded statement reminding member national associations about their obligations and responsibilities toward any violation of human rights and inadequacies in the provision of health care in their own countries.*

The Toronto Group's three representatives came to the conclusion that much had been achieved in getting the council to change its position in a number of areas as requested by the Toronto Group, and believed that, at this time, the WMA would be unlikely to accept recommendations for further changes. As a result of their careful deliberations, the representatives recommended to an interim meeting of the group in Bournemouth, England, on June 27, that the member associations of the group join or rejoin the WMA. The General Council, meeting in Regina in August 1990, approved the motion that the CMA reapply for WMA membership.

It was agreed by the member associations of the Toronto Group that the body should not be disbanded and that it should continue to meet to discuss common problems. It was further agreed that such meetings be at the time and place of the WMA General Assembly. At the end of 1994, the only member of the Toronto Group not a member of the WMA was the Medical Association of Jamaica.

Aid Program to Caribbean Countries

Canadian physicians had shown an increasing interest in delivering health care in developing countries and, in keeping with the WMA's recommendation that its member associations develop medical aid programs for developing countries in their respective regions, the CMA Executive Committee in 1967 established a Special Committee on International Health. The CMA received many requests from Canadian physicians who wished to volunteer for service in developing countries, and the new committee was set up to provide a coordinated response to such requests. The committee's terms of reference were:

(a) The Special Committee on International Health shall recommend to the Executive Committee, programmes in international health and, with the approval of the Executive Committee, shall implement such programmes.

(b) The CMA should begin an aid-programme in the field of international health in a small but ongoing way, depending on the availability of medical and other health manpower.

At the beginning it was proposed that the CMA organize a project in the West Indies, with the objective of providing a teaching program conducted by consultants from Canada. In 1968, Dr. Arthur D. Kelly and Dr. Guy Joron undertook a feasibility study funded by the Canadian Executive Service Overseas (CESO). The brief study confirmed a widespread need for assistance in the area. It was recommended that a program of teaching and service components, staffed by volunteer physicians from Canada, be established. Volunteers would have their travel and minimum maintenance expenses paid but there would no other remuneration. On the basis of the study, the CMA entered into an agreement with CESO whereby requests for assistance from Caribbean countries would be met by CMA "recruits." The CMA would administer the program and funding would come from the Canadian International Development Agency (CIDA) through CESO.

Between December 1968 and June 1969, 24 physicians went to Caribbean countries, providing voluntary service for up to 1 month. In late 1969, a further joint study was undertaken by a representative from each of the following organizations: CMA, Canadian Dental Association, the Canadian Teachers' Federation and CESO. The study group travelled from Guyana in the south to the Bahamas in the north, and from Barbados in the east to the Cayman Islands in the west. Twenty-one separate jurisdictions were visited and many meetings held with government ministers, government officials, health professionals, and the general public in urban and rural communities, to assess the areas of most need in the three disciplines (medicine, dentistry and education) and how those needs might be best met.

By the time the General Council met in June 1971, more than 200 physicians had provided health care to countries in the region. It soon became obvious that the health care program was making demands on the CESO budget that it could not sustain, and after meetings between the CMA, CIDA and CESO, it was agreed that there be direct funding from CIDA to the CMA, and that the CMA would take over the entire administration of the program.

The program expanded rapidly and soon the CMA was providing volunteer health care personnel, other than physicians. By 1973, the CMA was sending nurses, dentists, radiology technicians, laboratory technologists, pharmacists, hospital architects, health administrators and health care planners. Several groups of Canadian physicians undertook to provide ongoing care at specific sites so that there would be continuity of care. For example, physicians from the Courtenay-Comox area on Vancouver Island undertook to provide care for the small community of Dennery on the east coast of St. Lucia. The clinic's staff and the physicians' spouses provided money and material to equip a small hospital in the village, and the physicians rebuilt the "doctor's house." They also cleared away the undergrowth and planted a vegetable garden for patients and staff.

Specialists lectured and demonstrated new techniques at the University of the West Indies in Mona, Kingston. Ophthalmologists examined the eyes of hundreds of children and adults, carried out surgery on all age groups and, through the good offices of the Ontario Department of Education, provided glasses for those in need.

It had been intended that local personnel would be trained wherever possible so that reliance on the expatriate would diminish. Unfortunately, this did not work out as planned. As soon as an individual had been trained, he/she took off for greener pastures, usually one of the three economically viable islands — Barbados, Jamaica or Trinidad and Tobago — the US or Canada. Some administrations became so dependent on the CMA program that they made no attempt to obtain the necessary personnel to whom they would have to pay a salary nor did they make available training for local people. In one or two cases, Dr. Bennett, the CMA administrator of the program, was taken to task by ministers of health and/or senior officials when a volunteer could not be found to meet their needs. Discussions were held with CIDA and it was agreed that the program, while filling many needs, was not of itself providing a long-term solution, and so it was discontinued in late 1977.

In 1978, the CMA administered a program whereby academicians were being sent down to provide periods of teaching at the University of the West Indies. The CMA gave $1200 toward travel expenses for speakers and doctors from the Caribbean countries to enable them to attend a 3-day scientific meeting in Jamaica. When the program wound down, the CMA remained involved in the region by directing the many enquiries it received to other possible sources of help.

Instituto Naçional de Cancer (INCa) Brazil

In 1985 the governments of Canada and Brazil entered into an agreement whereby physicians and others from INCa in Rio de Janeiro would come to Canada for further training in their respective disciplines. The CMA was asked by CIDA to administer the program, and the Board of Directors acceded to the request. The CMA then entered into agreements with the Princess Margaret Hospital (PMH) in Toronto and with the Montreal General Hospital (MGH); both institutions would undertake to provide the appropriate teaching and facilities for the proposed training programs. At the PMH, the program was under the direction of Dr. John Simpson, training program director for radiation oncology, and Mr. J. Alan Rawlinson, director of the Department of Physics. At the MGH, the program was under the direction of Dr. Witold B. Rybka of the Department of Hematology.

In addition to the training programs, there was the matter of updating the equipment being used at INCa, and the CMA entered into negotiations with Atomic Energy of Canada Limited (AECL) on the question and purchase of the new equipment. This phase became very time-consuming and frustrating inasmuch as the equipment — a radiation beam data acquisition system — approved by INCa after inspection by Mr. Rawlinson and two physicists from INCa, developed problems and could not be guaranteed to be available within the time frame allotted for purchasing new equipment. With INCa's concurrence a substitute was found — a treatment planning computerized program — and this was purchased and shipped to INCa. AECL personnel supervised the installation and the instructional element.

Under the program, two physicians came to Canada. One came for 2 years' training in radiation oncology at the PMH; the other, who had done his training in oncology at the PMH, spent 2 weeks upgrading his knowledge and skills at the MGH. Two physicists each came for a 6-month period at the PMH, and one came for 2 weeks at the MGH. Two nurses went to the MGH for training in bone-marrow transplantation — one for 6 months and the other for 15 months.

The contributions of CIDA and the CMA were recognized by the installation, by INCa, of an appropriately worded plaque in its Department of Radiation Oncology. Ongoing evaluation for the next 2 years showed that the program had been well worthwhile and was proving effective in the enhancement of radiation oncology and bone-marrow transplantation for the people of Brazil.

In summary, members of the CMA and senior staff of the CMA Secretariat have contributed much to the improvement of health care in developing countries. Many CMA members have participated in programs and projects in developing countries, not involving administration by the CMA, and although their commitment and good works are not described here, their contributions to improving the health of the less fortunate have not gone unnoticed. Others have formed part of delegations or have been hosts to visiting physicians from other countries, and yet others have served as volunteers in appalling conditions in war-torn countries. The end result for some has been chronic ill health; others have given their lives in their service to others.

Civic Reception given by the City of Montreal, Tuesday, Sept. 8, 1959, for the delegates of the Word Medical Association Assembly.
L–R: The Honourable Senator Sarto Fournier, Mayor of Montreal; Dr. Renaud Lemieux, President, World Medical Association; Dr. E. Kirk Lyon, Deputy to the President, Canadian Medical Association; Dr. Murray Douglas, Chairman of the Council, Canadian Medical Association.

Chapter VIII

PUBLICATIONS

The *Canadian Medical Association Journal*

IN HIS REPORT to the 1954 General Council in Vancouver, Dr. T. Clarence Routley, general secretary and managing editor, stated that the financial position of CMA publications was not as healthy as in previous years, and that a deficit of $20 000 had been budgeted for 1955. He proposed that in that year the CMA journal be published on a twice-monthly basis.

Following General Council, space was found for the CMA editorial offices in 176 St. George Street, Toronto, in a house owned by Dr. T. Tweed Samis, a CMA member active in CMA affairs. The location could not have been better, as it was near the Toronto Academy of Medicine and the CMA general secretary's office at 244 St. George Street. After the completion of renovations of the new quarters, the associate editor, Dr. Stanley B. Gilder, and the advertising manager, Miss. M.E. Moyse, moved from Montreal to set up the operation of the *Canadian Medical Association Journal (CMAJ)*. The editor, Dr. Hugh E. MacDermot, and two staff members remained in Montreal where it was anticipated that the office would be closed in mid-1955.

Twice-monthly issues of the *CMAJ* began on Jan. 1, 1955. The CMA Publications staff was increased by the appointment of Mr. Robert Randall as editorial assistant. Mr. Randall had supervised for a number of years the publication of the *Canadian Public Health Journal*. Budget forecasts for the year were revised and the projected loss was increased to $35 000. This gloomy prognostication contrasted markedly with the great financial success of the *CMAJ* in the 1950 to 1954 period — profits had been $2532.11 in 1950, $4853.59 in 1951, $9121.79 in 1952, $36 299.79 in 1953 and $20 433.13. in 1954 — and the budgeted revenue had risen from $100 000 to $260 000. Costs, however, were rising rapidly and it was unlikely that profits could be maintained at the previous levels.

In 1955, Dr. MacDermot retired after a 31-year association with the journal. He had been editor for 13 years from 1942 to 1955. His many contributions to the Association were praised widely, in particular his writing of Volume I of the *History of the Canadian Medical Association 1867–1921*. His valedictory address to the 1955 General Council bears repeating and was as follows:

> *Mr Chairman and Members of General Council:*
>
> *I beg to report an encouraging year for the Journal. The chief point of interest has been the expansion of the Journal to two issues per month, as planned. I am glad to report that this development has been carried out smoothly and successfully. The supply of material is adequate, and we are confident that the increased rate of publication will be fully justified. We are more dependent than ever on the help of our Provincial representatives, and of all who provide us with a variety of material.*
>
> *Two special issues are planned. The first will be the Educational Number, which will appear in July. This will contain material concerning various aspects of medical teaching, of licensure, and of internships. The second, which will appear in the fall, will commemorate the rebirth of the Montreal General Hospital, the oldest teaching hospital in Canada, whose new establishment opens in May. These special issues have been in preparation for many months. It is felt that they will be of considerable interest. The Montreal office, in which some of the editing and makeup, all of the illustrations and the indexing have been carried on through the winter, is being closed down.*
>
> *Since this will be my last opportunity to speak as the Editor of the Journal I should like to make some remarks in retrospect.*
>
> *My association with the Journal extends over the last 31 years. Dr. A.D. Blackader in 1924 was kind enough to accept — and improve — some of my work, and I was fortunate in being able to keep in close association with the Journal from then on. The more I look back over its older issues the deeper is my respect for Dr. Blackader. It wasn't only that when he took up the editorship he was long past the retiring age; that he worked devotedly; that he took practically no pay for his work; these things were remarkable, no doubt, but it is not of them that I am thinking. It was his unquestionable faith in the Journal that impressed me. He knew it was young and weak, as was its raison d'être, the Association itself. But he also knew that we had men in Canada whose work and writings were of high quality. With their support he believed that the Journal could eventually take its place with other good national journals. It was by his faith and incessant labour that at the time of his retirement in 1929 (he was then 82), the Journal was set on a solid foundation. One could truly apply to him Wordsworth's*
>
> > *Give all thou canst; High Heaven rejects the lore*
> > *Of nicely calculated less or more.*

His successor, Dr. A.G. Nicholls, whilst less aggressive, still had the excellent qualities of clear expression and patience, and I learned much as his assistant. When I received my appointment as Editor in 1942 I became acutely aware that there was a war on. At some other time it would have been interesting to look back on history and comment on the embarrassments of the Journal in the days of the First Great War, but from 1940 on I was too much absorbed with my own similar editorial struggles to be able really to feel much concern with those earlier woes, much as I could appreciate them. Before long I was given the task of preparing a Bulletin to be sent to overseas medical officers. I have never been able to find out what anyone thought of this effort, which is only to be expected when I add that we learned at the end of the war that the large bundles of Bulletins which had been sent over for distribution, were still lying peacefully but quite uselessly tied up at an otherwise probably efficient headquarters.

I am extremely proud of the Journal as it is at present. An editor must expect some degree of censure, and therefore he may be allowed to claim whatever glory is due him. But there are too many people involved in the production of a journal for any one to take too much credit to himself. However, as a journalistic achievement one can look with some complacence at the row of neatly bound volumes representing thirteen years' work. A perverse friend of mine has remarked that they might also be regarded as coffins. But they are coffins which are always being opened for valuable information.

There have been changes and improvements in the physical aspects of the Journal, and of course the latest and most significant is that of the twice monthly publication. I proposed this change because I felt that we had reached a stage when we had to meet the gradually and naturally increasing demand for more space. No doubt we shall eventually become a weekly publication. There will be changes in journalism which we should try to foresee. The special fields must eventually want their own publication, and the Association may some day have to consider the possibility of helping to provide these extra channels. At present, however, and for a long time to come our Journal should continue to provide the wider outlook and to encourage variety of interest.

With my retirement I wish to record my deepest appreciation of the work of my staff. The Journal has been the work of a faithful and harmonious team, and cannot continue otherwise. I know that my successor, Dr. Gilder, will receive the same support as I have had. I can wish him little else. The prospects of the Journal are bright. May it prosper and go on from strength to strength.

> *All of which is respectfully submitted,*
> *H.E. MacDERMOT, Editor*

In response to the address, the Resolutions Committee brought in the following:

> *THAT WHEREAS this year marks the retirement of Dr. Hugh Ernest MacDermot, the efficient and beloved Editor of The Canadian Medical Association Journal*
>
> *AND WHEREAS under the guidance of Dr. MacDermot the Canadian Medical Association Journal has become a vital force in medical education and journalism in Canada and throughout the world*
>
> *THEREFORE BE IT RESOLVED that this General Council of the Canadian Medical Association spread upon its permanent records an expression of its appreciation of the able, scholarly and untiring efforts of Dr. Mac-Dermot in promoting the activities of this Association through the columns of the Canadian Medical Association Journal. The Canadian Medical Association has always appreciated the kindly and modest personality of Dr. Mac-Dermot and wishes him many happy years of retirement when his undoubted literary gifts may continue to flourish unhindered by the onerous duties of the office to which he gave so many years of distinguished service.*

The motion was carried unanimously. In his retirement Dr. MacDermot went on to write two more books: Volume II of the *History of the Canadian Medical Association* and *100 Years of Canadian Medicine.*

The twice-monthly issue of the *CMAJ* was received very favourably by the readership. It was noted that the increase in the number of issues had not diminished the number of pages but, to the contrary, had markedly increased them, allowing more coverage of Association activities. The policy of bringing the readership scientific, medicosocial and organizational topics was maintained; enlarged were the columns on continuing medical education, short notes and review articles, and a new section titled "Medical News in Brief" had been added to help the busy practitioner keep in touch with scientific medical literature from other countries.

As a result the financial picture for 1955 turned out to be much rosier than predicted. A profit of $29 523 was realized. Since 1954, the number of pages of advertising had increased by 30%, or 1505 pages. The total number of copies printed had risen from 155 605 in 1954 to 327 383 in 1985, an increase of 110.4%. The possibility of a weekly issue of the journal was discussed at the 1956 General Council, but no firm decision was made on this matter. The editor raised the question of specialty organizations publishing their own journals and that if this came to pass, the advertising dollar would be spread more thinly.

At the General Council meeting in 1957 Dr. Gilder reported that he had been invited by the World Medical Association to become the associate editor of the *WMA Journal*. This duty would run in concurrence with his other CMA obligations. Dr. Maurice R. Dufresne of Montreal was appointed assistant editor for CMA publications and took up his post in March.

By 1957, the Association had had 3 years of experience with the twice-monthly publication of the *CMAJ*, and during that period an operating profit of $117 000 had been realized. The economic recession had led to a reduction in contracts by some of the larger advertisers, but a deficit was not forecast for 1958, even though printing costs had risen by 2%. Offsetting the rise was a reduction to 8% in the commission rate charged by the journal's advertising agents and this had produced a savings of over $4 000. When the audited figures for 1958 became available it was seen that, although advertising volume for the year was down by 3.56%, overall revenue had risen by 14% as a result of higher advertising rates and an increase in the number of copies printed — 24 161 more than in 1957. Profit on the revenue of $399 214 was $69 988.

On Mar. 1, 1959, the *CMAJ* masthead carried the title in both official languages — *The Canadian Medical Association Journal* and *Le Journal de l'Association médicale canadienne*. This was not the first time that a conjunction of this nature had been used on a document as it had been used on the old minute books of the Association. The journal carried a new feature, titled "New Drugs," which listed new therapeutic agents and a brief description of their use, accompanied by descriptive monographs written by clinical investigators who had used the drug in practice and set out objectively the advantages and disadvantages, contraindications and so on.

The Apr. 1, 1959 issue was a special one on medical education and included articles from contributors in the United Kingdom and the United States. Dr. Gilder reported that the flow of original articles had been steady and the backlog within acceptable limits. In his report he welcomed the advice and assistance to the *CMAJ* that was forthcoming from members of the Association. Consideration had been given to the advisability of launching a specialty journal in the fields of clinical medicine and clinical investigation. The Pharmaceutical Manufacturers' Association of Canada (PMAC) had expressed its interest in such a venture, seeing the publication as providing a medium through which drug trials and research in therapeutic agents could be publicized. No recommendations on the subject were submitted to the Executive Committee.

A recommendation which received approval from the Executive Committee was one that converted the *CMAJ* to a weekly publication, effective Jan. 1, 1960. To show General Council how far the journal had come over three decades, the revenues were presented for comparison. In 1928, revenue was $36 868; in 1938, $36 017; in 1948, $88 552; and in 1958, $399 214. The increase in the last decade — more than 450% — was deemed to be remarkable.

In 1960, the Publications Department moved into the new CMA House at 150 St. George Street, Toronto, taking over the second floor. In February, Dr. Gilder, who earlier had been appointed editor of the *WMA Journal*, resigned as editor of the *CMAJ* and returned to the UK, where he intended to continue his editorial involvement with the WMA's journal. Twenty-three applicants for the position of editor were interviewed, resulting in the appointment of Dr. Donald C. Graham, to be effective July 1, 1960. Dr. MacDermot was lured out of retirement to act as interim editor for 2 months. The *CMAJ* was published every Saturday, and made a profit of $32 019 during the first 3 months of 1960; this amount compared most favourably with the profit of $33 752 made in the whole of 1959.

In his first report to General Council in 1961, Dr. Graham dwelt at length on a number of aspects of CMA publications, pointing out both the plus and minus components. The CMA Department of Publications, as it was then called, was producing close to one million journals annually, involving business operations well in excess of half a million dollars. Revenue in 1960 was $556 000, and of this, more than $507 500 came from advertising, mostly from the pharmaceutical industry. Dr Graham stated:

> *The CMA Journal must also provide a forum for publication, in this country, of the work of those engaged in the ever-increasing volume of research and clinical investigation being conducted across Canada. It is my impression that a certain amount of such investigation is not being reported and that some work of this nature is being submitted to general medical journals in other countries. This comment is not in any sense a reflection of editorial paranoia, but the fact is that until the major proportion of such material is published in Canada's national medical journal, our publication will not achieve its potential standard of excellence and the quality of Canadian medicine will not be presented to the world with true accuracy. That the CMA Journal is viewed as a mirror of Canadian Medicine has been impressed upon me during my brief tenure of editorial office by evidence of the extent to which it is read in diverse areas of the world beyond this country. To a large extent, irrespective of the ability and industry of the editorial staff, the standard of any medical periodical is, in the final analysis, dependent upon the volume and quality of the submissions of those who contribute to its contents. The active and continued cooperation of all components of the*

profession is therefore solicited in our endeavour to elevate the CMA Journal to the highest possible standard of quality.

Two special editions of the *CMAJ* had been published that year. The first was in recognition of the journal's 50th anniversary; the second was an issue on medical education. In July 1960, Dr. Dufresne resigned. Dr. Gordon T. Dickinson, who had been appointed associate editor, had been of great assistance to the editor, but the workload had reached the level at which more editorial component was needed, and in mid-1961, Dr. John O. Godden joined as associate editor. Dr. Graham believed that even with three people, the operation was understaffed and there was no leeway to fill absences or to have the time to develop and improve the publications. Profits in 1960 were $72 871, down slightly from the 1959 profit of $74 893.

As of June 1962, circulation of the *CMAJ* was 18 775, an increase of 700 over the previous year. The Executive Committee authorized hiring an additional associate editor having bilingual capability. The number of manuscripts submitted continued to increase and a considerable backlog had built up. From a financial point of view, 1961 was not a good year. There was a considerable drop in advertising revenue, production costs rose sharply and the result was a profit of only $6457. The actual decline in advertising was 10.4% (from 2009 to 1800 pages); advertising revenue declined 9.43% (from $507 702 to $459 676). In spite of the gloomy picture, members of the General Council were reminded that the journal's net profit between 1951 and 1961 was $456 816, and that if there was only one lean year in every 10, there should be little cause for complaint.

Efforts continued by the editorial staff to stimulate and promote the publication in its journals of reports from top level Canadian scientific investigators and educators. Specialist and affiliate societies were encouraged to submit the reports of their annual meetings for publication. The editor and associate editors attended meetings in Canada and overseas, and reports of those meetings were included in the journal. An example of this was a report of the 1962 annual meeting of the Canadian Society for Clinical Investigation, published in the form of abstracts of all papers presented or read by title at the meeting. Annual meetings of the Manitoba, Ontario and Saskatchewan medical associations were attended by the editor and written up in the journal.

A policy on the criteria for advertising copy submitted to the *CMAJ* was developed and, after approval by the Executive Committee, a brochure outlining it was produced for general distribution. In arriving at the policy, advice and input had been sought from a wide variety of sources, including the CMA

Committee on Pharmacy, the Food and Drug Directorate of the federal Department of National Health and Welfare, the *New England Journal of Medicine* and the American Medical Association (AMA).

The number of copies of the journal printed in 1962 exceeded the one million figure by 14 000, or 42 574 more than were printed in 1961. Weekly circulation was about 19 000. Out of a total revenue of $564 468 there was a profit of $59 134. During the year three special editions were published: the annual issue on medical education, clinical research in Canada, and a symposium on Canada's Emergency Health Services. Unfortunately, the backlog of submissions was such that a long period lay between submission and acceptance.

A new section was planned for the journal in which there would be a series of short articles dealing with current concepts of pharmacologic therapy in certain pathological states. The project would be the responsibility of an editorial subcommittee of the CMA Committee on Pharmacy, and articles would be recruited from centres across the country. Another innovation was to run abstracts of 150 words or less, printed in box format adjacent to the title of each major article.

The Nov 17, 1962 issue contained an article with nostalgic and historical connotations — the reminiscences of the surviving members of the research and clinical teams responsible for the discovery of insulin and its application to practical therapeutics. The same issue carried a reprint of the first article ever published on the clinical use of insulin, which had appeared in the March 1922 issue.

In June 1963, in Toronto, General Council was told of the death of Dr. Routley, managing editor of CMA publications for more than 13 years. Dr. Routley, CMA general secretary, had been president of the CMA and the BMA in 1955–56 and honorary CMA president for life, having been so appointed in 1962. During his tenure as managing editor he had displayed a business acumen among his many other widely recognized qualities, and this had been of great value to the Department of Publications during the transition from Montreal to Toronto and afterwards. His last report to General Council, prepared shortly before his death, was read by the general secretary, Dr. Arthur D. Kelly.

The brochure outlining the policy on advertising in CMA publications was in great demand. The editorial staff and the Advisory Committee on Advertising reviewed 353 new pieces of advertising copy; most of it met the criteria, but a number were returned for changes or rejected. Advertising revenue lost through rejection was estimated to be $5200.

Up until 1964 the search for a bilingual associate editor had not been successful, but that year an agreement was reached between the CMA and

M. Georges Lambin of Montreal to provide translation of copy into French. In this he was to be assisted by his son, Dr. Jacques Lambin, a surgical resident at the Hôtel-Dieu Hospital in Montreal. It was strongly believed that the abstracts of all major articles in the two journals should be in both English and French.

Two special editions were published in 1964. The first was on Jan. 25, when the whole issue was devoted to the complete proceedings of the International Symposium on Angiotensin, Sodium and Hypertension, held in Ste-Adèle-en-Haut, Que., from Oct. 11 to 14, 1963. The symposium was under the joint auspices of the Hôtel-Dieu Hospital and the University of Montreal Faculty of Medicine. In the past, the usual interval between an important medical meeting and the publication of proceedings could be up to 2 years. The CMA editors believed that they had set a world record by publishing the proceedings only 3 months after the symposium had taken place. The second special edition was the annual issue on medical education, containing a mixed bag of 15 articles pertaining to all levels of the education of a doctor of medicine. The proceedings of the symposium were bound and offered for sale at $3 per copy; the symposium sponsors paid the CMA $3000.

The pharmacologic articles referred to earlier were now being published in the journal. In cooperation with the editorial subcommittee, chaired by Dr. Denys Ford of Vancouver, articles were assigned across Canada. The first in the series was "Antibiotics for staphylococcal infections," published on Nov. 16, 1963. Subsequent articles appeared in every other issue throughout 1963 and 1964.

The Department of Publications claimed another "first" when the advertising manager, Mr. Thomas Wells, was elected member of the Province of Ontario Legislature, representing Scarborough North. In answer to a question from a member of the General Council, Dr. Kelly said that "Mr. Wells combined his CMA and parliamentary duties without evident neglect of either."

The work of the department continued to grow: in 1964, 1 075 920 copies of the *CMAJ* were printed, involving 5050 pages of which 3339 were editorial content. The journal's profit was $65 659 on revenues of $593 671. Seven hundred and eighty abstracts were printed and 117 of these were in a language other than English. More than 800 books were received for review. In his report to General Council in 1965, Dr. Graham spoke at length and in detail on matters pertaining to the publication of the two journals — the *CMAJ*, published weekly, and the *Canadian Journal of Surgery (CJS)*, published quarterly. Part of his presentation read:

The shepherding of all types of material along the production line from the original manuscript stage to the final finished product is an extremely labo-

rious process that can only be understood and appreciated by those who have actively engaged in this type of work. Simply to read, at an ordinary reading pace, the 13,405 typescript pages that went into the publication of the Association's two journals would take approximately 400 hours, or 50 eight-hour man-days. This amount of time would be required for relatively rapid, uninterrupted, reading with no attempt to understand or critically evaluate the material read. These 13,405 typescript pages represent only a small fraction of the material that your editorial staff must read each year to produce your weekly and quarterly journals. The preparation of a scientific article for publication in a medical journal has become an increasingly complex process. New Vistas of scientific knowledge are being revealed daily and the time has long since passed when a small editorial staff, no matter how seasoned and knowledgeable they may be, can properly evaluate the avalanche of new information that is now being submitted for publication in general medical and surgical journals. If for no other reason than the very extent of the scientific information explosion it has become increasingly important for editors to exercise critical judgment and discrimination in the selection of material for publication, to sort the wheat from the chaff and, by no means of least importance, to labour in cooperation with authors in an endeavour to present the finished product to the reader in a form that is clear, concise, logical and understandable. That this ideal may not be achieved in no way detracts from the thesis that it must be striven for. This process of selection and polishing of material for publication is a complicated and time-consuming one that often involves the referral of an article for evaluation and comment to one or more editorial consultants with particular expertise in the subject concerned. This is frequently followed by an exchange of lengthy correspondence with the author that results in one or more complete revisions of the original product before it is accepted for publication.

Medical journalism has long since become a specialty in its own right. The vast body of new scientific and clinical knowledge is of no practical value unless it is communicated effectively to those engaged in the practice of medicine in order that they may apply it in the improvement of the quality of medical care and the advancement of the public health. Much has been said and written in recent years about the inadequacies of medical journals as vehicles for the dissemination of the overwhelming volume with which physicians must keep abreast. If they are to fulfil their rightful role, the editors of medical journals must constantly explore and exploit new and better techniques whereby current knowledge can be more effectively conveyed to those who need it. To do so they need to establish and maintain close contact with their journalistic colleagues in other countries, attend and participate in the many conferences and symposia on medical journalism, medical bibliography, medical education and the communication of scientific information that are now being held on a regional and international basis throughout the world. As well, from time to time, one or more members of the editorial staff should enroll in certain formally organized courses in order that they be may be adequately informed on such matters as medical statistics or the design of new drug trials, for example, a basic knowledge of which is fundamental to the understanding and evaluation of an increasing proportion of scientific articles.

Dr. Graham went on to describe the work of the Department of Publications library staff. In 1964, the three staff members checked 7586 bibliographic references. Of these 3717, in other words 49%, were incomplete or incorrect as submitted and an additional 1950 required editorial revision because of incorrect form. Other activities included the answering requests for information, preparing indexes for both journals and cataloguing items for the library collection.

Dr. Graham retired as editor in 1965, and was succeeded by Dr. Dickinson who had been an associate editor since 1959. On Mar. 14, 1965, Dr. James R. Anderson from Peterborough joined the CMA as an associate editor. Dr. Kelly resigned as general secretary and was succeeded by Dr. Arthur F.W. Peart. Dr. Kelly agreed to continue as managing editor. Two new features were introduced in the *CMAJ*. One was the "Report from Ottawa" written by Mr. Gerald Waring, a member of the parliamentary press gallery. The other was a medicolegal column written by Dr. Trent Fisher, secretary-treasurer of the Canadian Medical Protective Association, which appeared in each issue. Four symposia were the subject of special issues:

- ✦ the Symposium on Aging, Oct. 9;
- ✦ the Symposium on Antibiotics, Oct. 16;
- ✦ the Symposium on Nutrition, Oct. 23;
- ✦ the Symposium on Toxic Factors in Food, Mar. 19, 1966.

The financial health of the *CMAJ* remained good as shown by its net profit of $87 388. Members were reminded that the net profits from CMA publications went to the Association's general revenues and were not retained by the Department of Publications for its own use. Because it was becoming increasingly obvious that the editorial complement was below minimum requirements to meet the heavy work load, the Executive Committee approved the addition of an associate editor, and, on Sept.1, 1966, Dr. Lawrence Rabson of Winnipeg was appointed.

In the year ending June 1967, the *CMAJ* published five symposium issues, two issues on medical education and 15 reports on national and international medical meetings. It was rumoured that the Royal College of Physicians and Surgeons of Canada (RCPSC) was examining the feasibility and desirability of establishing a new medical journal. Dr. James H. Graham, secretary of the college, said that what was visualized was more likely to be described as a bulletin or house organ, which might contain some material of a scientific nature. He was of the opinion that this kind of publication would complement the journal rather than compete with it.

The *CMAJ* carried a new section titled "The Medical Research Council," which gave details of MRC activities. At the same time, a new organization — the Society of Canadian Medical School Directors of Continuing Education — had been invited to enter into a cooperative arrangement with the journal in the selection of subjects for critical review and the recruitment of papers on those subjects for publication on a regular basis. Dr. Kelly's columns under the sobriquet "Aequanimitas" were extremely popular with the journal's readership. Unfortunately, the CMA did not avail itself of the opportunity to publish these articles in a book after Dr. Kelly's death. After negotiations broke down, the collection of articles was published in a limited edition by Dr. Kelly's family; the book is a collector's item and much sought after, particularly by those who had had the good fortune to know Dr. Kelly and to savour the views and comments in his columns.

The year 1966 saw new highs being reached in journal advertising revenue ($655 603) and in printing costs ($472 146). In early 1967, 22 359 copies of the *CMAJ* were printed weekly. The costs of printing and paper had risen markedly, as had the administrative expenses of publishing. Nevertheless, the new profit for the year was $34 249.

The following year, 1967, was the Association's centennial year, and a record number of symposia issues, 16 in all, were published along with two medical education issues. The editorial staff was considering publishing reports on clinicopathological conferences and trauma rounds. To mark the centenary, the cover and internal format of the journal were changed, but the celebratory mood was somewhat chastened by a deficit of $19 443. Factors contributing to the deficit were the decrease in advertising revenue, a 2% increase in printing and paper costs per page, more engraving and the use of more colour. It was noted that for 10 months of 1967, pharmaceutical industry figures revealed that the CMA received 22% of that industry's budget; the balance of 78% was shared by 14 other publications.

Dr. Kelly reported to the 1968 General Council that very serious consideration had been given to returning the journal from a weekly to a twice-monthly publication, but at that time no firm decision had been made. A questionnaire, designed for a 10% sampling of Association members, asking for a frank appraisal of the *CMAJ* and suggestions as to if and how it could be improved, was proposed by the General Council. For nearly a year the CMA had been negotiating with respect to the statutory second-class mailing rates and privileges the journal had enjoyed since 1911. A regulation not applied previously to the journal required that a publisher have in his/her possession signed papers indicating that each member of the organization was aware that a portion of his/her annual dues covered subscription to the organization's publication(s). The divisions had amended their annual dues notices to make this point clearly, and the Association hoped that the regulations could be met by submitting copies of the papers signed by the divisions.

The move of the CMA headquarters to Ottawa was imminent and Dr. Kelly echoed the concern of the editor, Dr. Dickinson, on the matter of moving the Department of Publications to Ottawa, recommending that the production staff remain in Toronto and maintain publication operations from that city. Investigations had revealed that there were no printers in Ottawa who could provide services similar to those provided by Southam/Murray. These concerns led to the approval by the General Council that: "in view of the remarks made by the Editor, we recommend that the Executive Committee study the advisability and feasibility of leaving the publishing of the CMA Journal in its present location." On Sept. 1, 1967, Dr. Godden, the journal's associate editor, moved from that full-time position to the part-time position of associate editor of the *CJS*, with the appointment to end on Aug. 31, 1969. He was replaced on the *CMAJ* by Dr. Alexander W. Andison, an obstetrician-gynecologist from Winnipeg, on Jan. 1, 1968.

The Executive Committee studied the question of the Department of Publications' future location and decided that the department, including the library, should remain in Toronto until 1971. The Executive Committee and a Special Subcommittee on Publications had numerous meetings at which they wrestled with the matter of frequency of publication of the journal. The subcommittee had recommended that it remain a weekly publication, that the staff remain in Toronto and that new features be introduced to increase readers' interest. At first, the Executive Committee agreed with these recommendations, but after reflection and further analysis of the financial situation, including the cost implications of a large increase in postal rates, it was decided that the frequency of publication of the *CMAJ* should revert to semi-monthly, i.e., 26 issues per annum, beginning no later than July 1, 1969. The AMA provided consultative services through Mr. Robert W. Mayo, executive managing editor of AMA publications, and Mr. Norman D. Richey, managing editor of the *Journal of the American Medical Association (JAMA)*.

There were deficits in both 1967 and 1968; in the latter year the deficit was $82 324. The budgeted deficit for 1969 was $114 097. The editor, Dr. Gordon T. Dickinson, resigned effective May 16, 1969. Dr. Kelly, who had taken over the task of managing editor, resigned effective Dec. 31, 1969. Dr. James R. Anderson was appointed acting editor of CMA publications and Mr. John Cox was appointed business manager.

Despite representations on behalf of the CMA in the House of Commons as well as direct discussions with the postmaster-general and his officials, and cooperative efforts with other publishers, the Association was unable to forestall or modify the drastic increases in postal rates which came into effect on Apr. 1, 1969, as a result of amendments to the *Post Office Act*. Under the amendment, the CMA had its statutory second-class mailing privileges withdrawn and replaced by third-class mailing privileges. The reasoning behind this change was the decision by the government that "a publication which is published primarily for the benefit of the members of a particular profession may not be transmitted by mail at a second-class rate of postage" applied to the *CMAJ* and the *CJS*. This decision translated into an increase in mailing costs for Department of Publications from $18 500 to $130 000! The average circulation figures for the *CMAJ* for the last 6 months of 1968 were 22 330 copies. The deficit came in at $101 631, slightly lower than the budgeted figure, but it was still the largest in its history. For 1970 the budgeted deficit was $43 221.

Dr. James R. Anderson was appointed editor of the *CMAJ*, effective May 1, 1970, and Mr. Clifford K. Goodman was appointed business manager of CMA Publications. Neither of these men saw any major problems in moving the Department of Publications to Ottawa, even though there were reservations about the availability of adequate library facilities. There would be a savings of $15 225 in rent as the department would be located in CMA House. Based on these opinions and figures, the Executive Committee instructed the general secretary to initiate and implement the transfer of the department to Ottawa.

By the time General Council convened in 1971, the financial picture for the Department of Publications had improved, and the *CMAJ* showed a profit of $27 777. Mr. Goodman had been able to obtain increased advertising revenue and tighter controls were imposed on expenditure. The department was ensconced in its new quarters in CMA House in June 1971. Minimal difficulties were experienced in the transition from Toronto to Ottawa as some experienced staff chose not to move and new personnel had to be found in Ottawa. Once again the red ink was evident in the journal ledger; there was a deficit of $29 994, due in the main to the development of a new format which was not offset by a compensatory increase in advertising revenue.

The Board of Directors reviewed the journal's philosophy. In general terms the publication policy was to provide members and others with interesting and informative scientific and medical business matters — in other words, a scientific publication combined with a house organ. It was also considered to be the optimum medium through which advertisers could promote their products. The Board of Directors made the decision that each issue would contain a minimum of 48 pages of editorial content, approximately two-thirds of which would be material of a scientific/clinical nature and the remaining one-third would be non-scientific material, such as Association and affiliate society news and articles on such subjects as medical economics and other special features.

Problems with the post office continued to plague the CMA publications, and the Association came around to the view that it was being the victim of discrimination by having to use third-class mailing rates. The position maintained by government appeared to be that anything connected with the practice of medicine was a bottomless pit of money and that no changes in mailing privileges were likely. The CMA objected to the discrimination on the grounds that the Association paid much more in postage than its competitors but received an inferior delivery service. Options considered included a move to first-class mailing with resultant near-prohibitive costs or establishing a separate publications corporation. The problem with the latter option would be the loss of control by the CMA over its own publications. The Board of Directors instructed members of the senior secretariat to bring to the attention of the postmaster-general, his staff and physician members of parliament, the inequity of the application of the legislation.

In June 1972, the Board of Directors established the Publications Committee to comprise a board member as chairperson, two representatives from the membership, one coming from clinical practice and the other from the scientific/ research community, the Association's general secretary, the editor and the business manager of CMA Publications, and the director of communications. The board appointed Dr. Louis R. Harnick as chairman; the two representatives from the membership were Dr. Lloyd Stern of Montreal and Dr. Peter B. Heaton from Ottawa. The terms of reference of the Publications Committee were:

(i) *To serve in an advisory and consulting capacity to the Board of Directors and staff in respect of all aspects of CMA Publications.*
(ii) *To review the quality, scientific and educational standards of CMA Publications.*
(iii) *To assess the effectiveness of CMA Publications as an instrument of communication within the profession on matters pertaining to CMA affairs.*

    (iv) To be acquainted with the business aspects of the Publications' operation, including the promotion of advertising and circulation, and the maintenance of acceptable advertising standards.
    (v) To review the staffing requirements for CMA Publications.
    (vi) To make recommendations on the above functions, and to advise the Board on any matters referred to the Publications Committee.

In the calendar year ending Dec. 31, 1972, the financial picture of the *CMAJ* improved, showing a profit of $40 995. The Board of Directors recommended and the General Council approved that the Association publish a tabloid-format newspaper called *Mediscope*, and that it be directed to the members of the health care team, including such health professionals as pharmacists, physiotherapists, radiology and laboratory technicians, senior nursing administrators and teachers, medical administrators and clinic managers. The publication was not intended to replace the component in the *CMAJ* that dealt with the affairs of organized medicine. *Mediscope* would appear bimonthly, beginning in January 1974, and Mr. Milan Korcok was appointed its editor. The Board of Directors accepted that an initial deficit would be very likely and that the future of the paper would depend on its financial health. A preliminary readership survey conducted in late 1973 showed a favourable reader response, particularly from allied health professionals. Eighty percent of respondents indicated that they wished to continue receiving the tabloid.

The first glow of success was soon dulled as problems mounted. The post office decided that it would not grant *Mediscope* second-class mailing privileges, and the end results were inevitably increased costs and delays in delivery. In December 1973, the Board of Directors extended the life of the tabloid up to June 1974. One issue was planned for January and two for February. The board instructed the Publications and Finance committees to review the paper's operation in late March and submit a report at the board's April meeting. The reviews concluded that advertising could not be sustained at the hoped-for level and the board, therefore, discontinued publication at the end of April. The tabloid lost $46 197 in 1973 and $72 416 in the first 4 months of 1974.

The *CMAJ* was growing in strength with increasing numbers of pages; half the increase was in editorial content and the other half in increased advertising. French-language content grew to the extent of two and a half pages per issue and it was proposed that the French-language content of the scientific section be further increased, with special emphasis on review articles. In 1973 profit was $55 797; in 1974, it was $11 568.

The battle between the Association and the post office continued in 1975. The attempt to obtain second-class mailing privileges for the CMA publications was rebuffed once again. As the face-to-face meetings were nonproductive, correspondence was entered into between the two parties, but the post office continued its tactics of obfuscation by not giving any reasons for its decision. Its discriminatory attitude was exemplified when the chairman of the Publications Committee, Dr. Estathios W. Barootes, reported that officials pleaded the general intent of the legislation, but qualified that statement by saying that such legislation was susceptible to different interpretations. There was absolutely no doubt in the minds of the committee that the intransigence shown by the post office was based on its perception that the Association was "well-heeled" and able to afford the excessive burden of third-class mailing privileges. Unfortunately, this opinion could not be substantiated after a meeting between the Association's legal advisers and those of the post office, at which the Association learned that under its existing structure there was no way that it could qualify for second-class mailing privileges. Consideration was given to a wholly owned corporation publishing the journals, and while this would appear to meet the requirements of the legislation, the post office did indicate a protocol that would comply with its interpretation and would in all likelihood permit the mailing privileges requested.

This would require setting up a corporation in which no common voting share was owned by an officer or official of the Association, but one in which the Association could own preference shares that controlled the profits of the company. The format required was the formation of a corporation, to be known as the Canadian Medical Journal Publications Limited, located in the journal sales office in Toronto, with 100 common voting shares owned by the directors of the corporation and 10 000 participating, but nonvoting, shares owned by the CMA. The latter would enable the shareholder to share in the profits and assets of the company on a par with one common share. The business, sales and production staffs would have to be transferred to the corporation with no loss of benefits; the Editorial Department would remain as part of the CMA staff and its services purchased by the corporation. The CMA would have to sell the *CMAJ* to the corporation for approximately $500 000, receiving in return notes bearing a 10% to 12% interest rate.

This option was given searching study by the CMA Board of Directors, and concern was evident over the ramifications if such a format were adopted. Of particular concern were the change in name of the publication and the delisting of the CMA as publisher, leading to a loss in advertising revenue. The Board of Directors decided not to proceed with the creation of an independent publishing corporation.

Dr. Anderson resigned as scientific editor of the *CMAJ*, and Dr. David A.E. Shephard was appointed in his place. Dr. Earl M. Cooperman was appointed associate scientific editor. In 1977, the *CMAJ* introduced a redesigned cover and a new format of contents. There were more practice-oriented scientific articles, shorter in length than in previous issues; an increased number of editorials and review articles; articles from the Department of Communications; and reports of special projects carried out by the Association. In the year 1976–77, the journal's profit was $44 057. Sales of advertising were good, with 55 to 60 pages of advertising in issues of 120 to 130 pages, in keeping with the Association's policy of a 45% advertising component. Two-thirds of the editorial content was devoted to the scientific section and one-third to the news and features section. The May 6, 1977 issue of 170 pages was the largest to date in the publication's history.

Dr. Shephard resigned on July 9, 1977, and was replaced by Dr. N. Jack Wiggin, who assumed the position on Jan. 9, 1978. On Apr. 1, new postage rates came into effect, increasing the annual mailing costs of CMA publications by more than $60 000. It was found that advertising rates could not be increased to a level which would compensate for the extra mailing costs and the logical conclusion was that there would be a decline in profits.

In 1978, the *CMAJ* published approximately 34 000 copies with a page total of 3138. The number of scientific articles published increased substantially, but the number submitted for publication dropped slightly. The Publications Committee was concerned over the potential long-term implications of the combination of increased publishing requirements and a reduction in manuscripts, and the scientific editor was directed to visit a number of faculties of medicine and teaching hospitals to outline the *CMAJ*'s publishing policies and describe the type of manuscript required, and the benefits and merits of publishing in the *CMAJ*. It was hoped that this effort would result in more articles being submitted for consideration of publication.

On the other side of the coin, the number of editorials submitted more than doubled and letters to the editor increased substantially. Advertising page sales reached 1500, 200 of which were of the classified category. Reprints of 320 articles realized a net profit of $12 000. Postal rates continued to be a major irritant, and it was noted that the ever-upward spiral of those rates was not accompanied by any improvements in the delivery of CMA publications to members and others.

At the end of 1978, Dr. Cooperman returned to full-time practice of pediatrics and Dr. Peter Morgan was appointed in his place. Two part-time contributing editors, Dr. Clifford L. Jarrett and Dr. Donald T. Wigle, were retained, and Mr. David Woods, former editor of the *Canadian Family Physician*, was appointed a contributing editor with the responsibility to increase the journal's news and features content, particularly as it applied to primary health care. Dr. Alexander W. Andison, who had retired in 1974 after a number of years as associate editor of the *CMAJ* and the *CJS*, and who had been persuaded to return to the publications when his experience and expertise were required, retired once again.

The year 1979 was a record one for the journal in terms of advertising sales and the number of pages printed. Independent and in-house readership surveys indicated a high rate of acceptance. After 9 years Mr. Goodman resigned as business manager of CMA publications, and was succeeded by Mr. Neil Hutton as director of advertising sales. Mr. Goodman was recognized as having been a major contributor to the journal's success during his tenure. Mailing costs had risen by more than 300% between 1969 and 1979, and it was predicated that in 1980 they would be more than $400 000.

The journal's swings in revenue manifested themselves once again with a deficit of $64 206 in 1980, mainly due a drop of more than $100 000 in advertising revenue. Dr. Wiggin resigned as scientific editor and Dr. Andrew Sherrington was appointed to succeed him. A redesigned journal appeared on July 1, and the dates of publication were changed to the 1st and 15th of each month. Mr. Woods was appointed director of publications.

At the 1981 General Council, when the report on CMA publications was presented, the matter of postal rates, particularly in view of the impending increase of about 35% in mailing costs, received a lot of attention. Complaints from members over late or irregular delivery of the journal were increasing, and the Board of Directors was instructed to reopen discussions with the new post office crown corporation on ways and means whereby the problems might be solved.

After 12 years of being repeatedly denied by the post office, CMA publications were finally given back the second-class mailing privileges that had been taken away from them. The victory was marred somewhat by the lengthy mail strike in the summer of 1981, which led to a loss of advertising revenue, particularly in classified advertising. The Association was forced to find other means of delivery during the strike. Advertising revenue was just under $2 million, but the greatly increased costs resulted in a profit of just $5194.

At the beginning of 1982, the journal changed to computerized typesetting and web offset printing, using the firm RBW Graphics. Dr. Sherrington resigned as the *CMAJ*'s scientific editor and the position was taken by Dr. Morgan. During the year, the journal faced increased competition from four new medical journals in Canada but was still able to increase its share of advertising revenue. The year-end profit for 1982 was $293 667. In the first 6 months of 1983, advertising pages increased by 75. Covers of the journal carried reproductions of the works of living Canadian artists. Beginning in February 1983, a four-page insert in French was introduced. Changes in content included an editor's column and brief items on medical research. The *CMAJ* became a member of the Canadian Business Press Association, and the CMA's director of publications became a member of its board of directors.

Studies of CMA publications showed that the average reading time for the journal was 42 minutes and that there was an increase in readership for the French insert. In 1983, the profit was $518 632, again due to a marked increase in advertising revenue. Advertising linage increased by 160 pages and this, despite new competing publications, moved the journal from fourth to second place among 23 Canadian medical publications. In the first half of 1984 the journal carried 130 more pages than for the same period in 1983. Plans were afoot for the acquisition of computer typesetting hardware. Over the year, it increased its advertising by 270 pages; this translated to a 50% increase in just 2 years. There was doubt that that rate of growth could be maintained because competition was increasing. In attempting to forecast the journal's financial future, the Association was handicapped by uncertainty about the amount of postal rate increase and by doubts about the effectiveness of new federal legislation designed to protect the Canadian publishing industry.

Dr. Bruce P. Squires came to the journal as part-time scientific editor, and Dr. Lawrence Hart joined as the CMA's first fellow in medical writing and editing. The Board of Directors approved a new format for the scientific section of the journal and the Publications Committee was given the mandate to act as an editorial board. Profit for 1984 was $537 203 out of a revenue of $3 317 623. In 1985 the corresponding figures were $121 765 and $2 933 168.

The journal was 75 years old in 1986, a year of uncertainty in the publishing of medical journals. The Toronto *Globe and Mail* described the medical publishing industry as "volatile and highly competitive." Pharmaceutical manufacturers were showing caution in their planning for advertising because of their uncertainty over the application of the amended *Patent Act*. Strong competition for the advertising dollar was coming from the manufacturers of generic drugs. In January the journal was mailed to its readers in a clear plastic cover to minimize damage in its travels through the mail system. To celebrate its anniversary, its covers carried reproductions of art work by Canadian physicians. In mid-year, Dr. Morgan devolved his position to a halftime one so that he could devote more time to teaching and to the writing of books. The halftime vacated by Dr. Morgan was filled by Dr. Squires. Ms. Ann Bolster was appointed managing editor. The Board of Directors directed that the membership of the Publications Committee be increased from four to eight. Net profit in 1986 amounted to $60 221 out of a total revenue of $3 045 074. Monies were coming in from reprint orders and royalties as well as from advertising and paid subscriptions.

In a study of the publications department in late 1986, the Board of Directors regarded the *CMAJ* as its first priority and the flagship of the Association. As far as the journal itself was concerned, the study looked at physical presentation, marketing, readership and editorial concept. It was recognized that advertising by the pharmaceutical manufacturing industry was spread over 40 medical publications in Canada. A marketing campaign was initiated by an outside communications consultant agency, targeting marketing and media personnel. The results were deemed to be unsatisfactory, and a reassessment of the entire marketing strategy, based on long-term and short-term components, was initiated. Outside experts were retained to redesign the journal using more pictures, graphs and colour.

The financial results of the journal's operation in 1987 were described at General Council as "disappointing." The budget for the year had predicted a net income of $180 000, but in fact it turned out to be a loss of $319 264 out of a revenue of $2 586 088. The deficit was due to a significant decrease in the number of display advertising pages — from 1200 in 1986 to 940 in 1987. Postal rates, however, rose less than had been anticipated. On July 1, Dr. Morgan resigned and Dr. Squires was named scientific editor.

One of the results of a readership survey was that the journal was weak in its acceptance by general practitioners/family physicians; in Quebec this low level of acceptance applied to both general practitioners/family physicians and specialists. To redress the problem, beginning Mar. 1, 1988, the journal was mailed to all nonmember general practitioners/family physicians in Quebec for a 6-month trial. Reliable sources in Quebec told the CMA that there was minimal cost-ratio benefit in having a French insert in the journal and recommended its discontinuation. The Publications Committee accepted this opinion and the insert was discontinued, effective with the Feb. 1 issue, bringing about an annual savings of $80 000. The budget for 1988 projected a revenue of $2.5 million and expenditure of $2.9 million. In December 1988, a readership study, carried out by FOCUS, showed that the CMA was ranked first in total readership and highest in reading frequency numbers.

As it turned out, there was no deficit attributed to the journal for 1988, but a profit of $34 190. Pharmaceutical industry advertising amounted to

$1 714 000 and classified advertising to $659 000. In February 1989, the Association, in keeping with its commitment to reduce damage to the environment, changed the type of polywrap in which the journal was being mailed, replacing it with a biodegradable type of wrapping. A further independent survey confirmed the journal's first place in total readership, and this fact did not go unnoticed by the pharmaceutical manufacturers — display advertising revenue rose to $2 480 979. Classified advertising brought in $733 380 and the net profit for the year was $403 191.

In January 1990, the journal underwent further changes, increasing the bilingual component and improving the legibility and overall appearance of the contents. Photographs that tied together cover and contents were an innovation well received by the readership. Dr. Squires became editor-in-chief of CMA Publications in addition to being scientific editor. Journal revenues continued to increase and in 1991 were $4 723 990; display advertising was $3 142 453, and net revenue (profit), amounted to $800 413. Further independent readership surveys in 1991 continued to place the journal ahead of the rest of the field and undoubtedly was the reason for a 33% increase in display advertising in 1992, bringing in $4 334 869. Classified advertising contributed $950 870. Total revenue was $6 127 413 giving a net revenue of $1,389,552. In 1992, Dr. Patricia Huston was appointed associate editor-in-chief.

In 1993, the total number of journal pages was double that of 1988. Editorial content was consistently given high marks in readership surveys and there was no decline in the high level of readership numbers. Net revenue for the year was $1 087 041, slightly lower than the forecast of $1 201 848. A downturn in advertising revenues was experienced across the board by all publishers, but the high ranking held by the journal kept the loss to a minimum. In 1994, total revenue was down by over $300 000; net revenue was $1 155 961.

Changes in design and format were under consideration with a view to introducing approved changes in early 1995.

The *Canadian Journal of Surgery*

At the 1956 General Council there had been a brief discussion on the concept of producing a Canadian journal of surgery. Shortly after that meeting, Drs. Gilder, Routley and Kelly were invited to attend a meeting of the Council of the RCPSC and to present a brief on the establishment of such a journal. At the meeting, the CMA was led to believe that the college would welcome a journal as proposed and would be happy to see it published under the aegis of the CMA. The CMA representatives believed that the demand for such a publication should come from members of the profession and not be superimposed upon it by the CMA. Later the Association would be very pleased to learn that Dr. Ronald C. Laird of Toronto had called a meeting of an organizing committee to consider the ways and means of creating such a publication. The committee was composed of representatives of the RCPSC and the surgical specialties. It was the unanimous decision of the committee that a Canadian journal of surgery be established and that it be published by the CMA. The meeting suggested that the editorial board, in the beginning, be made up of the department of surgery heads from the Canadian medical schools. By invitation, those professors met with Drs. Gilder and Routley and responded with enthusiasm to the invitation to form the editorial board.

In March 1957, the *CJS* editorial board met in Toronto. The meeting was chaired by Dr. Robert M. Janes, professor of surgery at the University of Toronto. Dr. Janes planned to retire later in the year but was willing to continue as chairman. His experience with medical publishing in the United States would turn out to be valuable in helping the fledgling journal develop its wings and fly on its own. In addition to the editorial board, each of the surgical specialties appointed advisors to the CMA.

In October 1957, the first issue of the *CJS*, a quarterly, made its appearance. The initial readership gave it good marks as did advertisers, and after three issues there were 975 paid subscriptions, just 25 short of the target of 1000 set for the first year. By the end of 1958, the *CJS* had a net revenue of $1317 out of a total revenue of $26 110. By the end of 1959, it was well established and receiving an increasing number of manuscripts submitted for publication. Many of the papers presented at the meeting of the RCPSC in Vancouver in January 1959 were received for publication. Submissions were also coming in from other countries, and articles from Australia and Central Africa had been accepted for publication. At the end of 1959, paid subscription was 1014 and the net revenue for the year was $984.

By June 1961, the number of subscribers had risen to 1436. A promotional campaign conducted by the managing editor and his staff in January had led to 250 new paid subscriptions. The steady improvement in quality was largely due to the expert guidance provided by the editorial board, chaired by Dr. Janes. More subscriptions were coming in from overseas and the publication's acceptance was confirmed by a readership survey. The balance sheet for that period showed a loss of $4426, but this was attributed to a changing of the financial year to conform with the calendar year and not to a decline in revenue. Up to that time the Association had been using outside advertising representatives but, in December 1961, this practice was discontinued and all advertising sales were handled by the advertising manager, Mr. Thomas Wells, operating out of CMA House.

During 1962, the *CJS* was made available to trainees in surgical specialties in approved Canadian centres of graduate instruction at a reduced subscription rate of $5 per annum. The credibility of the publication increased and it was accepted by three major abstracting publications — *Surgery, Gynaecology and Obstetrics, The Yearbook of Surgery* and the *Annual of British Surgical Practice.* Abstracts of the scientific articles in each issue were submitted to and published in the *JAMA.* In 1962 the profit was $108. The managing editor, Dr. Routley, expressed concern, in his written report to the General Council just before his death, over the fact that circulation of the *CJS* was still only 1425 out of a potential of 2700 surgeons in Canada.

The editorial board, at its Jan. 19, 1964 meeting in Quebec City, was told that Dr. Janes would be stepping down as chairman. His expertise and leadership during the formative years of the *CJS* had been of inestimable value, and many compliments were paid to him on that account. Professor Frederick G. Kergin was elected chairman of the editorial board in his place. In 1963 the *CJS* made a profit of $4696 on a print run of 7677 copies. In 1964, profit had increased slightly to $5782 but the number of copies had decreased to 7205. Total page count was 634, of which 492 were editorial.

In spite of readership approval and the best efforts of the managing editor and staff, paid subscriptions continued to hover around the 1440 mark. Revenue in 1965 was $36 419; $19 386 came from advertising and the net revenue was $3107. By the end of 1966, revenue had risen to $41 773, with the increase coming entirely from advertising; profit for the year was $10 567. The ratio of advertising to editorial had remained around 1:3 for several years but in 1967 the ratio changed slightly with an increase of 4% in advertising. Net profit for that year was $9399 out of a total revenue of $48 951. The profit figure was welcome news for the association, as the *CMAJ* had shown a deficit of $19 443 for the same period.

Dr. Kelly, managing editor of CMA Publications, reported to the 1968 General Council that a certificate of qualified circulation, issued by the Canadian Circulations Audit Board, showed that the January 1968 issue of the *CJS* was 1173 in Canada and 282 abroad. The editor of CMA Publications and the chairman of the *CJS* editorial board advised the CMA Board of Directors that the staff of the *CJS* should not move to Ottawa with the *CMAJ,* but that it should remain in Toronto for a further year following that move. It was held that moving the operations of the two publications at the same time would be very disruptive and a year's grace would give the editorial board the opportunity to assess the future of the publication. Under the existing format, the editorial board had the responsibility for the editorial content of the *CJS,* but the

CMA was the publisher and carried out the sale of advertising and administration of the publishing. The editorial board believed that it might wish to align itself with another organization, leading to increased circulation and a corresponding increase in revenue. The editorial board appointed a small executive committee to study all aspects of the *CJS* and to report back. The Board of Directors approved the recommendation.

The January 1969 issue of the *CJS* was a memorial issue dedicated to Dr. Janes with contributions prepared by members of the Janes Surgical Society. In the introduction Dr. Kergin wrote:

> *It is appropriate that an issue of the Canadian Journal of Surgery be dedicated to the late Dr. Robert M. Janes. It was his foresight, enthusiasm and confidence in Canadian surgery and surgeons that led to the establishment of the Journal in 1957. He served as Chairman of the Editorial Board during the critical first seven years of the Journal's history, when standards were set and format determined.*

The revenue in 1969 was $42 949, leading to a profit of $2607. A loss of $20 575 was budgeted for 1970, but things turned out better and the loss was $10 699. The subscription rate was raised from $10 to $15, effective Jan. 1, 1971, and the number of issues went from quarterly to six issues a year. For 1971, the budget was set for a revenue of $66 000 and an expenditure of $70 000. Mrs. Gillian Pancirov was appointed assistant editor.

In 1971 the Board of Directors directed that the *CJS* operation be moved to Ottawa no later than July 1, 1972. The duties of managing editor would be taken over by the general secretary. Because of his intention to leave Canada later in the year, Dr. Kergin resigned as chairman of the editorial board. Dr. Kergin, a Rhodes Scholar, spent 2 years at Oxford before returning to Toronto where he joined the Department of Surgery, then headed by Dr. Gallie. Dr. Kergin's contributions to the *CJS* were recognized by the Board of Directors who decided that one of the future regular issues of the *CJS* be devoted to articles written in his honour. The March 1973 issue was a Festschrift prepared by the Kergin Surgical Society. Drs. Lloyd D. MacLean and C. Barber Mueller succeeded Dr. Kergin as coeditors of the *CJS*. The deficit for the year was $8881, even though revenue from advertising increased by $8000 over the 1970 figure; unfortunately, increased expenses counteracted the potential net profit. The budget for 1972 forecast a deficit of nearly $6000; the actual loss was $1862 on a revenue of $64 614. Revenue rose to $71 679 in 1973, but a sharp increase in printing and production costs offset the increase in revenue and the net profit was $1443.

During 1973, representatives of the Association met with representatives of the RCPSC on the matter of a joint sponsorship of the *CJS*. The meeting had been called because of inadequate revenue from subscriptions, and the CMA believed that the publication should be available to all surgeon members of the Association. The RCPSC was of the opinion that the publication should be improved and distributed to all surgical fellows. As a result of the meeting and subsequent discussions, an agreement was reached whereby there would be joint sponsorship of the *CJS* by the two parties, with the CMA continuing as publisher and retaining final responsibility and authority for production, advertising sales and business management. The RCPSC assumed responsibility for editorial policy and content. A *CJS* joint advisory board with representatives from both organizations was established to serve as a liaison between the co-sponsors. The agreement was for a 3-year period ending Dec. 31, 1977, and subject to renewal if mutually acceptable. A deficit of $4950 was budgeted for 1974.

In 1975, the General Council was told that circulation had risen to 7400 and that the actual deficit for the 1974 operations had been decreased by a grant of $8000 from the RCPSC, thus giving a deficit of only $530. In 1976, *CJS* revenue rose to $122 159, with $91 155 coming from advertising; profit for the year was $4116. Comparable figures for 1977 were $118 544 in revenue, with advertising contributing $81 315; the deficit was $7153.

The co-sponsorship agreement expired at the end of December 1977, and was renewed for a further 3 years, expiring at the end of 1980. Arising out of the new agreement was the decision that the *CJS* would be published in a new size, with a new format and cover. Pages allocated for editorial copy were increased to 64 per issue, a 45% increase in editorial copy. The RCPSC increased the annual subscription rate from $3 to $4.50 for each fellow receiving the publication. Advertising pages had increased to an average of 31 in the first three issues of 1978. For the year 1977, the deficit was $7153 on a revenue of $118 544. The budgeted deficit for 1978 was $14 329.

Sales of advertising increased by about 15% and total revenue rose by 17%, but the deficit was still present, recording an amount of $9411 on a total revenue of $144 539. The RCPSC returned to the CMA the sum of $2058.73 as its portion of the *CJS* profits in 1976. The budgeted deficit for 1979 was $10 261. In 1979 the editorial pages were increased from 64 to 72 and advertising rates were increased by 15%. Dr. Joseph Shugar of Montreal assumed the position of part-time associate editor in January 1979. At the General Council in 1979, a special tribute was paid to Drs. MacLean and Mueller, coeditors of the *CJS*, who were carrying out their task on a voluntary basis. The actual deficit for 1979 was $9007, slightly less than had been forecast.

The budgeted deficit for 1980 was $8933. The General Council received with some dismay the news that the true deficit for 1980 had reached $21 352. Advertising revenue had decreased by nearly $20 000 and expenses were down by $8000. The report was optimistic in that it predicted a turnaround for the *CJS* in 1981, basing that assessment on the likelihood of a substantial increase in advertising sales. The General Council's concerns were echoed by the RCPSC, some of whose members were worried about the financial support required in the operation of the publication. Advertising revenue for 1981 was budgeted at $150 000, an amount $30 000 above the actual advertising revenue in 1980, and a budgeted deficit of $12 309 was predicted for 1981. Mrs. Pancirov was appointed associate editor.

The agreement on the matter of joint sponsorship was renewed. The General Council approved a motion that financial support for the *CJS* should be terminated in 2 years. The true figures lived up to the prognostications and advertising revenue did increase substantially, achieving a height of $191 297. This permitted a profit of $682, albeit a small but welcome change from 7 straight years of deficits! It was hoped that savings in printing and postage costs could be achieved and a larger profit reported for the coming year. The long postal strike of the previous year had had an adverse effect on the amount of revenue from classified advertising. A profit of $10 942 was budgeted for 1982.

In March 1982 Dr. D. Laurence Wilson stepped down as chairman of the Publications Committee. In the Board of Director's report to the 1982 General Council, Dr. Wilson was described as "having lent enormous support and judgement and literacy to the role of Chairman." Dr. Wilson was replaced by Dr. Gerald Caron. On the matter of the Association's financial statement showing advertising revenue for 1982 at $236 510 and a net profit of $28 149, one long-time member was heard to remark that "The *CJS* has gone from the ridiculous to the sublime!"

At the beginning of 1983, the *CJS* underwent major changes in its design. There was a high level of acceptance by the readership, but a drop in advertising revenue in the early months, although this was offset later. A profit of $22 612 was budgeted for 1983, but when all the figures were in, the true profit was just less than half at $10 595. Advertising revenue was $207 119, down nearly $30 000 from the 1982 figure.

On Aug. 23, 1984, the CMA Board of Directors ratified a 5-year agreement, which had been reached by the Joint Management Committee of the CMA and the RCPSC. Under the agreement, profits accruing from the publication during the life of the agreement would be placed initially in a reserve fund and retained there until such time as the fund reached a level of approximately 20%

of the *CJS*'s operating revenue. With the proviso that no distribution of such profits in excess of the reserve fund requirements would be permitted in the first 3 years of the term of the agreement, profits would be divided equally between the two parties. In 1984 the *CJS* made a profit of $47 560. Mailing costs during that year had increased by more than $28 000; advertising revenue had increased by $77 000.

The "boom or bust" story of the *CJS* finances continued in 1985 when a deficit of $44 357 was recorded. Advertising revenue decreased by $82 000 from the previous year. This scenario was seen right across the spectrum of advertising in medical publications, but the Association's publications were affected to a lesser extent than those of its competitors. The trend continued in 1986 when the deficit was $44 528, again largely due to a decrease of $33 000 in advertising revenue. There were no signs that "the bleeding had stopped" when it was reported to the 1988 General Council that the deficit for 1987 was $100 788, almost twice the budgeted deficit. Advertising revenue was down by 34% and total revenue declined by 23%. Display advertising pages fell from 117 in 1986 to 81 in 1987.

The Board of Directors approved a review of the *CJS* and its operations and this was done by D. Elkins Management Limited late in the year. Five recommendations came from the review:

(i) *Redesign the cover and contents.*
(ii) *Reduce editorial costs while maintaining the existing editorial style.*
(iii) *Develop a formal marketing programme and sales kit.*
(iv) *Consider the use of a new marketing rep. house more in tune with the pharmaceutical manufacturing industry.*
(v) *Search for opportunities to develop paid subscribers and other financial support.*

Readers saw the results of the redesigned cover and contents in the September 1987 issue. A new printer, RBW Graphics, printed four issues in 1988. The selling of advertising space by an agency, beginning in early 1987, had not been as successful as had been hoped and consideration was given to other options before that contract expired at the end of 1988. Consideration was given also to selling *CJS* on a single-sponsor basis, thus allowing a given revenue stream for a specific period. There are problems inherent in such an arrangement. The recommendation was made that new marketing representation might be a more attractive option. The budgeted deficit for 1988 was $118 000; the true deficit was slightly under that at $104 500.

The financial viability of the *CJS* continued to be of great concern both to the CMA and the RCPSC. The projected deficit for 1989 was $70 900. The RCPSC, since 1984, had contributed $4.50 per surgical fellow in exchange for the right to appoint the editors and the editorial board and to have input into editorial policy. This had amounted to $38 025 in 1988. The RCPSC also published the abstracts of the college's annual meeting. In April 1988, the council of the college voted to discontinue financial support for any periodical other than its own *Annals*. The position was put before the 1989 General Council and, after discussion, the following motion was placed before the meeting: "That the Canadian Medical Association cease publication of the *Canadian Journal of Surgery* and include the contents of this Journal in the *CMAJ*."

The speaker ruled that the motion be taken in two parts. The motion to cease publication of the *CJS* was defeated by 84 votes to 80, making redundant the second part of the motion.

The decision by the Council of the RCPSC opened the way for the CMA to consider acting independently to alter the *CJS* in such a manner as to ensure its long-term viability and to develop a publication that could function without the financial help of the CMA. Following the decision by the General Council, the CMA Board of Directors examined the options, taking into account that the budgeted deficit for 1989 was $70 950. The true deficit for the year turned out to be $40 080. The picture was brighter in 1990 when the true deficit was $3541.

Negotiations with the RCPSC led to an agreement whereby the college would provide support to the amount of $30 000 as part of its phase-out strategy. Further negotiations led to an agreement whereby a number of specialty societies would provide financial and editorial support over the following 5 years. Partners to the agreement were the CMA, the RCPSC, the Canadian Association of General Surgeons, the Canadian Society of Cardiovascular and Thoracic Surgeons, the Canadian Society for Vascular Surgery and the Canadian Society of Surgical Oncology. In 1991, the Canadian Orthopaedic Association joined the agreement. The RCPSC distributed a letter to its members asking for a voluntary donation of $25 to support the *CJS*; the appeal resulted in the receipt of more than 250 donations.

In 1991, advertising revenues were on the rise again, reaching $240 880 and this contributed to a profit of $6542 for the year. Drs. MacLean and Mueller resigned effective July 1, 1992. The two surgeons had been coeditors of the *CJS* for 20 years and had enjoyed the triumphs and suffered the tribulations during that period. Given that they had been at the helm for nearly two-thirds of the journal's existence, it was no wonder that their dedication was warmly recognized at the 1992 General Council. Their successors were Drs. Jonathan L. Meakins and Roger G. Keith. They began their tenure as coeditors by initiating improvements in the editorial content. The editorial process was decentralized to Saskatoon and Montreal, and the reviewing process was upgraded. Although advertising revenue was down by $15 000 during the year, the net revenue at year-end was $7177.

The actual revenue for the *CJS* in 1993 was $265 783; deficit was $30 774; in 1994, the deficit was $30 146 on a revenue of $233 860. It is difficult to understand why such an excellent publication, for that is what it is, suffers the indignities of having a financial track record where year-end deficits are more frequent than net revenues. Examination of the layout, perusal of the articles and of the expertise listed on its masthead, leads one to the conclusion that the *CJS* deserves a future better than its past.

Other CMA Publications

In 1986 the Board of Directors discussed the question of expanding the mandate of the Publications Department; the outcome was approval of such expansion into new publishing ventures and related activities. It was believed that the expansion into previously unexplored waters had the potential not only for enhancing the CMA's reputation, but also leading to increased revenue for the Association. The decision was made that a detailed study of the department be undertaken, and this took place in 1987. In fact, two studies were carried out, one in-house and the other by DCH Consultants, Inc., of Ottawa. The result of both studies showed that the Publications Department faced strategic and financial problems, and indicated that in order to increase the financial base of the department, steps needed to be taken to increase its "stable" of products. It was deemed that the department would need to become more business oriented and that the existing publications, such as the *CMAJ* and the *CJS*, would have to be repositioned in the marketplace. On the basis of the findings, the Board of Directors approved the new mandate for the department.

On the matter of the Association's two journals, it was agreed that the *CMAJ* would remain as the flagship of the Association for the foreseeable future. In view of the recommendation that the Association become more business oriented if its new mandate was to succeed, the Board of Directors approved that a search be instituted to find someone who could steer the vessel through waters unfamiliar to the Association. The search for a CMA director of publications led to the appointment of Mrs. Barbara Drew who had had a 16-year association with the publications of the National Research Council, where she had been director of Administrative Services and Publications. In

1990 Mrs. Drew was appointed executive director of Administration and Membership Services and Mrs. Susan Stockwell took over as director of publications. In 1992 Mrs. Stockwell went on leave of absence and was replaced by Mr. Stephen Prudhomme; on her return to the Publications Department in 1994 she was appointed associate director.

The following narrative describes the various ventures undertaken by the Publications Department from 1988 onwards.

Net Worth

Net Worth was the first new publication in the expanded stable, beginning with the first issue in December 1987. It was described as "a financial newsletter for physicians," designed to be a "quick read," with the object of assisting its readers to make sound financial decisions. The publication was a monthly one, made up of eight pages of editorial content and up to four pages of advertising in colour. The first issue went to 54 000 physicians across Canada. There were seven different editions, including an MD Management edition, each with similar editorial content but with different advertising. MD Management Ltd. made a payment of $35 000, net of advertising revenue, to each of the first two issues, and agreed to purchase $15 000 of advertising per issue during the year. Various manufacturers within the pharmaceutical industry sponsored 36 500 copies. The January and February 1988 issues were combined into eight editions; the March, April and May issues were each four editions. A French version, *Valeurs Nettes*, became available, beginning in September 1988.

It was clear from the response that the publication had met a need and it was decided that in future issues the editorial emphasis would reflect that need in greater measure. Facilities for inhouse publication were not adequate and so *Net Worth Inc.* was set up, with Mr. David Elkins as publisher. Advertising revenue was slower coming in than anticipated, and MD Management was allotted the unsold advertising space. The post office did not permit the publication to enjoy second-class mailing privileges, in spite of ongoing attempts to obtain them.

By late 1989, the Association wished to have more editorial control, and in order to make changes in format and methods of distribution, as well as increase the publication's availability to advertisers, the joint publishing venture was ended. Publication was moved in-house as facilities were then available, and the name of the publication was changed to *Strategy*. In October, a new multi-sponsored format was introduced and each issue was distributed in the *CMAJ* polywrap. Editorial material was either written or commissioned by MD Management and transmitted to the CMA Publications Department for publication via a desktop publishing system. The General Council was told in 1991 that the publication's advertising revenues were on the increase and that a readership survey was commissioned. This survey of 1200 readers was very favourable, and advertisers responded. By the end of 1991, advertising revenue had risen to a level that enabled the publication to be self-supporting. In 1993, the publication was redesigned and its contents expanded.

Humane Medicine

Since 1954, this journal of the art and science of medicine had been published by Humane Medicine, Inc. It had been founded by Dr. Dimitrios G. Oreopoulos and Dr. John O. Godden, a former associate editor of the *CMAJ*. The publication provided physicians with a forum for an exchange of ideas on the types and quality of care provided to patients. In 1989, negotiations were entered into between the CMA and Humane Medicine Inc., resulting in the CMA taking over the publication. Dr. Oreopoulos was appointed editor-in-chief and Dr. Godden became executive editor. The CMA appointed Dr. Athol L. Roberts as the editor of the CMA Ethics Section.

Under the agreement with Humane Medicine Inc., and with a separate agreement with Keith Health Care Communications, financial independence was guaranteed for the first year's publication of four issues and assured for the second year. During the 2-year period, the publication would be a supplement to the *CMAJ*. The first year ended with a net revenue of $2103. The advertising had been of a corporate nature as opposed to product information, giving pharmaceutical companies a platform on which to publicize their contributions to health care rather than a promote their products, and their contributions to research and development formed their presentations. The Publications Department proposed that additional revenue be sought from other commercial sources and a wider range of subscribers be targeted.

In 1991, it was reported to the General Council that the publication was attracting excellent submissions from Canadian and international sources. Sir John Templeton, who had had a long association with investment components of the Association's savings plans, generously donated $60 000 to the publication. The Canadian Nurses Association promoted the publication in its journal, reaching 108 000 members of their association , and the CMA approached other health organizations with a view to obtaining the same type of promotion.

In January 1992, *Humane Medicine* was redesigned and a review of editorial strategy and content was undertaken. Corporate advertising was discontinued in 1991 and in mid-1993, product advertising was accepted. Dr. John R. Williams, director of the CMA's Department of Ethics and Legal Affairs, introduced a new section on bioethics. The name was changed to *Humane Medicine: A Journal of the Art of Healing* and the cover design reflected the changing editorial content.

CMA News

The Board of Directors agreed with the views of the Publications Department that the Association needed to promote itself more actively to its members, and to this end *CMA News* was developed. The first issue came out in April 1991 and was distributed in the polywrap to all CMA members. It consisted of four pages in both official languages, and the articles were cross-referenced to other CMA publications. By the end of 1994, under the senior editor, Mr. Patrick Sullivan, it was published 12 times a year, and each issue of eight pages was sent to each member of the CMA as part of the benefits of membership. Others could receive the publication on payment of a yearly subscription fee. Membership of the CMA at the end of 1994 was 44 000.

Canadian Association of Radiologists Journal

In 1989, a number of options for CMA involvement in the publication of the *Canadian Association of Radiologists Journal (CARJ)* were offered to the Canadian Association of Radiologists (CAR). Following discussions, an agreement was arrived at whereby the *CARJ* would be published as a joint venture, beginning in January 1990. The CAR retained total editorial control, and the CMA assisted in its search for and selection of a new editor. At the end of the first year of operation under the new arrangement, a net revenue was realized, and by the end of 1991, net revenue came to $20 000.

RRT: The Canadian Journal of Respiratory Therapy

An agreement was reached with the Canadian Society of Respiratory Technology to publish its official journal on a fee-for-service basis. The first issue was published in April 1991 and sent to the society's 300 members. Publication was scheduled for five issues per annum. Both the Association and the society were pleased with the success of the first year. In 1992, the structure of the editorial board was changed, leading to the society's Board of Directors taking a more active role in the production of its journal.

Mediscan

In the autumn of 1991, the CMA agreed to assume responsibility for the publication and distribution of *Mediscan*, the official publication of the Canadian Federation of Medical Students. The motive behind this venture was twofold: to have the CMA support and promote the activities of Canada's future medical practitioners, with the hope that they would become full members of the CMA, and to have the publication generate net revenue for both parties.

Books

In its new role, the Publications Department became involved in a number of joint ventures in the writing and publication of books. Some of these are described here.

The Canadian Medical Association Guide to Prescription and Over-the-Counter Drugs

This was the first joint venture for the CMA with Dorling Kindersley Ltd. and the Reader's Digest Association (Canada) Inc. The book was published simultaneously in English and French in January 1990 and was an immediate success. The CMA component was made up of the coeditors, Dr. Mark S. Berner from Montreal and Mr. Gerald N. Rotenberg from Toronto, supported by a 12-person editorial board, plus a physician liaison from Health and Welfare Canada. The book, described as "an authoritative guide, edited by Canadian experts in the fields of drugs and drug therapy" and "the most reliable home reference guide to all major prescription and over-the-counter medications used in Canada," sold out its first printing of 130 000 very quickly. It was available through retail outlets and, for members of the Association, through the *CMAJ* at a special rate. The CMA received royalties of $1 per copy from bookstore sales and 4¢ a copy from direct mail sales. A second printing was done, and it was noted that up to the early months of 1993, 161 000 English and 49 000 French copies had been sold. A second edition was planned for 1995.

The Canadian Medical Association Home Medical Encyclopedia

This was another venture for the CMA with Dorling Kindersley and Reader's Digest. Dr. Peter Morgan, a previous scientific editor of the *CMAJ*, was the editor. The book was launched in January 1992 and made available to the public through retail outlets, and to members through the *CMAJ*. By mid-1993, over 60 000 copies had been sold. A French version was planned for 1994. The royalty arrangements were the same as those for the earlier joint venture.

Guidance and Support in Caring for the Elderly

In 1990, this book was published in both French and English by Grosvenor House Press. The costs of publication were partially offset by an Eldercare Grant from Parke-Davis, a manufacturer of pharmaceuticals. The book was based on the report of the CMA Committee on Health Care for the Elderly. It was available to the public through bookstores, and through the CMA to Association members. Sales exceeded 1300 copies in the first weeks after publication.

Everyone's Guide to Cancer Therapy
In a cooperative venture with a Canadian publisher, Somerville House Books Ltd., the guide was published in 1992. Sales were satisfactory with more than 500 copies being sold in the summer of 1993.

The Canadian Medical Association Complete Book of Mother & Baby Care
This was another joint venture with Dorling Kindersley and Reader's Digest. Agreement was reached in 1991, and the book went on sale in the autumn of 1992. By mid-1993, sales were approaching 20 000, and in that year it went into a second printing.

In 1992–93, the CMA entered into an arrangement with Grosvenor House Press to publish four books. They were:
1. *Breathing to Live. A Physician's Companion to Managing COPD and Counselling Patients.*
2. *Worried Sick…Generalized Anxiety Disorder. A Physician's Guide to Care and Counselling.*
3. *Depression: Diagnosis and Treatment in Primary Care.*
4. *A Prostate Problem: Benign Prostatic Hyperplasia. A Physician's Guide to Care and Counselling.*

Other publications included: *Nutrition of the Elderly; The CMA Guide to Medical Administration in Canadian Hospitals; Quality of Care: Issues and Challenges in the 90s. A Literature Review; Physicians in Canada Volume III* (a joint publication with the Association of Canadian Medical Colleges), *The Patient–Physician Relationship; Physicians, Ethics and AIDS; Challenges and Changes in the Care of the Elderly; A Compendium of Quality of Care Developments in Canada 1994.*

In 1993 and 1994, CMA Publications and Key Porter Books Ltd. completed negotiations for a series of medical books titled *Your Personal Health Series.* The series was established to provide information to the general public so that it might become a better informed consumer of health care resources.

Another agreement was entered into with Dorling Kindersley and Reader's Digest, which led to the publishing of the *Canadian Medical Association Complete Guide to Medical Symptoms.* In February 1993, an agreement was concluded with Harold Starke Publishers Ltd. whereby the CMA became the exclusive agent in Canada for the distribution and sale of *The Illustrated History of Medicine*.

In 1994, the General Council was told that in the previous year, 6900 CMA books were sold through Membership Services. Included in this total were 1000 copies of the *Canadian Medical Association Complete Book of Mother & Baby Care*, 300 copies of the *Canadian Medical Association Home Medical Encyclopedia*, 250 copies of *The Illustrated History of Medicine*, and more than 400 copies of *The CMA Guide to Medical Administration in Canadian Hospitals*. In mid- to late-1994, a number of new publications were brought on stream, including the *Directory of Canadian Clinical Practice Guidelines 1994* and the *Canadian Immunization Guide — Fourth Edition*. In addition to the publications listed, many other booklets were available to members and to the public. The Association also publishes numerous policy summaries and position statements.

More books and booklets are in various stages of production and will be available in 1995.

Chapter IX

SPECIAL PROJECTS

A NUMBER OF SPECIAL PROJECTS have been undertaken by the Association, some of them leading to the creation of new organizations. For example, it was the CMA that, on Oct. 9 and 10, 1867, formed two important committees concerned with granting licences and medical education, out of which came the need to have a *Canada Medical Act* and that subsequently led to the creation of the Medical Council of Canada in 1912. Another example is the initiating role played by the CMA in the creation of the Royal College of Physicians and Surgeons of Canada (RCPSC). In some instances, the Association acted as an animateur or a catalyst in working with other health care organizations to establish a new multidisciplinary or multi-organizational body. Other projects have been initiated and carried out by the Association with the results having a direct bearing on the delivery of health care to Canadians. This chapter describes some examples.

The College of Family Physicians of Canada

In 1947, the CMA formed a committee, chaired by an internist, Dr. Wallace Wilson from Vancouver, with the aim of improving the status of general practitioners both in and outside the CMA. Difficulties were experienced in coming up with recommendations that pleased everyone, and it was not until April 1953, that the report of the Meeting of the Exploratory Committee on Accreditation of General Practitioners was presented to the Executive Committee for consideration. In the report was a recommendation for the establishment of a body to be known as the College of General Practitioners of Canada. Eight aims and objectives were put forward.

1. To establish an academic body with broad educational aims.
2. To arrange for postgraduate education for general practitioners.
3. To arrange for research in general practice.
4. To arrange undergraduate teaching by and for general practitioners.

5. To arrange for publication of original articles by general practitioners.
6. To arrange for hospital staff appointments for general practitioners.
7. To provide suitable recognition to members in the field of general practice.
8. To do all things necessary to maintain a high standard in general practice.

Questions arose as to how such a body could be created. The response was that the CMA had successfully organized the creation of the RCPSC in 1928, leading to Royal Assent in 1929, and its *Act of Incorporation*, that it was the CMA that had initiated the Royal College's certification program in the following decade, and with that background of experience, no problems were foreseen in adopting similar procedures for the establishment of a College of General Practitioners. In 1953, the General Council endorsed the Executive Committee's approval of the concept and established an organizing committee to proceed with the creation of such a college. The committee was made up of Drs. Murray R. Stalker, John H. Black, Glen Sawyer, Charles L. Gass, W. Victor Johnston and Armand Rioux. Later Dr. J. Wendell Macleod was added, representing the Association of Canadian Medical Colleges (ACMC). The committee was given $3600 to finance its operations up to the time of enrolment of the first members of the new college. A request was made by the committee that the CMA grant sums up to $10 000 to aid the work of the new college in the ensuing 3 years.

On June 17, 1954, in Vancouver, the new College of General Practice of Canada was officially launched. It was celebrated by a number of general practitioners over a lunch of Pacific salmon at the Palomar Supper Club; at the head table were Dr. Routley and Dr. Kelly. Dr. Stalker became the college's first president and Dr. Johnston its first full-time director.

The CMA was also involved in matters pertaining to the college's headquarters, whose first home was next door to the headquarters of the CMA and the OMA. The house belonged to Dr. T. Tweed Samis, an ophthalmologist, who not only had supported the concept but had also become a foundation benefactor with a generous donation. Accommodation for the college was provided rent-free, and it was in the basement of 174 St. George Street that Dr. Johnston began the first of his 10 years as the college's director.

Over the 40 years that have elapsed since that beginning, the college has gone on from strength to strength. Its name was changed to College of Family Physicians of Canada (CFPC), and it now occupies its own building at 4000 Leslie Street, Toronto. The expanded role of the college, particularly in relation to its certification and fellowship programs, and in its involvement at the international level through its membership in The World Organization of

National Colleges, Academies and Academic Associations of General Practitioners (WONCA), have given it a status that is the envy of many other organizations.

The college's relationship with the CMA has, by and large, been of mutual benefit to both organizations. Periods of disagreement have never been long-lasting and have not carried any lingering animosity between the two. Cooperation has been frequent and fruitful as will be seen in the following narrative.

Task Force on Education for the Provision of Primary Care Services

In 1981, the General Council approved "That a Task Force be established to review Family Practice training in Canada." The CMA had expressed concern over the intention of the CFPC to eliminate the practice-eligible route to certification, and the mandate of the task force was to review the implications of such an intent and make appropriate recommendations to the CMA. Similar concerns had been expressed by the Canadian Federation of Medical Students (CFMS), which believed that the acceptance of a rotating internship should not take the place of the practice eligible route. It was the college's view that residency training was superior to a 1-year internship.

Dr. D. Laurence Wilson, a past president of the CMA, was named to chair the task force. Members were Drs. L.W. (Sandy) Nash, Dennis A. Kendel, Claude A. Murphy, Michael Dixon, Robert Tingley and Constance Lapointe. The working terms of reference were:

1. *To determine in broad outline the objectives of training for physicians entering primary-care practice and in particular to:*
    (a) *review the scope of current primary care practice, recognizing regional, local and specialized patterns;*
    (b) *identify present problems and future trends;*
    (c) *agree on the characteristics of primary-care practice patterns in the next decade.*
2. *To examine the content, strengths and weaknesses of pathways currently available to physicians preparing for some sort of primary-care practice, considering such characteristics as the setting, content, evaluation methods and duration of the programmes.*
3. *To make recommendations for future training of primary-care physicians with consideration of both core and optional training components.*

Between October 1982 and May 1983, the task force carried out a series of onsite visits and met with many family practitioners and others. It found that, in Canada, this area of study was fragmented, with no clear direction to ensure the best health care in the coming years. In August 1984, the task force presented its findings and recommendations to the General Council. The following recommendations were approved:

1. *That the family physician be competent to provide primary, continuing and comprehensive care to all age groups. He should be competent to recognize and treat common illness, including severe illness, with episodic help from other specialists. He should have hospital privileges and should participate in the active care of patients in hospitals. His core training should include training in obstetrics.*

2. *That there be a single national standard of training for all family physicians. The standard should embrace the nature of clinical training to be undertaken, careful and well-documented in-training evaluation, and terminal evaluation in the form of a common national certification programme.*

3. *That the prescribed training and evaluation procedures be available to all trainees proceeding to the specialty of Family Medicine.*

4. *That the CFPC administer the national programme of training and evaluation for family medicine.*

5. *That sufficient extra residency training positions be funded to allow some of the family physicians to develop areas of special competence.*

6. *That the CFPC temporarily extend a practice-eligible route to certification for practising family physicians who have been in an acceptable form of clinical practice for five years or more, have been active members of the CFPC for a prescribed period, and have fulfilled special continuing medical requirements prescribed for them by the College.*

7. *That the National Joint Committee on Accreditation of Pre-registration Physician Training Programmes and the Federation of Provincial Medical Licensing Authorities of Canada (FPMLAC) take steps, in consultation with the CFPC, to incorporate elective rotations in family practice in all PG-1 programmes.*

Two recommendations were not approved but were referred to the Board of Directors, as were two notices of motion. The Council on Medical Education was requested to organize a mechanism whereby a national consensus on the recommendations, as well as the content of the other motions, could be achieved. Dr. Albert R. Cox, dean of medicine at Memorial University of Newfoundland, chaired a series of national invitational meetings, attended by representatives from the CMA, CFPC, RCPSC, ACMC, CFMS, Canadian Association of Internes and Residents (CAIR), FPMLAC, Committee on Accreditation of Pre-registration Training Progammes and the Fédération des médecins, internes et résidents du Québec.

The multi-organizational group met in CMA House in February and April 1985 and recommended the establishment of a postgraduate family medicine education joint committee and a national family medicine advisory training council. The recommendation was approved by the General Council, as were the recommendations on the matter of membership in the two bodies. The General Council also approved the continuation of the multi-organizational group called The Family Practice Training Committee, and directed that it report to the 1986 General Council on the matter of "a design and acceptance of an educational continuum embracing the clinical clerkship, a newly designed, flexible PG-1 year and a period of family practice residency."

In 1986, Dr. Cox presented the committee's report, "Continuing the Evolution." The report recommended, inter alia, that integrated 2-year family medicine training programs should continue to be the preferred route to family practice, but that a postgraduate year, common to all medical disciplines, was not feasible. It was further recommended that all Canadian faculties of medicine offer a flexible PG-1 year composed of three training streams, viz., one for graduates intending to complete a family medicine residency of 2 years; a second stream for graduates proceeding to a RCPSC specialty; the third stream being a transitional arrangement.

After discussion of the report by the General Council in 1986, the following recommendations were approved:

1. *That integrated two-year family medicine training programmes should continue to be the preferred training route to general and family practice.*
2. *That university faculties of Medicine and provincial governmental departments of Health and Education increase the number of Family Practice residency training positions and the educational resources to meet training requirements.*
3. *That all faculties of Medicine offer a flexible PG-1 made up of three training streams:*
   (i) *The first year of the integrated CFPC Residency Training Programme.*
   (ii) *First-year programmes that would accommodate the diverse needs of the various RCPSC programmes (straight, rotating, mixed and comprehensive internships).*

(iii) An objective based transitional training stream that would:

(a) *provide core training in subject areas common to a number of disciplines (e.g. emergency medicine and internal medicine) and specific training in areas of major disciplines which could be eligible for some credit towards the training requirements of the CFPC or the RCPSC.*

(b) *Meet the needs of students who do not enter PG-1 programmes of the RCPSC or the CFPC postgraduate training due to the limited number of positions.*

(c) *Provide broad training options and experience for those students who are undecided about their career choice or who wish a broad training experience.*

4. *Recommended to all Faculties of Medicine, the Federation of Medical Licensing Authorities, the CFPC and the RCPSC that all programmes in the newly designed transitional PG-1 training stream be university affiliated.*

5. *That the CFPC, the RCPSC, the Federation of Medical Licensing Authorities, and other bodies as appropriate, collaborate in developing general and discipline-specific objectives for the transitional PG-1 stream for which credits can be given.*

6. *That university training programmes invite, and the CFPC, the RCPSC, and La Corporation Professionelle des Médecins du Québec, undertake a collaborative review and accreditation of the transitional PG-1 training stream for the assignment of appropriate credit.*

7. *That the Federation of Provincial Medical Licensing Authorities of Canada review the transitional PG-1 training stream programmes for credit towards pre-registration training.*

8. *That the CFPC, the RCPSC and La Corporation Professionnelle des Médecins du Québec, review and expand the mechanisms that give credit for appropriate training to students who change from one discipline to another.*

9. *That all Canadian medical schools require family medicine clerkships or an equivalent family medicine clinical experience.*

The CFPC responded to the resolutions by stating that

The College of Family Physicians of Canada is committed to working towards implementing these Invitational Family Practice Committee recommendations. The College believes that this process should start at the medical school in each area with the postgraduate deans and the directors of family practice residency training programmes. At the same time, national policy will be developed by the National Advisory Committee on Family Medicine

Training (NACFMT), objectives will be developed by the postgraduate edu-
cation joint committee with its working groups in each discipline and the
CFPC Committee on Assessment and the postgraduate education joint com-
mittee will attempt to be as flexible as possible during this period of transition.

The CMA is represented on NACFMT by two members and shares equally with the CFPC the travel and maintenance expenses for the public member.

Hospital Accreditation

The matter of evaluation of hospitals received its baptism in 1911 when the Clinical Congress of Surgeons of North America set up a standardization committee to look at how a mechanism might be created for evaluating hospitals for their suitability to train surgeons. The committee's research led it to the conclusion that there were no guidelines, rules or benchmarks by which comparisons between hospitals could be made, and it informed the United States Congress of its findings. Subsequent to that, two decisions were made: one to introduce the category of Fellow of the American College of Surgeons, and the other to set up a program of standardization to determine a hospital's standing. In 1918, under the direction of the American College of Surgeons (ACS), the standardization program was initiated. By the mid-1940s more than 90% of the hospitals in the US and Canada met the minimum standards.

It was becoming logistically difficult for the ACS to manage and maintain the program, and so, in 1951, the Joint Commission on the Accreditation of Hospitals (JCAH), was formed. The first meeting of the JCAH was held in Chicago in 1951, and its membership was: American Hospital Association, seven members; American Medical Association (AMA), six members; ACS and the American College of Physicians (ACP), three members each; CMA, one member. The CMA's responsibility was one-twentieth of the budget; its representative was Dr. E. Kirk Lyon of Leamington with Dr. Arthur D. Kelly as his alternate.

It was agreed that the provision of field inspection service would be a responsibility of the constituent organizations, but all such field inspectors would be doctors of medicine, and the surveys would be conducted in a uniform manner. The standards followed would be those set out by the ACS. In Canada, regular inspection of hospitals of 50 beds or more had been carried out by the ACS inasmuch as the Canadian Hospital Association was not in a position to cover the costs.

In the same year, 1951, the General Council approved the following:

1. That the CMA should take the lead in setting up a body "for the Stan-
dardization and Approval of Hospitals in Canada."

2. *That cooperation be sought from other interested bodies such as the RCPSC, the Canadian Hospital Council (CHC) and the Catholic Hospital Association of Canada.*

3. *That a committee be set up to implement the foregoing recommendations and that such committee be expected to explore acceptable possibilities for financing this program.*

The CMA committee that was formed was named the Committee on Standardization of Hospitals, and a meeting was convened in Toronto on Jan. 18, 1952, attended by representatives of the CMA, the RCPSC and the CHC. That meeting recommended setting up a Canadian Committee on Hospital Accreditation (CCHA), with five members from the CMA, five from the CHC and two from the RCPSC. It was further agreed that the CMA membership would include a representative from l'Association des médecins de langue française du Canada (AMLFC) and that the CHC membership would include a representative of the Catholic Hospital Association. In 1953 the committee was renamed Canadian Commission on Hospital Accreditation. Funding assistance was sought from the Department of National Health and Welfare, but none was forthcoming. This led to concerns among the "trinity" over the costs of proposed activities and how these would be met. After hearing of these concerns, the 1953 General Council placed a moratorium on activities until such time as funding could be assured. Until then, the CMA would continue as a member of the joint commission.

By 1954, funding from participating organizations became available and the Canadian commission appointed its first surveyor, Dr. Karl E. Hollis, a former superintendent of the Sunnybrook Hospital in Toronto. Dr. Jean-Jacques Laurier of Montreal was appointed shortly afterwards and carried out surveys for 6 months of the year. Dr. Hollis carried out surveys for 9 months during the year. In 1954 in Canada there were 853 general hospitals of more than 25 beds, and of that number, the joint commission gave full approval to 230, provisionally approved 44 and did not approve 22. In 1956, 136 Canadian hospitals were surveyed; 87 were given full accreditation, 34 were provisionally accredited and 15 did not meet the requirements.

In his report to the 1956 General Council, Dr. Lyon reported that the AMA had formed a committee, known as the Stover Committee, to examine the operations of the joint commission and that the CMA had been invited to attend a meeting of that committee; this was found to be unfeasible, and Dr. Kelly submitted a detailed written opinion stating that the CMA was well satisfied with the joint commission's work. In his report on the activities of the Canadian Commission on Hospital Accreditation (CCHA), Dr. Lyon stated that it was assessing hospitals for the CMA's intern training program as well as carrying out surveys for the RCPSC graduate training programs. Dr. Laurier resigned and was replaced by Dr. M. Langlois. Dr. Hollis was designated the director of the CCHA. Following the two reports, there was much discussion on the subject of an all-Canadian survey program that led to approval of the following:

> *That this General Council is in favour of an all-Canadian programme of hospital survey and accreditation and recommends to the Executive Committee that this be instituted as soon as possible; and that the CMA indicate to the CCHA that when the latter is prepared to take over the whole programme, the CMA will withdraw from the Joint Commission and will make available the funds now going to the Joint Commission, to the Canadian Commission.*

At a Sept. 29, 1956 meeting of the CCHA, Jan. 1, 1958, was set as the date of the recommendation's implementation, and a liaison committee of four CMA members was established to work out the terms of separation from the joint commission. Subsequently, the date was changed to Jan. 1, 1959. Principles and operational methods were laid down. In 1958, 99 out of 128 surveys of Canadian hospitals were carried out by CCHA surveyors. In December 1958, the secretary of state granted the Canadian Council on Accreditation its Letters Patent and the CMA resigned its seat on the joint commission.

The CCHA now operated out of CMA house in Toronto. By 1960, the CMA was contributing $15 000 to the annual revenue of $36 501. Expenditures, however, amounted to more than $52 000, and the CMA announced that the membership fee in the CCHA would be increased to $4000 per seat. In 1960 the CCHA issued its first accreditation guide. There was no direct funding forthcoming from the federal government, but it did provide about $30 000 through a public health grant via the provinces on a per capita basis. Budgets continued to rise as the number of surveys increased and, beginning on Apr. 1, 1966, hospitals were charged for survey services with rates being based on the number of beds.

Accreditation surveys began to be done on facilities other than general hospitals, i.e., long-term, mental health and rehabilitation facilities. In 1988 the name of the council was changed to Canadian Council on Health Facilities Accreditation (CCHFA). Surveyors now included hospital administrators in addition to physicians and nurses. The council moved away from the concept of minimal standards to one of optimal achievable standards, defined "as the best possible level that can be reached taking into account the availability of resources."

The accreditation process by the CCHFA and its predecessors has gone on for 36 years, and during all that time the CMA has been an active participant in setting standards for institutions providing health care and in evaluating the degree of compliance with those standards. From 1969 to 1979, the Council on Health Services reported to the CMA Board of Directors and to the General Council on the activities of the CCHA; from 1979 onward this responsibility fell to the Council on Health Care. In 1994 the CMA had three seats on the Board of Directors of the CCHA, having given up one of its seats to the CFPC.

Connaught Laboratories Ltd.

In early 1975, the Toronto *Globe and Mail* published a series of articles on Connaught Laboratories Ltd. (CLL). Those articles, as well as subsequent articles and letters raised concerns about CLL products, concerns that were not only raised by physicians but also by some members of the general public. In discussions with CLL, the CMA indicated that it was willing to take action necessary to review the areas causing concern. This offer was accepted by CLL and the CMA established an expert committee to examine the criticisms and allegations and then report to the CMA on their validity. The committee was also to report on aspects of CLL's activities that might have a bearing on the matter. Implicit in the committee's terms of reference was the requirement to assess the nature of CLL's national and global roles and to determine if Canada needed a biologicals industry.

The Expert Committee was chaired by Dr. Robert C. Dickson of Halifax, a past president of the RCPSC; members were Dr. J. Alistair Dudgeon from the Hospital for Sick Children, London, England; Dr. Frank T. Perkins from WHO in Geneva; Dr. Jack C. Witt from the University of Manitoba; and Dr. Cornelia J. Baines from the Toronto Western Hospital. One of the first tasks of the committee was to familiarize itself with the role that the CLL and its predecessors had played in the production of biologicals in Canada. The history formed part of the committee's report to the CMA and is reproduced here in part.

The story begins with a University of Toronto professor, Dr. J.G. Fitzgerald, who, in 1913, began the production of an anti-rabies vaccine at 5, Queen's Park. There were other needs, however, in the field of biologicals. In 1914, diphtheria was still a major scourge in Canada. Antitoxin, required to save victims of diphtheria, could only be purchased from the New York Board of Health. As a consequence of cost and limited supplies (and therefore a precursor of what may occur in the future), many patients with diphtheria were unable to receive any treatment and others received only inadequate treatment.

In response to this need, Dr. Fitzgerald established an antitoxin laboratory in the Department of Hygiene where he was associate professor. This laboratory was to provide diphtheria antitoxin, at cost, for the Province of Ontario. By 1916 the provincial government was purchasing diphtheria antitoxin and distributing it free of charge within the province. The antitoxin was being sold to other provinces as well. Already the needs of Canada were being recognized and met.

As World War I unfolded, the need grew for tetanus antitoxin for the wounded. Colonel George Gooderham, Chairman of the Ontario Red Cross Society, asked Dr. Fitzgerald to meet this need. Production of tetanus antitoxin began in early 1915 under the direct supervision of Dr. Robert D. Defries. The antitoxin laboratory had become, in fact, a national serum institute. The antitoxin could only be produced with capital assistance from the Ministry of National Defence. So began a long relationship of interdependence between government and what was to become in 1917, the Connaught Antitoxin Laboratory.

Because facilities for antitoxin production had been inadequate, Colonel Gooderham had purchased in 1915, property north of Toronto at Steeles Avenue and Dufferin Street. There, a new laboratory opened in 1917, its name honouring the then Governor-General of Canada. For the remainder of the war, the Connaught Antitoxin Laboratory produced diphtheria and tetanus antitoxins, and rabies vaccines. Production of smallpox vaccine, using modern methods, was initiated.

The interval between World Wars I and II was characterized by great activity at "Connaught" under the leadership of Dr. Fitzgerald. In 1921, insulin was discovered by Dr. Frederick G. Banting and Charles H. Best, and in 1922, the Connaught Antitoxin Laboratory offered to assist in the production of insulin. To this day [1976], Connaught has provided virtually all of Canada's insulin requirements. Moreover, the institution has been in the forefront of development of new insulins beginning with protamine zinc insulin and including sulfonated insulin, developed by Dr. P. Maloney for use in patients who have developed antibodies to Insulin-Toronto.

In 1924, Dr. Fitzgerald, while in Europe, learned that Dr. Gaston Ramon at the Institut Pasteur was producing diphtheria toxoid. While antitoxins are used once illness is established, toxoids are used to prevent illness. Since the preventive approach is preferable, Dr. Fitzgerald cabled instructions to what was "Connaught Laboratories" to begin production of diphtheria toxoid. This was done under the supervision of Dr. Maloney.

When World War II began, Connaught Laboratories were able to pro-

tect Canada's armed forces by providing smallpox vaccine, tetanus toxoid, typhus vaccine, gas gangrene antitoxin, T.A.B. and dried blood serum. By the end of the war the laboratory was also manufacturing penicillin. Between 1939 and 1944, the staff increased from 252 to 900 persons. Since 1945, Connaught has given emphasis to the production of virus vaccines, including influenza, measles and mumps vaccines, but most importantly, poliomyelitis vaccine.

Reflecting the commitment to research was the adoption in 1946 of a new name for the institution: Connaught Medical Research Laboratories. During the 1950's and 60's, the Connaught enjoyed an excellent and worldwide reputation due to the scientific contributions of its staff, to its influence on foreign scientists through graduate training and research programmes, to the use of its products abroad, and in particular, to its role in poliomyelitis production. Its reputation was further enhanced by its contribution to the WHO's programme for the eradication of smallpox, a programme in which Drs. R.J. Wilson and P. Fenje were particularly involved.

By 1970 Connaught needed a lot of money in order to carry out renovations and construction of new facilities. Money was not forthcoming from either the University of Toronto or the Government of Ontario and so Connaught Medical Research Laboratories ended up being bought by the Canada Development Corporation and being renamed Connaught Laboratories Ltd. There was a view that the importance of research had diminished since the sale and it was against that background that the CMA's Expert Committee set out to review the criticisms and allegations.

These included:- a deteriorating scientific base; the purchase of foreign holdings; the need for a strong research and production base; termination of staff positions; demolition of buildings; a growing emphasis on production and profitability at the expense of research; regulatory exceptions made by the federal Health Production Branch; poor peer interchange; and failure to seek patent protection. Specific criticisms and allegations were levelled at the components of insulin production and distribution; smallpox, poliomyelitis, measles, mumps and rubella vaccines; human blood products; multi-antigen vaccines; diagnostics; and poor marketing practices of Protein-Purified Derivative (PPD).

The Committee carried out several onsite inspections and hearings, and interviews were carried out in Toronto and in Ottawa. Numerous interviews and discussions were held with CLL staff and many verbal and written submissions were received from members of the scientific community, some of whom had either worked at or had been closely associated with Connaught Laboratories Ltd. At the end of 1976, the Expert Committee submitted its *report to the CMA Board of Directors. The Committee found that many of the criticisms and allegations were without foundation; in particular, those directed against CLL in the areas of insulin production and smallpox vaccine that had received most of the publicity, were answered by the Committee's statement that in those areas, CLL were blameless. The Committee found that the fundamental functions of CLL had been conducted with a high degree of scientific integrity and that it had full confidence in the quality of Connaught products.*

Recommendations

A. National
   1. Canada needs and should support a biologicals industry for both national needs and the export market.
   2. Facilities producing biologicals should be financially supported by government subsidies.
   3. Such financial support should underwrite completely the cost of:
      ◆ Production of biologicals which are essential for the health needs of the nation but which may be financially unprofitable;
      ◆ Stockpiling of necessary reserves of biologicals to cope with national emergencies;
      ◆ Provision of biologicals to developing countries as may be deemed necessary;
      ◆ Research.

B. Connaught Laboratories Ltd.
   4. Connaught should be a facility producing biologicals for national needs and the export market. In addition to the subsidies for the function outlined in 3 above. Connaught must receive adequate funds so that its plant may meet modern standards. Renovation of some buildings and the construction of new ones are required.
   5. Research must gain much higher priority and this without delay in order that Connaught regain its position in the forefront of the development of biologicals.
   6. The new president of Connaught should be a scientist of high standing, preferably with an appreciation of the problems associated with the manufacture of biologicals.
   7. The scientific direction at Connaught requires complete reorganization with greater involvement of the senior staff in decision and policy-making. It is undesirable for the scientific director to be chairman of the board.
   8. An active cross-fertilization of ideas between universities and Connaught

should be encouraged. This could be achieved in a number of ways, such as:

- ◆ The establishment of a peer review committee involving Connaught and the university community to discuss research programs;
- ◆ The endowment of a university chair in a field relevant to Connaught;
- ◆ The secondment of staff both to and from Connaught and universities which may lead to the employment of new graduates by Connaught.

9. The lines of communication extending from production through quality control to the president must be clearly defined and clearly followed. With respect to release of products, the ultimate decision of the director of quality control must be final.

10. Connaught should continue in association with the Red Cross to provide blood products for Canada; collaboration with the Red Cross should be improved. Improvements must be made to the production facilities and procedures in the Blood Products Division at Connaught.

C. Bureau of Biologics (Canada)

11. The inadequacies in number of staff, laboratory space and animal facilities at BOB (Canada) must be corrected. The increase in staff must be sufficient to enable adequate site inspection of all facilities providing biologicals for Canada and to enable adequate laboratory control procedures to be carried out.

12. Research must have a high priority at BOB (Canada) so that it may keep abreast of technological developments in the control of biologicals. The responsibility for the safety and potency of biologicals used in Canada rests with the Canadian regulatory authority. A free exchange of ideas between Canadian producers and BOB (Canada) should be encouraged rather than allowing dependence on the standards and requirements of another country, the USA, to grow.

As this story of the CMA's involvement with CLL was being written in 1994, CLL was very much in the news as a result of the inquiry being conducted by Mr. Justice Horace Krever. The report of the CMA's Expert Committee was requested by the inquiry as part of its investigation into procedures that resulted in many Canadians being infected with hepatitis C and HIV in the early 1980s.

In early 1980, Dr. William A. Cochrane, chairman of the board and CEO of CLL, presented to the CMA Board of Directors a report on the progress made by the implementation of the 1976 recommendations. He noted that, whereas it was widely accepted that Canada should have a viable biologicals industry, neither the federal nor the provincial governments had come forward with any subsidies, limiting their involvement to lending a sympathetic ear to CLL's requests for aid. Renovations to the plant had been made and the scientific staff complement increased.

Health Care of the Elderly

The release in 1984 of the report of the CMA's Task Force on Allocation of Health Care Resources, in which much attention had been paid to Canada's elderly population, moved the Association to establish a special committee to examine the delivery of health care to the elderly and the chronically ill.

The task force had drawn attention to what it perceived as inadequate health care services for the elderly and the perpetuation of the philosophy of institutionalizing them. The task force had heard over and over again that independence and living in one's own home were rated very highly by the elderly. Examination of demographic statistics revealed that if the present philosophies and policies were continued, the demand for institutional facilities would produce unmanageable fiscal and logistical problems. In the words of one presenter to the task force, "Health services for the elderly, per se, are but one important element in the total spectrum of the provision of the needs of old people. Social services, income support, housing, transportation, employment opportunities and a host of other factors affect the health and quality of life of the elderly."

The Special Committee was chaired by Dr. Dorothy Ley from Beaverton, Ont.; members were Drs. A. Mark Clarfield from Montreal, Gordon Ferguson from Fredericton, W. Murray McAdam from Kitchener, Ont., Mark D. Schonfeld from Vancouver and Gerald R. Zetter from Edmonton. The committee's terms of reference were:

- *To carry out a comprehensive analysis of the current state of health care for the elderly in Canada.*
- *To identify the strengths and weaknesses of existing Canadian health care systems as they affect the elderly.*
- *To examine alternative models of health care delivery to the elderly and study their possible applications to the Canadian scene.*
- *To present realistic options and make recommendations to improve the system so as to provide humane and economical delivery of health care to the elderly.*
- *To recognize that while clinical issues are important, social, economic and political matters must be considered. The Committee will strive to make recommendations which will serve to maintain, protect and promote, the quality of life of Canada's elderly.*

In its early meetings the committee reviewed health care for the elderly in the provinces and territories and studied a number of reports relevant to that review. The committee then surveyed types and levels of care, recognizing that these terms are not synonymous. The view automatically equating aging with illness was found to be a common mindset, and this was something that had to be challenged and shown to be false.

Onsite visits were carried out both in Canada and the United Kingdom. In the latter, committee members were very impressed by the level of community support, the emphasis on rehabilitation both inside and outside institutions, and the effectiveness of the team approach. In Canada, the committee identified what it described as "fundamental problems," viz., confusion in terminology; fragmentation of care; inadequate community services; inadequate education in the teaching of geriatrics and gerontology; inappropriate attitudes towards the elderly; and inappropriate financing of health care.

The committee's final report, *The Elderly — Challenges for Today — Options for Tomorrow*, was approved by the Executive Committee and the Board of Directors early in 1987 and presented to the General Council in August of that year. The report contained recommendations aimed specifically at the CMA and its divisions; other recommendations were directed at governments.

In developing strategies for implementation of its recommendations, the committee established a set of principles that it considered essential in the provision of health care for the elderly. They were:

1. *Care of the elderly should be seen as mainstream health care.*
2. *No elderly person should be denied health care because of age.*
3. *Health care of the elderly should not be viewed as episodic; it is essential that each elderly person has a family physician familiar with that person.*
4. *The elderly must participate in planning services that affect them.*
5. *Geriatric patients should be assessed in their own environment.*
6. *High-quality health care in the home has to be supported by high-quality support services.*

Four components formed the core and focus of the report: education (professional and public), research, environment and service community.

The Board of Directors was aware that the philosophies espoused in the report and the implementation of the recommendations would require considerable attention by the Association, a view shared by the General Council. Arising from the discussion, it was approved that a Special Committee of the Board of Directors be formed to direct and monitor the implementation of the recommendations.

The CMA formed a presidential steering committee chaired by Dr. John O'Brien-Bell with members Dr. Ley; Dr. Rory H. Fisher from Sunnybrook Health Science Centre in Toronto; Ms. G. Parker, coordinator of a geriatric assessment and treatment centre; Mr. L. Batterson, president of the National Pensioners and Senior Citizens Federation; and Mr. A. Fagnant, administrator of a long-term health care facility.

The committee devised three strategies: dissemination of information, lobbying for change and direct action by the CMA. On the dissemination strategy, 4400 copies of the report were distributed through articles in the *Canadian Medical Association Journal (CMAJ)* and other publications, and meetings with interested groups. In February 1988, in Saskatoon, the committee took part in an international symposium on research and public policy on aging and health. Lobbying and direct action were undertaken on several fronts, particularly at provincial levels.

Among other areas studied by the committee were education, research, drug usage by the elderly, attitudes and ethics in health care of the elderly. The Department of National Health and Welfare made a grant of $45 000 to the CMA, indicating its supportive participation in areas of health care to the elderly under its jurisdiction. To permit the committee to continue its work, the CMA Board of Directors extended its life to August 1989. After that time, the ongoing work in connection with the implementation program would be taken over by existing departments within the Association.

In the period 1988 and 1989, the committee, now chaired by Dr. Ley and with the addition of Ms. P. Chartrand as an observer from the Department of National Health and Welfare, focused on five priorities: the need for improved education of health professionals in the care of the elderly; the needs of the demented elderly; medication use by the elderly; models of reimbursement for professionals caring for the elderly; and publication of the proceedings of a CMA–Department of National Health and Welfare co-sponsored national/international workshop called "Challenges and Changes in the Education of Health Professionals in the Care of the Elderly."

In December 1988, the Board of Directors approved the committee's Joint Statement on Education for Health and Social Service Professionals on Gerontology and Geriatrics. Four national associations — the Canadian Hospital Association, the Canadian Nurses Association, the Canadian Longterm Care Association and the Canadian Public Health Association — approved the joint statement. On the matter of medication use by the elderly, Dr. Ley reported to the 1989 General Council that efforts had been made to establish a functioning coalition of national organizations to address the issue of inappropriate medication use by the elderly, and recommended that the CMA join such a coalition and undertake appropriate activities commensurate with its expertise and resources. The committee encouraged the Council on Economics to pursue the issues outlined in a discussion paper titled *Payment for the Delivery of Physicians' Services to the Elderly*. The teaching of care of older adults who have impaired cognitive function was one of the major topics discussed at the aforementioned co-sponsored workshop.

In early 1990, Dr. Ley was invited to make a presentation on the CMA's policy and the work of its committee to the House of Commons Committee on Health and Social Affairs. In the same year, Grosvenor Press published *Guidance and Support in Caring for the Elderly* in English and French. The book was based on the CMA's Report on Health Care for the Elderly and was available for general sale.

Health Action Lobby (HEAL)

In February 1991, the federal budget indicated that "the existing freeze on Established Programme Financing (EPF) would be extended for a further three years." This action quite clearly showed that it was the government's intention to reduce its involvement in specific program transference of funds to the provinces for use in the delivery of health care. The CMA's concern over this action was shared by other organizations, and to address this concern a multi-organizational conference was held on June 19, 1991. At the conference an organization called the Health Action Lobby (HEAL) was formed with member organizations being the CMA, the Canadian Public Health Association, the Consumers' Association of Canada, the Canadian Hospital Association, the Canadian Nurses Association, the Canadian Psychological Association and the Canadian Longterm Care Association.

HEAL's mandate was to represent a cross-section of opinion of national health organizations in safeguarding the five basic principles of medicare. The initial approach was in three phases:

> (i)   To document the financial impact of the federal government's policies in the health sector;
>
> (ii) To identify and assess the various options available in terms of legislative, financial and administrative safeguards via expert reports, and from that develop a position paper;
>
> (iii) To communicate HEAL's proposals via provincial/territorial divisions and chapters.

The CMA Board of Directors, in October 1991, established an ad hoc steering committee to keep the CMA informed of HEAL's actions and to provide direction to the CMA staff. Committee members were Drs. Carole Guzmán, Hugh Scully and Colin McMillan. In January 1992, HEAL produced a consensus document titled *Medicare: A Value Worth Keeping*. The document contained the following five-point action plan:

(a) that the five principles of Medicare be incorporated into the proposed Canadian Constitution;

(b) that the federal government reaffirm its shared responsibility for the financing of the health care system;

(c) that a joint federal/provincial Health and Finance Ministers meeting be convened in the first six months of 1992;

(d) that a national "arms-length" monitoring process be established around interprovincial agreements and be enforced, where necessary, under federal legislation;

(e) that a national task force be established under the auspices of the Federal/Provincial/Territorial Conference of Ministers of Health, with representation from key stakeholders to define, clarify and expand on the criteria of Medicare.

On Feb. 4, 1992, HEAL made a presentation to the federal Constitutional Committee, stressing the need to include health care as a core value of Canadian society. This concept was the subject of debate at the 1992 General Council and led to a recommendation that the CMA oppose such a move. The motion was defeated. A motion was approved recommending that changes be made to the *Canada Health Act* to permit creative problem-solving initiatives and additional funding measures necessary for the continuance of implementation of the five principles of medicare and the survival of high-quality health care for all Canadians.

In 1993, HEAL decided to participate in the next federal election by campaigning on its five-point action plan. Involvement was to be nonpartisan and non endorsing of specific candidates. This did not preclude individual members of HEAL's member organizations from involving themselves in the election campaigns, on the understanding that they did not purport to represent HEAL.

During 1993 and 1994 HEAL produced the following papers:

✦ *The Importance of Federal Health Transfer Payments to Canada's National Health Care System.*

- *Committing to the Future of Canada's Health Programmes.* This paper was submitted to the federal minister of finance in February 1994, prior to the federal budget.
- *Getting to the Core of Comprehensiveness.* This was a discussion paper produced in March 1994.

Leadership Conferences 1989 to 1994

In 1989, the CMA turned its thinking inward and asked itself a number of searching questions: What is leadership and whence does it come? Who should provide health care? New knowledge and advances in technology have changed the practice of medicine and at the same time there have been many changes in the environment in which medical practice takes place. The health care system is publicly funded, and as the share of gross national product devoted to health care increased so, *pari passu,* has the direct involvement by governments in the area.

Out of the self-questioning grew the concept of a forum in which answers might be found. Thus it was that the first CMA leadership conference was born. The chosen site for the hoped-for revelations was the Delta Hotel in St. Sauveur, Que., and plans were made for a registration of 125 people. At the opening of the conference on Mar. 5, 1989, there were 230 registrants. They came from the CMA divisions, from the AMA and the Michigan State Medical Society, from all branches of medical practice and from federal and provincial governments. They had come together to increase their understanding of the multiplicity of factors affecting medical practice and to learn about leadership.

Prior to the conference, the CMA had defined the characteristics that it believed were paramount in leadership, viz., "The successful medical leader must be willing to direct change rather than react to it and, perhaps most importantly, must be capable of acting in concert with other leaders in the healthcare system." The roster of speakers was broad and catholic, and included a dean of law, a federal deputy minister of health, a former provincial minister of health, a dean of medicine, academics, ethicists and health care administrators.

Some speakers expressed concern over what they perceived as an abrogation of leadership roles by physicians and warned that non-physicians would step in to fill the gaps. Physicians who became managers were reminded that they should not forget that they represented patients, and that good patient care should never be compromised by governments' overwhelming fiscal concerns. During the sessions, it was stressed over and over that as long as physicians were in a reactive mode, medical leadership would be beyond their grasp.

A topic that received much attention was that of quality assurance. One speaker opined that quality in health care could only come from attention to structure and process, an approach that must begin in undergraduate studies and continue through the lifetime of medical practice. In his summary of the proceedings, Dr. A.R. Cox, vice-president of Health Sciences and Professional Schools, Memorial University of Newfoundland, challenged participants to meet again to discuss the topics on which consensus had not been reached, i.e., maintenance of competence, innovations in health care funding, physician reimbursement and the correction of regional disparities in the provision of health care. He believed that consensus had been reached on the need for improved communications and collaboration between all parties involved in health care; that there was a need for physicians in managerial positions; and the recognition of the importance of quality assurance.

If the idea of a leadership conference had arisen from a "navel-gazing exercise," it was clear from post-conference assessment that the CMA had provided a forum — previously lacking — for meaningful discussion on important matters. There had been a marked ripple effect from the conference, and the CMA was asked by many to repeat the event in 1990. Some participants went even further and suggested that the CMA leadership conferences should become an annual event. After review the CMA agreed to hold a second leadership conference in 1990.

The second conference was held in Ottawa from Mar. 1 to 3, 1990, and its theme was allocation and decision making: balancing access and quality with affordability. The conference opened with Sister Nuala P. Kenny, Head of the Department of Pediatrics at Dalhousie University in Halifax, reviewing the ethical issues inherent in health care planning and the many conflicts that physicians have to face in decision making. Much time was devoted by some speakers to the factors leading to choices and to the apparently inevitable question of the rationing of health care when faced with cost constraints. A presentation of note on this subject was given by Dr. A. Mark Clarfield, chief of geriatrics at the Sir Mortimer B. Davis-Jewish General Hospital in Montreal, when he described the care of the elderly. Professor Greg Stoddart from the Centre for Health Economics and Policy Analysis, McMaster University, Hamilton, Ont., presented a paper outlining the problems of transferring new knowledge into clinical practice. Professor Harry E. Emson, from the Department of Pathology, Royal University Hospital, Saskatoon, presented views on cost–benefit factors, including the sometime absence thereof, in screening procedures. A topic that stimulated discussion in both plenary and group sessions was the allocation of scarce health care resources and ways and means whereby optimum use could be obtained. In the final session, a panel wrestled with two case vignettes in which participants played roles revealing how choices about the allocation of resources have to be weighed and how implemented when all aspects are taken into consideration.

The CMA decided that the conferences should be held annually, and the Third Annual CMA Leadership Conference opened in Ottawa on Feb. 28, 1991, and ran until Mar. 2. The theme was autonomy and accountability. The program was designed to include contentious issues and the speakers were selected on the basis that their presentations would engender lively debates. The conference opened with a debate titled "Physician autonomy is dead," and saw Dr. John O'Brien-Bell, a CMA past president, square off against the Hon. Monique Bégin, a former federal minister of national health and welfare; the debate was moderated by Ms. Pamela Wallin, CTV's national affairs correspondent. Among the next presenters was the Hon. Mitchell Sharp who had been federal minister of finance when medicare was introduced and who described to his audience the paradox created by the successes in medical care leading to people living longer and falling prey to illnesses in later life. He stressed that there would never be enough money to provide everything for everyone and warned that if the medical profession did not help governments to contain costs, governments would take unilateral action unacceptable to the profession.

There were divergent views as to whether or not physicians had autonomy. The spectre of two-tier medicine crept in to some of the debates, particularly the one in which the health care industry was compared to the automobile manufacturing industry. Speakers from the United Kingdom and the United States highlighted the good and the bad in health care in their respective countries. The consensus was that physicians needed to become more cost-conscious and that autonomy was not incompatible with accountability.

The Fourth CMA Leadership Conference was held in Ottawa from Feb. 27 to 29, 1992. Its theme was quality of care — effectiveness, efficiency, excellence. Can they coexist? The objectives were: to emphasize and demystify quality management from theory to practice; to identify and debate roles for physicians in quality management; and to position the CMA as a leader and a resource on quality of care issues. Close to 300 people registered to hear presentations from Canadian physician leaders, international experts and those who did not have kind words for the present systems of health care delivery. The keynote speaker was Dr. Donald Berwick, a pediatrician and principal investigator for the US National Demonstration Project on Quality Improvement in Health Care. It was his opinion that efficacy, appropriateness, execution and values were the cornerstones of research into quality of health care; furthermore, he presented nine myths connected to the quality of care and dispelled each one with practical realities. Speakers urged their audiences to be more understanding of the needs of patients and to be aware that the age of paternalism and diagnosis sugar coating was past.

Dr. Pranlal Manga, a health economist with the Health Administration Program at the University of Ottawa, told his audience that physicians were going the wrong way to improve the quality of care, even though their efforts were well intentioned, and that the objective should be the optimization, not the maximization, of health care. He defined maximization as "using the necessary resources to continuously improve the health of a single patient or patients of one physician or hospital" whereas optimization was seen as "a much more holistic view toward making the best use of health resources for the benefit of the entire patient population." Mr. Ovide Mercredi, national chief of the Assembly of First Nations, spoke about patients' culture and how it affected the quality of care. He asked that health care providers to the indigenous peoples be sensitive to cultural issues when making decisions.

One plenary session was devoted to "crystal-ball gazing." Titled "Looking Ahead: Public Trust, Professional Progress and Future Challenges" it brought together speakers from the general public, medical licensing authorities, governments and practising physicians. Dr. Richard S. Stanwick, a Winnipeg pediatrician and medical officer of health for that city, described a program that took health care to "street people" — a culture/environment with non-traditional patient–physician relationships made necessary by inadequate conventional services.

The CMA reviewed each conference critically and took corrective action where weaknesses were found. Success brought with it pressures to maintain the high standards. The first four conferences had not been financially self-sustaining, but it was believed that the annual event was on its way to becoming the premier health conference in Canada and that it should continue. Many suggestions for themes were received, and the CMA's Planning Committee considered other topics, including updating of matters discussed at earlier conferences. It was decided that, for the foreseeable future, the site of the conferences would be Ottawa.

The Fifth CMA Annual Conference was held from Feb. 25 to 27, 1993, and the theme was "Patient–Physician Relationships: Understanding The Message." The objectives were: to increase awareness of physician leaders about patient–physician communication issues in a complex, ever-changing world; to make those leaders aware of solutions to problems arising from such issues; and to help practitioners cope with new roles. More that 250 people registered for the conference. There was agreement among a number of the speakers that the traditional patient–physician relationship must be rethought, not to introduce something new, but to bring back something that had been lost. It was argued that there was an increasing tendency for care, in its purest sense, to be lost in the use of technology. There was a need for teaching attitudes to change, particularly in the way language and listening skills were taught. Video presentations were being used more frequently to explain to patients detailed, comprehensive and specific information on procedures and outcomes, enabling them to be better informed in decision making. Not everyone was enthralled with the use of such technology, arguing that it was impersonal and did not give the patient opportunities to express any doubts and fears.

The word "unconventional" well described the way in which Dr. William B. Dalziel, an Ottawa geriatrician, greeted the participants in his workshop on doctors' relationships with elderly patients. By making his audience use earplugs, glasses and physical restraints, he gave them some idea of the frustrations experienced by the elderly. He recommended most strongly that, when dealing with a state of depression in the elderly, physicians should look to environmental/situational factors as a possible cause before seeking solutions in pharmaceutical products.

The theme of the Sixth CMA Annual Leadership Conference, held from Mar. 3 to 5, 1994, was "Evidence and Experience: Rediscovering Practice-Relevant Research." This theme was chosen as a result of concerns about health care expenditures that, along with often ill-defined clinical decision processes, had stimulated interest in evidence-based medicine (EBM). The 300 registrants heard from speakers that EBM places less value on clinical experience, the study of physiologic principles, traditional medical training and common sense, in favour of moving to systematic observation, understanding of rules of evidence and critical interpretation of original literature.

In response to this "creed," many questions were raised about the need for physicians to become believers; many of the physicians present believed that EBM denigrated experience, clinical judgement and, in the end, the art of medicine. It was postulated, heretically in the views of some, that many physicians learn about advances in medicine in the same way that their patients do — through the news media! The increased use of computer technology was seen as one way in which physicians could remain *au fait* with advances in medicine.

Dr. Bruce P. Squires, the editor-in-chief of CMA publications, told his audience that the dissemination of information had been made more difficult due to increased volume and complexity. The *CMAJ* had addressed the problem by instituting specific changes, including development of the structured abstract, a focused clinical review of relevant literature dealing with a specific topic and the development of practice guidelines. Professor Jonathan Lomas, of the Department of Clinical Epidemiology and Biostatistics, McMaster University, gave the closing address, "Linking Research Evidence and Clinical Epidemiology and Biostatistics," in which he advanced the view that EBM would be of little use to "frontline physicians," that it is loved by paying agencies, which believe it has potential for cost containment, and that it should be directed to the attention of policy makers rather than to clinicians.

The CMA took the opportunity at the conference to release its bilingual publication *Guidelines for Canadian Clinical Practice Guidelines*. These guidelines had been prepared under the direction of the Council on Health Care and Promotion, and input had come from more than 40 health organizations, all of which had endorsed the final version. The booklet contains 14 guidelines set out in three categories — philosophy and ethics, methods, and implementation and evaluation — designed to assist physicians in making clinical decisions and improving the quality of care that they deliver.

Staff of Aesculapius. This replica of the model displayed in CMA Alberta House was presented on behalf of the Alberta Medical Association by its president, Dr. R.K.C. Thomson (right) to the Canadian Medical Association on Dec. 7, 1962, and accepted by Dr. M.R. MacCharles of Winnipeg, President of the CMA.

Chapter X

MYTHOLOGY, HERALDRY, INSIGNIA AND AWARDS

IT IS DIFFICULT to understand why the argument over what is the "official" badge of medicine continues to find its way into the media and into the corridors of CMA House. In the fall of 1994, a major Canadian newspaper carried a series of letters from protagonists of various views, demonstrating their respective biases in verbiage worthy of the pamphleteers of earlier times. Let it be clearly understood that there is absolutely no reason for medicine to be associated with the wand and two snakes, whether or not the wand is surmounted by two wings. The fact that various medical units of the armed services in some countries, including Canada, still have this caduceus as their insignia, should be discounted as proof that the caduceus represents medicine. In the words of Dr. Arthur D. Kelly, "The Caduceus of Hermes or Mercury should be relegated to the banks, the postal services and oil companies for their properly commercial purposes." After all, Mercury's reputation as a thorough rascal would hardly be one with which the members of the medical profession would wish to be associated! Son of Zeus and Maia, said to have been born on Mount Cyllene in Greece, one of his first recorded crimes was the theft of some of Apollo's cows. He was appointed messenger of the gods, and one of his duties was to escort the souls of the dead to the Underworld, at which time he used the caduceus as a protection. The caduceus originated from a herald's staff, and one day Mercury separated two serpents that were fighting and had become entwined on his staff. Because snakes were involved and were thought to have healing powers, the caduceus with the two serpents was mistakenly thought to be the symbol associated with medicine, a mistake perpetuated over the years. It is the Rod of Asklepios that is the true symbol of the art and science of medicine.

In the Old Testament (Numbers 21: 8–9), there is written, "And the Lord said unto Moses, Make thee a fiery serpent and set it upon a pole; and it shall come to pass, that every one that is bitten, when he looketh upon it, shall live. And Moses made a serpent of brass and put it upon a pole, and it came to pass, that if a serpent had bitten any man, when he beheld the serpent of brass, he lived." Now Moses lived many years before Asklepios, but it seems probable that the symbol was adopted as one of healing and handed down through the years.

Asklepios, also known by the Romans as Aesculapius, was said to be the son of Apollo and the nymph Coronis. He was brought up by centaurs in the mountains of Greece. He had four children: two sons, Machon and Podalarius, both of whom became military surgeons, and two daughters, Hygeia and Panacea. The opening sentence of the Hippocratic Oath reads, "I swear by Apollo the physician, by Aesculapius, Hygeia and Panacea, and I take witness all the gods, all the goddesses, to keep according to my ability and my judgement of the following Oath." Asklepios was worshipped from 400 BC to 300 AD in many temples where psychotherapeutic medicine was practised by his followers, known as Asklepiads. Asklepios was killed by a thunderbolt from his father Apollo, who believed that his son's medical work was interfering with nature and rendering man immortal.

For centuries, serpents were held to have the power of healing, said to arise from their ability to shed their skin and appear anew. The parallel was drawn that man could shed his disease and emerge anew in health. As far as the Rod of Asklepios is concerned, the combination of the staff and the snake is said to arise from an incident in which the snake restored life to a dead child and then entwined itself on the staff.

Armorial Bearings

In the CMA archives is a small green-covered booklet titled *Origin and Organization of the Canadian Medical Association with the Proceedings of the Meetings, held in Quebec, October 1867 and Montreal, September 1868*. On its cover is emblazoned what appears to be a device. It is the figure of Asklepios on a shield, holding the staff and the serpent, with the whole being surmounted by a crown. A garland of maple leaves and a beaver, surrounded by a belt signifying unity or banding together, and the motto *ope doctrinae levamen*, embellish the device. The motto was translated by a classical scholar as "aid or succour by the resources of knowledge." The booklet was printed by John Lovell, Printer, St. Nicholas Street, Montreal.

Enquiries were made to the College of Arms in London and to the Lord Lyon of Scotland in Edinburgh to see if this device had been patented for the Association. It was learned that there was no record of the device being patented by either. The College of Arms pointed out that it was improper for the crown to be used without proper authority. It was later learned that the device had appeared on medical publications prior to the creation of the CMA, also published by John

Lovell. *The British American Journal (Second Series) 1860–1862* and *The Canadian Medical Journal and Monthly Record of Medical and Surgical Science 1864–1872* both bore the device, and it was subsequently used in the *Canadian Medical and Surgical Science Journal 1873–1888* and its successor, *The Montreal Medical Journal 1888–1910*. Because John Lovell had used the device on the first two publications, it is highly likely that he had done the same for the booklet.

In July 1972, CMA President Dr. Gustave Gingras directed that enquiries be made to the College of Arms as to armorial bearings for the CMA. The College of Arms had its beginning when King Edward I appointed two heralds, Norroy and Surroy. In 1411 Henry IV appointed Clarenceux, but it was Henry V who proclaimed that no one could use armorial bearings without permission from either the king or his heralds. This was upheld by the Earl Marshal's Court, but it ruled that the king was the ultimate authority. It was Henry V who instituted the Garter King of Arms and his Pursuivant, Blue Mantle. There are 10 degrees of armorial bearings; the CMA, if it were granted them, would fall into the 10th category, described as "arms of concession," more commonly known as "augmentations."

Correspondence between the CMA and the College of Arms led to Dr. John S. Bennett visiting the college, where he had a number of meetings with the Windsor Herald of Arms, A. Colin Cole, Esquire. Records in the college library, dating back to the mid 1300s, were viewed, as were robes of office and livery. A prescribed form of application, known as a prayer, was required; this was to be handwritten and submitted to His Grace the Duke of Norfolk, Earl Marshal and Hereditary Marshal of England. The prayer was handwritten by Dr. Bennett, and in December 1972, the CMA was informed that it had been found acceptable by the Earl Marshal and the Kings of Arms. Suggestions as to what should be depicted in the armorial bearings were relayed to the college, and out of these was developed a number of draft designs. In early 1973, the CMA Board of Directors reviewed a design, which it approved after minor alterations in June 1973. Dr. Gingras unveiled a painting of the Association's new armorial bearings, as approved by the Kings of Arms, at the ceremonial session of the joint CMA and BMA annual meeting in Vancouver. Several months later, letters patent, depicting the armorial bearings, badge and supporters, signed by the three Kings of Arms — Garter, Clarenceux, Norroy and Ulster — were prepared and illuminated, the text being in Canada's two official languages.

The English version of the letters patent reads:

To All and Singular to whom these Presents shall come, Sir Anthony Richard Wagner, Knight Commander of the Royal Victorian Order, Garter

Principal King of Arms, John Riddell Bromhead Walker, upon whom has been conferred the Decoration of the Military Cross, Clarenceux King of Arms, and Walter John George Verco, Esquire, Commander of the Royal Victorian Order, Norroy and Ulster King of Arms, Greetings. Whereas Gustave Gingras, Esquire, Companion of the Order of Canada, Commander of the Most Venerable Order of St. John of Jerusalem, Doctor of Medicine of the University of Montreal, Fellow of the Royal College of Physicians and Surgeons of Canada, President of the Canadian Medical Association, hath represented to the Most Noble Bernard Marmaduke, Duke of Norfolk, Knight of the Most Noble Order of the Garter, Knight Grand Class of the Most Excellent Order of the British Empire, upon whom has been conferred the Territorial Decoration, Earl Marshal and Hereditary Marshal and One of Her Majesty's Most Honourable Privy Council, that The Canadian Medical Association was founded on the Ninth day of October 1867 and by the enactment of His Majesty King Edward VII by and with the advice and consent of the Senate and House of Commons of Canada on the Nineteenth day of May 1909 was constituted a corporation in the name of The Canadian Medical Association, and has among its Objects (provided for by Chapter 62, 1909 as amended by Chapter 73, 1959 of the Statutes of Canada) the promotion of medical and related arts and sciences and the maintenance of the honour and interests of the medical profession: the furtherance of measures designed to improve the public health and to prevent disease and disability: the promotion of the improvement of medical services, however rendered, and assisting in the promotion of measures designed to improve standards of hospital and medical services: That the affairs of The Canadian Medical Association are conducted by a Board of Directors which said Board is desirous of having Armorial Ensigns duly assigned with lawful authority and therefore he, as President of the Association and on behalf of the said Board of Directors, hath represented the favour of His Grace's Warrant for Our granting such Arms and Crest and in the same Patent such Supporters and such Device or Badge We may consider fit and proper to be borne and used by The Canadian Medical Association upon its Common Seal or otherwise according to the Laws of Arms, And forasmuch as the said Earl Marshal did by Warrant under his hand and Seal bearing date the Eighteenth day of December 1973 authorize and direct Us to grant and assign such Arms and Crest, such Supporters and such Device or Badge accordingly, Know Ye therefore that We, the said Garter, Clarenceux, and Norroy and Ulster in pursuance of His Grace's Warrant, and by Letters Patent of Our several Offices to each of Us respectively granted, do by these presents grant and assign unto The Canadian Medical Association the Arms following, that is to say: .

Or a Rod of Aesculapius entwined with Maple all Gules on a Bordure Gules four Fleur de lys and as many Leopard's Faces alternately Or. And for the Crest Or a Wreath Argent and Gules Rising from within a Chaplet of Maple Leaves veined Or a Sun in Splendour Or, Mantled Gules doubled Argent and Or as the same as are in the margin hereof made plainly depicted. And by the Authority aforesaid We do further grant and assign the following Device and Badge, that is to say:- A Rod of Aesculapius as in the Arms entwined by a Crown Rayonny Or as herein depicted, And by the Authority aforesaid, I, The said Garter do by these Presents further grant and assign unto The Canadian Medical Association the Supporters following, that is to say:- On the Dexter side a Moose and on the Sinister side a Grizzly Bear both proper and gorged with a Chaplet of Maple Leaves Or, as the same as are in the margin hereof more plainly depicted, the whole to be borne and used for- ever hereafter by The Canadian Medical Association upon its Common Seal or otherwise, according to the Laws of Arms. In witness thereof We, the said Garter, Clarenceux, and Norroy and Ulster, Kings of Arms have to these Pre- sents subscribed Our names and affixed the Seals of Our several Offices this Twentyninth day of March in the Twentythird year of the Reign of Our Sov- ereign Lady, Elizabeth the Second by the Grace of God of the United King- dom, Canada and Her Realms and Territories, Queen, Head of the Commonwealth, Defender of the Faith and in the year of Our Lord One Thousand nine hundred and seventyfour.

Signed by Anthony R. Wagner, Garter
J.R.B. Walker, Clarenceux
Walter J. Verco, Norroy and Ulster

Beneath the armorial bearings is a scroll inscribed with the words
INTEGRITATE ET MISERICORDIA

The Shield

The main feature of the shield is the Rod of Asklepios entwined with maple leaves; around the edge of the shield are the heads of four leopards representing the Commonwealth and four fleur de lys representing the French role in Canadian history.

The Crest

The crest is a rising sun, symbolic of health and energy. The wreath is made up of white and red bands, a reminder of the striped poles which once designated the location of surgeon-barbers.

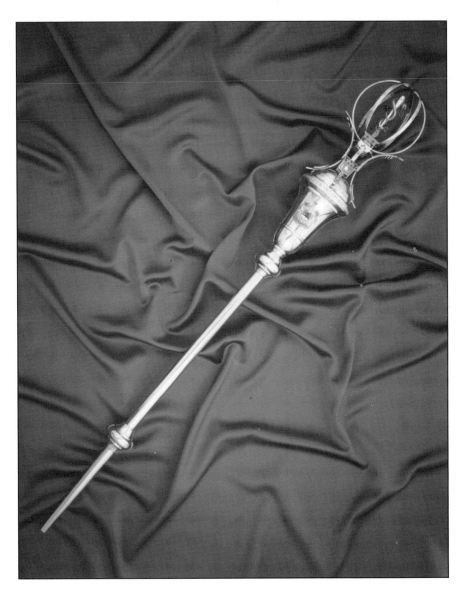

The CMA mace, gift of some of the past presidents of CMA. A showcase for the mace was presented to the CMA by BMA Scottish Council in 1969.

The Device and Badge

As described in the letters patent, the device and badge of the Association is the Rod of Asklepios, surrounded by maple leaves and surmounted by a crown whose finials are golden rays.

Insignia

The Seal

Up to 1961, the seal of the Association consisted of a circle containing the Rod of Asklepios with maple leaves, with "Canadian Medical Association" inscribed within the perimeter and the wording "Founded AD 1867" across the centre. In 1961, the General Council approved a new format for the seal, and it is now a circle in the centre of which is the Rod of Asklepios surrounded by maple leaves and with the figures 1867 across the centre. Around the perimeter is inscribed "The Canadian Medical Association — L'Association Médicale Canadienne."

Logo

The logo of the Association is the Rod of Asklepios without the maple leaves, placed in the centre of a stylized C. It appears on CMA letterhead, on the cover of the CMA journals, on the covers of Association books and on documents such as policy summaries and press releases.

The CMA Mace

At the 99th annual meeting of the CMA in June 1966, a number of past presidents gathered together to discuss what they might do in the way of making a gift to the Association in recognition of its centennial in 1967. Dr. Arthur D. Kelly, writing under the sobriquet "Aequanimitas" in the *Canadian Medical Association Journal* dated June 10, 1967, related how the matter was resolved.

> *Just before I left Edmonton, I went up to the President's suite for some refreshment to restore my wasted spirits. I was invited to join a group of Past-Presidents who found themselves standing together at the bar. They had formed an ad hoc committee from force of habit! The first order of business was an expression of surprise and gratification that so many Past-Presidents — twelve out of eighteen living — were able to attend the Annual Meeting. Someone proposed that we consider a suitable date for the next meeting of the Committee. Then an intermission to recharge the water pitcher. Just as I was slipping away there was mention of a mace.* (Eyewitness account by an unidentified person.)

Photograph taken at the 100th CMA Annual Meeting – Québec, Quebec, June 9–17, 1967.

The photo shows the past presidents who attended the meeting. They are L-R (back row): Dr. Renaud Lemieux, Dr. Arthur VanWart, Dr. Morley A. R. Young, Dr. William W. Wigle (Dr. Wigle portrayed the first CMA president, Sir Charles Tupper), Dr. Robert O. Jones, Dr. E. Kirk Lyon, (front row): Dr. Jack F.C. Anderson, Dr. Gordon S. Fahrni, Dr. Duncan Graham, Dr. Sclater Lewis, Dr. Norman H. Gosse, Dr. G.W. Halpenny.

So it was that the idea of an Association mace was born. Discussions with Henry Birk and Sons led to the CMA's ground rules for the manufacture of the mace:

❖ The mace was to be representative of Canada and its 10 provinces, with space left for subsequent territorial representation.

❖ The mace was to be distinctly "medical" in design.

❖ The CMA crest was to be incorporated.

❖ Inscriptions were to be in both official languages.

❖ The finished article had to be forward-looking both in concept and decor.

❖ The shaft of the mace to be hollow so that it could contain a scroll naming the original donors.

It was agreed by the past presidents that they would meet the costs of the making of the mace and that arrangements whereby future past presidents could contribute to a mace fund would be defined. On the matter of contributions, Dr. Kelly reported that "currency regulations which made it difficult for His Royal Highness, Prince Philip, Duke of Edinburgh, to remit his share, were surmounted and the appeals of his Canadian deputy president (Dr. E.K. Lyon) for a refund, on the grounds of 'double taxation' for the 1959 year of office, were ignored."

Executed in gold, silver gilt and enamel, the mace measures 105 centimetres overall. The central figure on the head of the mace is the Rod of Asklepios entwined with maple leaves. The Arms of Canada are displayed on two sides. The Arms of the Canadian Provinces and Territories decorate the arcs, which meet at the top, and the title of the Association is executed in relief in both official languages. The inscription reads: "Presented to The Canadian Medical Association on the occasion of the 100th Anniversary, 1967, by the living Past-Presidents."

The mace can be disassembled into three separate parts; the shaft is hollow and contains the scroll on which are penned the names of the original donors and the year in which they assumed the office of Association president. These are the names and dates:

Dr. Duncan Graham*	1940	Dr. Gordon S. Fahrni*	1941
Dr. D. Sclater Lewis*	1943	Dr. Frederick G. McGuiness	1947
Dr. Jack F.C. Anderson*	1949	Dr. Norman H. Gosse*	1950
Dr. Charles W. Burns	1953	Dr. J. Renaud Lemieux*	1956
Dr. Morley A.R. Young*	1957	Dr. Arthur F. VanWart*	1958
HRH Prince Philip	1959	Dr. E. Kirk Lyon*†	1959
Dr. R. MacGregor Parsons	1960	Dr. Gerald W. Halpenny*	1961

Presidential Badge and Chain of Office.

Dr. Malcolm R. MacCharles	1962	Dr. William W. Wigle*	1963
Dr. Frank A. Turnbull	1964	Dr. Robert O. Jones*	1965

†Deputy president *Attended presentation.

The presentation of the mace to the CMA was made by the senior past president, Dr. D. Graham, at the Association's centennial meeting in Quebec City, June 1967.

In 1969, a meeting was held in Edinburgh to commemorate the 10th anniversary of the conjoint BMA and CMA annual meeting in that city and to honour Dr. James Hamilton who had served as chairman of the Committee on Arrangements for the 1959 meeting. Dr. Ross M. Matthews, president of the CMA, was presented with a handsome display case for the mace by the Scottish medical fraternity. When not in use, the mace is displayed in that case at CMA House. At official functions such as General Council and the ceremonial session of the annual meeting, the mace is borne in procession.

Presidential Badge and Chain of Office

Dr. John Ferguson, a charter member and past president of the OMA, donated a presidential badge of office to the CMA. Dr. Ferguson was described as "the Nestor of the Canadian Medical Profession" and so highly was he regarded that, in 1930, at the age of 80, he became president of the OMA. The presidential badge was presented by Dr. Alexander Primrose to the CMA's president, Dr. Harvey Smith, at the CMA's 62nd annual meeting in Vancouver in late June 1931.

The badge is in the form of a pear-shaped medallion worked in solid gold. It is suspended in pendant style from a smaller medallion bearing the figure of Hygeia. On the lower rim of the medallion is inscribed "Canadian Medical Association" and below this the Association's founding date MDCCCLXVII. On the upper rim is inscribed "Praesidis Insigne." Surrounding the medallion are the shields bearing the arms of the Canadian provinces and territories. The smaller medallion depicts the Rod of Asklepios. The upper portion of the chain consists of four maple leaves (two on each side), linked in stylized form and attached to a red ribbon. The ribbon collar joins in framed letters CMA from which the smaller medallion hangs with the larger medallion suspended below. The badge was designed and executed by Ryrie-Birks of Toronto.

Over the 63 years since the badge was presented, presidents and deputy presidents have worn it as occasion demanded; five people have been entitled to wear it during their joint-presidency of the CMA and other national medical

President's Lady's Brooch.

organizations. The names and dates are in the chapter on International Health. Two deputy presidents have worn the badge — Dr. E. Kirk Lyon in 1959–60 and Dr. E.W. Barootes in 1976–77.

President's Lady's Brooch

Dr. Harry D. Roberts of St. John's, CMA president 1971–72, presented to the Association a beautiful brooch to be worn by the president's lady on ceremonial occasions. The design features the Rod of Asklepios with maple leaves in an oval setting; the whole is executed in gold and is encrusted with precious stones.

Past President's Pin

This is of teardrop shape and is suspended from a bar inscribed with "Past-President." In the centre of the medal is the figure of Hygeia surrounded by the inscription "Canadian Medical Association." The recipient's name and date of presidential office is inscribed on the back of the medal. The French equivalents, "Ancien président and "L'Association médicale canadienne," are inscribed when indicated.

Past President's Spouse's Pin

For the past president's lady there is a handsome miniature replica of the president's lady's brooch. When the spouse is male, appropriate mementoes, such as engraved cuff links, are presented.

Badge of Office of the Chairperson of the Board of Directors

In 1973, Dr. Gustave Gingras donated a badge to be worn by the chairperson of the CMA Board of Directors. The obverse of the badge features the Rod of Asklepios with maple leaves, surrounded by the inscription "Canadian Medical Association — L'Association médicale canadienne: Chairman of the Board — Président du Conseil." On the reverse is inscribed "Presented by Dr. G. Gingras, OC, MD, FRCPC. President 1972–73." The badge is fastened with a red ribbon.

Senior Member's Pin

Nominations for senior membership in the CMA are submitted by its divisions. The criteria for nomination are: CMA membership for 10 years immediately prior to nomination; the nominee to be aged 65 or older; and to be in good standing in his/her division. The membership requires the unanimous consent of the CMA Board of Directors.

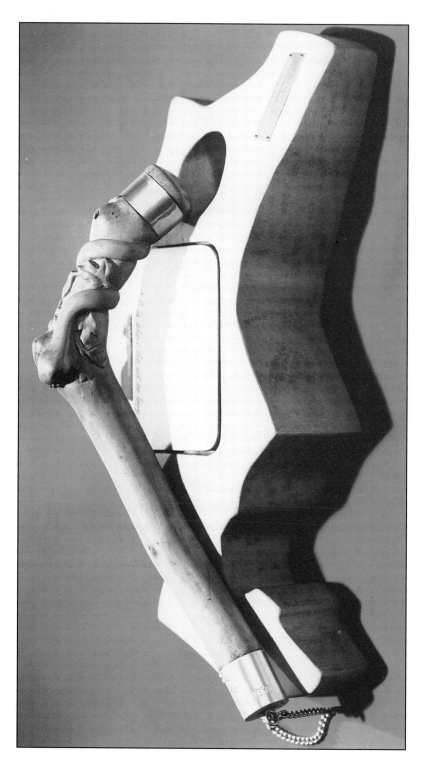

Gavel fashioned from a branch of Hippocates' plane tree on the Island of Cos. Presented by Dr. Wilder Penfield on the occasion of the CMA Annual Meeting in Montreal, June 1961.

The pin is shield-shaped surmounted by a crown rayonny and depicts the CMA badge, with the figures 1867. A banner gules (red) surrounds the shield. Below the banner is inscribed "Senior Member." When the pin is awarded to a francophone member, the appropriate wording is "L'Association médicale canadienne" and "membre émérite." The name of the recipient is inscribed on the reverse.

Board of Directors Member's Pin

At the beginning of their tenure on the CMA Board of Directors, members are presented with a pin, replicating the Association's logo.

Commemorative Pin

In 1987, a gilt enamel pin was fashioned to commemorate the CMA annual meeting in Charlottetown in August of that year. Although it was never an official CMA pin, the idea for the pin came from Dr. Athol L. Roberts who became president of the CMA at that meeting. The centre of the pin depicts the provincial arms of Prince Edward Island, with the date 1987; the perimeter of the pin carries the following gold lettering on a black background: Canadian Medical Association — Charlottetown, PEI.

Gavels

Details of the gavels owned by the Association are as follows.

1924   Presented by the Ottawa Medico-Chirurgical Society
1931   Presented by Dr. T. Clarence Routley, general secretary 1922 to 1954
1961   Presented by Dr. Wilder Penfield *
1962   Presented by Dr. Arthur D. Kelly, general secretary 1954 to 1966
1975   Presented by Dr. J. Douglas Wallace, general secretary 1970 to 1976
1981   Presented by Dr. Gordon S. Fahrni, CMA president 1941–42
        to be used at meetings of the past presidents of the CMA
1986   Presented by Dr. Léo-Paul Landry, secretary general 1986 —

Other insignia are: dark blue ties bearing a depiction of the device and badge; blazer badges depicting the shield and the motto; and an insignia that would have brought pleasure to lovers of automobile badges. Unfortunately, the

---

* This gavel was fashioned from a piece of the plane tree under which Hippocrates was reputed to have taught on the island of Cos and is in the shape of the outline of the island. The base is made of Canadian maple. Dr. Penfield made his gift at the time of his receiving senior membership in the Association.

ties and blazer and automobile badges are no longer available. It was in 1924 that the automobile badge was first introduced, primarily for the purpose of identifying the car as belonging to a CMA member. It is unfortunate that such identification is contraindicated in today's world, but in 1924 and 1925 nearly 500 were bought by CMA members. The emblem was designed to be attached to the car's grille and executed in blue enamel baked on French bronze. The design was that of the CMA's seal as described earlier. The price of $2.50 included postage and packing; each emblem was serially numbered, and the number and the name of its owner were recorded in a logbook kept by the general secretary.

President's Gown of Office
This gown was presented to the Association in 1966 by Dr. Arthur F. VanWart, CMA president 1958–59. The gown is faced with red, overlaid with gold trim.

President-Elect's Gown of Office
This gown is faced in green.

Chairperson of the Board of Directors' Gown of Office
In 1967, Dr. Gordon S. Fahrni presented a gown to be worn on ceremonial occasions by the person holding the office of chairperson of the Board of Directors. The gown is faced in red overlaid with silver trim.

Speaker's Gown of Office
In 1971, the president of the OMA, Dr. James T. Colquhoun from Thunder Bay, on behalf of the OMA, presented a gown to be worn by the speaker of General Council. The gown is faced in red, with red piping on the sleeves.

Other gowns of office are worn by the honorary treasurer, the secretary general and the mace bearer. All gowns are worn on ceremonial occasions by their respective holders of office or appointment.

Awards

The F.N.G. Starr Award
The Frederic Newton Gisborne Starr Award, first bestowed in 1936, represents the highest award that lies within the power of the CMA to bestow upon one of its members. Achievement is the prime requisite in determining the recipient of this award.

Medallists may have achieved distinction in one of the following ways: by making an outstanding contribution to science, the fine arts or literature (nonmedical), or by achievement in serving humanity under conditions calling for courage or the endurance of hardship in the promotion of health or the saving of life, in advancing the humanitarian or cultural life of his or her community, or in improving medical service in Canada.

Such achievement should be so outstanding as to serve as an inspiration and a challenge to the medical profession in Canada.

The CMA Medal of Honour

Established in 1982, the CMA Medal of Honour represents the highest award that lies within the power of the Association to bestow upon a person who is not a member of the medical profession.

The award is granted in recognition of personal contributions to the advancement of medical research, medical education, health care organization and health care education of the public; service to the people of Canada in raising the standards of health care delivery in Canada; and service to the profession in the field of medical organization.

The CMA Medal of Service

The CMA Medal of Service, first awarded in 1964, is awarded from time to time to individuals who have made an exceptional and outstanding contribution to the advancement of health care in Canada. This may be a service to their profession in the field of medical organization, to the people of this country by helping to raise the standards of medical practice in Canada or a personal contribution to the advancement of the art and science of medicine.

To qualify, a recipient must have made contributions in at least two of the above fields.

The names of recipients of the above three awards are listed in the appendices.

Special Medal for Outstanding Service to the CMA

Awarded to Dr. Gordon S. Fahrni in 1980.

Special Medal of Recognition

Awarded to Dr. Gordon S. Fahrni in 1987. In April 1987, Dr. Fahrni reached his 100th birthday. A graduate in medicine in 1911 from the University of Manitoba, he became interested in the diseases of the thyroid gland and soon became an acknowledged expert in the surgery of that gland. He was a pioneer in decreasing the operative complications associated with hyperthyroidism.

At a memorable meeting of the CMA in 1921, when it appeared that the debt-ridden CMA would founder, he led a movement to ensure that the

Association would survive. In 1923 he became president of the Manitoba Medical Association, and in 1942 he became president of the CMA. At the age of 64 he moved from Winnipeg to Vancouver and started a practice there, retiring in 1965. In 1987 he was made honorary president of the British Columbia Medical Association. His writings are many and include his autobiography, *Prairie Surgeon*.

The Osler Oration and Osler Scholarship

The Osler Oration was established to honour the memory of Sir William Osler. At the 60th annual meeting of the CMA in Montreal in 1929, a special day, June 20, was named The Osler Day and set aside for annual meeting attendees to visit the Osler Library in McGill Medical School and see Sir William's collection of rare books, photographs, correspondence, morbid anatomy specimens and Association memorabilia.

Among the *incunabula* could be found the following: the 1495 Aldine edition of Aristotle; the 1478 text of Celsius; the 1472 book on diseases of children by Bagellandus; the Venetian edition of Hippocrates (1526); the 1543 editions of works by Copernicus and Vesalius; Harvey's *Letters to Riolanus* (1649); and the first edition of William Jenner's *Treatise on Vaccination* (1798).

In the evening, Association members, families and friends, and invited guests, assembled in the Windsor Hall to hear the first Osler Oration. The chairman for the event was Dr. Alfred T. Bazin, CMA president, who stated in his introductory remarks that

> *a sum of $6000 has been generously donated to the Canadian Medical Association by Mr. J.W. McConnell. This money will be placed in a Trust Fund and will be invested in trust fund securities; the interest accumulating over three years will be available to a candidate nominated by the Faculty of Medicine of McGill University, to permit such candidate to undertake such special studies as will make him or her better fitted to teach clinical medicine. As the Montreal General Hospital was Osler's first hospital, the President and five members of the Board of Management have donated a like sum under similar conditions, the candidate for the Scholarship to be nominated to the CMA by the Medical Board of the hospital.*

Dr. Francis J. Shepherd, former dean and professor of anatomy at McGill and a close friend of Osler, was chosen to deliver the first Osler Oration (1929). Sadly, he died shortly after completing his manuscript, and the reading of it was entrusted to Dr. H.A. LaFleur, another of Osler's associates. Up to 1966, the Osler Oration was presented 11 times at CMA annual meetings.

The minutes of the CMA Executive Committee of November 1931 record that in June 1932, the 3-year period since the establishment of the Osler Scholarship had been reached and, under the terms of the award, it was time for a decision to be made. The remarks made by Dr. Bazin in 1929 had been formalized as follows:

1. *The $6000 donated by members of the Board of Management of the Montreal General Hospital was to be invested by the CMA; the interest accrued to June 1932, and every three years thereafter, shall be made available to and paid to a candidate nominated by the Medical Board of the Montreal General Hospital, in order that such candidate may pursue special studies to advance the knowledge of medicine and to improve the teaching of clinical medicine.*
2. *The $6000 donated by Mr. J.W. McConnell was to be invested by the CMA and the accumulated interest in June 1932 and every three years thereafter, was to be made available to a candidate nominated by the Faculty of Medicine, McGill University, Montreal.*
3. *The capital in each case shall not be disbursed, but shall remain intact.*

The CMA Executive Committee approved the following in early 1932:

That the General Secretary communicate with the Medical Board of the Montreal General Hospital and the Faculty of Medicine of McGill University requesting them to have their nominations made for the Osler Scholarships not later than May 1st, 1932; and that the Sub-Executive Committee be empowered to approve the nominations on behalf of the Executive Committee, in order that each candidate may be advised and that the announcement may appear on the Annual Meeting programme.

In response to that initiative, the following were recommended: Dr. Gordon Allan Copping by the Montreal General Hospital and Mr. Gerald Taylor Evans by McGill University.

The CMA had set up a Standing Committee on Awards, Scholarships, and Lectures to handle the requirements of the major orations and scholarships, and in April 1933, the Executive Committee directed it to investigate, report and recommend on the methods of payment of funds to the recipients of the scholarships. The committee responded as follows:

1. The Faculty of Medicine at McGill University and the Medical Board of the Montreal General Hospital be notified on or before April 1 each year of the amount of each Scholarship.
2. The Scholars shall receive on or before July 1, one half of the award, with the other half paid on or before November 1.
3. Scholars will submit to the General Secretary of the Canadian Medical Association, for approval of the Committee on Awards, Scholarships, and Lectures, on or before November 1, a brief interim report of their activities undertaken under the Scholarships.
4. On or before July 1 of the year succeeding the award, Scholars are to submit to the General Secretary for approval of the Committee on Awards, Scholarships and Lectures a full report of their activities and copies, when available, of reprints of such publications as have arisen from their work.

The next time the scholarships were awarded was on Apr. 1, 1936, when Dr. John G. Howlett of the Royal Victoria Hospital and Dr. Stuart R. Townsend each received $942.86. In 1937, the Executive Committee decided that the presentation of the scholarships would be made at the CMA's annual meeting. Scholarships were awarded in 1939, followed by a moratorium during World War II. Records do not give any details of the scholarships until 1957 when it was reported that Osler scholarships had been awarded to Dr. David Stubington and Dr. Douglas G. Kinnear.

In his report to General Council in 1961, the chairman of the Standing Committee, Dr. Robert M. Janes, stated "that the Committee is a Standing Committee of the Association but it cannot claim to being among the most active." However, he reported that the Faculty of Medicine of McGill University and the Board of Management of the Montreal General Hospital had selected the same nominee for 1960 and 1961 and that both scholarships had been awarded to Dr. Carl A. Goresky of Montreal.

There is a gap of 16 years before the next mention of the Osler Scholarship appears in CMA records. In 1978, with the agreement of McGill University and the Montreal General Hospital, the scholarship was awarded to Dr. Douglas A. Wasylenki, a lecturer in the Department of Psychiatry at the University of Toronto. In the same year, with the agreement of the two sponsoring bodies, the terms of reference for granting the scholarships were changed. There would be only one scholarship awarded each year. The scholarship fund would provide for $2000 of interest revenue to be awarded annually; the first recipient under the new arrangement in 1979 was Dr. Ronald T. Tanton of Halifax.

Administration of the scholarship was now under the Council on Medical Education and it reported that the 1980 recipient was Dr. Pierre Leichner, who planned to use his award to further knowledge of program planning and evaluation of clinical training, focusing particularly on the use of instructional videotapes. In 1981, Dr. Linda S. Snell of McGill University used her award to examine graduate clinical training in ambulatory care. Dr. A. Mark Clarfield of Montreal used his 1982 award to integrate the approach of community health with the teaching of geriatrics, and the 1983 recipient, Dr. David Dawson of McGill University, used the award to investigate certain aspects of the clinical clerkship. No awards were made in 1984 and 1985 and the accumulated 2 years' interest of $4000 was available. The 1986 recipient of the Osler Scholarship was Dr. Michel Desjardins, of Gaspé Harbour, Que., who planned to use it to measure the impact of various primary clinical teaching methodologies on the provision of quality care.

The $4000 was available for 1987 and 1988. The recipient of the Osler Scholarship for 1987 was Dr. John A. Rutka, a Toronto otolaryngologist, who used the award to assist in the purchase of new audiovisual equipment to be used in the teaching of complex anatomy and microsurgical instrumentation in aural surgery. At this point, the rates of interest were not capable of sustaining annual depletions of $4000 and it was agreed that the capital in the fund should not drop below $50 000. The 1988 recipient of the Osler Scholarship was Dr. Mark S. Gans, director of the Department of Neuro-ophthalmology at McGill University, who planned to use the award to develop an ongoing computerized teaching file of articles and slides for use in his department. The 1989 recipient was Dr. Elizabeth J. Latimer of McMaster University, Hamilton, Ont., who used the award to further the development of a learning package for trainee physicians in the areas of pain and symptom control, clinical decision making in life-threatening situations, and the overall care of patients and their families.

In 1988 and 1989, the Council on Medical Education reviewed the report of the Osler Scholarship Committee recommending changes in the awarding of the scholarship. It was held that the amount was not significant by itself in terms of funding research for any length of time, and that consideration should be given to changing the award to honour achievement and having it presented at the CMA annual meeting. In its report to the 1990 General Council, the Council on Medical Education presented the committee's report that recommended that the scholarship be awarded as an honour to recognize "an innovative contribution to the field of clinical medical education." Because the time now spent in postgraduate training has increased, it was recommended that the terms of reference be amended to indicate that applicants must have graduated from a Canadian faculty of medicine within the last 15 years and received a staff appointment to teach clinical medicine at a Canadian medical school within the last 5 years. No award was made in 1990, and in 1991 Council on Medical Education reported to the General Council that the Osler Scholarship Committee was still working on the terms of reference. It was decided in 1992 that there would be a moratorium until such time as the monies in the trust fund had reached a level to permit the scholarship to be reinstated.

The Listerian Oration

At the annual meeting of the CMA in Winnipeg in 1922, the idea of the Listerian Oration took shape. Dr. John Stewart of Halifax, who had been one of Lord Lister's dresser-clerks and had moved with him from Edinburgh to London, suggested that it would be well for the CMA to consider having an address in honour of Lister at every third association annual meeting. The General Council agreed with the suggestion and appointed Dr. Stewart to chair a committee to carry out the proposal. The committee had representatives from Nova Scotia, Quebec, Ontario, Manitoba, Alberta and British Columbia. In 1923, the CMA reappointed the committee for a further year and chose Dr. Stewart to give the first Listerian Oration.

Dr. F.N.G. Starr was asked to undertake the duty of collecting an endowment fund. At a meeting of the Ontario members of the committee it was decided that the best way to do this would be to organize a club to be known as The Lister Memorial Club. A subscription of $10 would entitle the subscriber to membership. The hoped-for objective was $5000, a sum that would yield about $800 interest in 3 years and would cover the expenses of the preparation, delivery and publication of each triennial oration.

The first Listerian Oration was given at the CMA's annual meeting on June 18, 1924, and reprinted in a special issue of the *CMAJ* in October. It was delivered under the auspices of the Lister Memorial Club of the CMA, and the Executive Committee of the CMA, acting on the club's behalf, presented every member of the Association with a copy of the Listerian Oration, including the foreword by Dr. Alexander Dougall Blackader.

Thirteen Listerian orations were given at CMA annual meetings between 1924 and 1964. Among the orators were Sir Charles Scott Sherrington, Lord Moynihan of Leeds, Sir Howard Florey and Sir Charles Illingworth.

The Blackader Lecture

In 1919, the fortunes of the CMA were at a low ebb and the *CMAJ* near to extinction. The journal's editor, Sir Andrew MacPhail, who was suffering from an old injury to this left eye, resigned, and the Association elected to go without an editor, leaving that responsibility with the Editorial Board, chaired by Dr. Alexander D. Blackader. At the CMA annual meeting that year, Dr. Blackader offered to act as editor, an offer that was gratefully accepted by the Association. It was not until 1923 that he was formally appointed editor. Dr. Blackader was a pioneer in the practice of pediatrics in North America, a distinguished physician, a teacher and author, and at age 72 was taking on a task that would have daunted many younger people. It was to his great credit that the journal was turned around, albeit at great personal sacrifice on his part. Although the position of editor was a voluntary one, the revitalization of the journal occupied Dr. Blackader almost to the point of obsession.

He continued thus until his resignation in 1929. A colleague noted that "it was impossible to work for him without feeling the intense and abiding keenness of his devotion to the association, and the true sense of humility with which he avoided self-seeking or even recognition." At the 1929 General Council, the following resolution was passed:

> *Members of Council have learned with regret of the resignation of Dr. A.D. Blackader as Editor of the Canadian Medical Association Journal. During Dr. Blackader's tenure of office, covering a period of ten years, the quality of the Journal, the sphere of its influence, and the character of the service it has rendered, have been the source of pride and satisfaction to every one interested in the welfare of the medical profession in the Dominion of Canada. As a tangible expression of deep and abiding appreciation of Dr. Blackader's efforts, as a mark of recognition, also, of his eighty-second birthday, and, finally, to signalize his pioneer and long-sustained interest in the field of diseases of children, and his devotion to the highest ideals in medicine, it is recommended to Council that there be established in the Canadian Medical Association the Blackader Lecture in Diseases of Children.*

Dr. Blackader was appointed editor emeritus and continued to contribute regularly to the journal up to the time of his death in 1932. The first Blackader Lecture was given at the 62nd annual meeting of the CMA, held in Vancouver in June 1931; the lecturer was Dr. Edwards A. Park, professor of pediatrics, Johns Hopkins University, Baltimore, whose topic was "Some Aspect of Rickets." Eleven Blackader Lectures were given up to 1965.

Names of orators/lecturers and dates for the Osler and Listerian orations and for the Blackader Lecture can be found in the appendices.

The Gordon Richards Memorial Lectureship

In 1951, the Ontario Cancer Treatment and Research Foundation established the Gordon Richards Memorial Lectureship and offered it to the CMA for its annual meeting in Winnipeg in 1953. The Association accepted the offer and the lecture was given by Dr. Douglas Quick of New York. In 1955, at the CMA's annual meeting in Toronto, the lecture was given by Dr. Ralston Paterson from Manchester, England.

The Tisdall Memorial Lecture

In his report to the 1955 General Council as chairman of the Committee on Awards, Scholarships and Lectures, Dr. D. Sclater Lewis stated that Merck and Co. had proposed the establishment of a lecture to be given every third year in honour of Dr. Fred Tisdall who had died in 1949. Dr. Tisdall had been the first chairman of the Association's Committee on Nutrition and had been very active in stressing the importance of proper nutrition. He had arranged for internationally known workers in the field of nutrition, such as Sir John Boyd Orr and Sir Edward Mellanby, to give addresses to Canadians.

The Association accepted the offer of Merck and Co. and arrangements were made for the first Tisdall Lecture to be given at the 1956 annual meeting in Quebec City.

The Roads Lecture

A number of citizens of Kingston, Ont., headed by Dr. Kenneth M. Adams, established in 1979 a fund to provide for a lecture at the CMA annual meeting in honour of Dr. William R. Ghent of that city. Dr. Ghent, a general surgeon, was recognized nationally and internationally for his work in the field of accident prevention. In 1981 he was appointed chairman of the CMA's Council on Health Care and held that position until August 1984. During his term in office and as a result of his direction, the CMA was in the forefront in pressing for changes in many aspects of road safety and in trauma prevention. Dr. Ghent himself gave the first Roads Lecture.

Appendices

CMA PRESIDENTS 1953–95

1953–54 Dr. Charles W. Burns
Manitoba

MD CM University of Manitoba 1913. CAMC 1916–18. FACS 1923. FRCSC 1931. FICS 1947. Professor and chairman, Department of Surgery, University of Manitoba. Professor emeritus. President, Manitoba Medical Association. President, College of Physicians and Surgeons of Manitoba. LLD (Hon) University of Manitoba. CMA senior member 1964.

1954–55 Dr. George F. Strong
British Columbia

MD University of Minnesota 1921. FACP 1938. President, American College of Physicians 1955–56. FACPS 1955. Clinical professor of medicine, University of British Columbia 1951–59. President, Canadian Heart Foundation 1956. President, British Columbia Medical Association 1936–37. DSc (Hon) University of British Columbia 1955. LLD (Hon) University of Minnesota. DSc (Hon) Laval University. FRCP (Hon) 1955. FRACP (Hon) 1956.

1955–56 Dr. T. Clarence Routley
Ontario

MD University of Toronto 1915. CMA general secretary 1923–54. Lifetime CMA honorary president. President, British Medical Association 1955–56. LLD (Hon) Queen's University 1931. LLD (Hon) Dalhousie University 1953. LLD (Hon) University of Toronto 1955. OBE 1945. F.N.G. Starr Award 1948. Founder member, World Medical Association.

1956–57 Dr. J. Renaud Lemieux
Quebec

MD Laval University 1926. RCAMC 1940–45. FRCPC 1957. Professor of medicine, Laval University 1934–67. President, Quebec Medical Association 1955–56. President, World Medical Association 1959. President, Canadian Cancer Society 1963–66. DSc (Hon) Laval University. LLD (Hon) University of Edinburgh. CMA Medal of Service 1970. CMA senior member 1967.

1957–58 Dr. Morley A.R. Young
Alberta

CATC 1918–19. MD McGill University 1921. FACS 1930. FRCSC 1933. LLD (Hon) University of Calgary 1977. President, Alberta Medical Association 1956–57. Order of Canada. Centennial Medal 1967. CMA senior member 1966.

1958–59 Dr. Arthur F. VanWart
New Brunswick

MA University of New Brunswick 1920. MB University of Toronto 1921. CRCPC (internal. medicine) CRCSC (general surgery). President, New Brunswick Medical Society. LLD (Hon) University of New Brunswick 1949. Member, Royal Commission on Health Services 1961. CMA senior member 1969.

1959–60 HRH Prince Philip,
Duke of Edinburgh

1959–60 Dr. E. Kirk Lyon
Ontario

CMA deputy president. MD University of Toronto 1923. CRCSC (general surgery). FACS. President, Ontario Medical Association 1950–51. CMA Medal of Service 1969. CMA senior member 1968.

1960–61 Dr. R. MacGregor Parsons
Alberta

MD University of Toronto 1930. FRCSC 1940. FACS 1944. President, Alberta Medical Association 1950–51. LLD (Hon) University of Alberta 1971. Centennial Medal 1967. CMA senior member 1972.

1961–62 Dr. Gerald W. Halpenny
Quebec

MD McGill University 1934. RCAMC 1939–45. FRCPC 1947. FACP 1949. President, Quebec Medical Association 1960–61. CMA honorary treasurer 1957–60. CMA senior member 1974.

1962–63 Dr. Malcolm R. MacCharles
Manitoba

CAMC 1914–17. MD University of Manitoba 1920. Charter fellow RCPSC. FACA. FRCS (Edin) 1924. Professor of surgery, University of Manitoba. DSc (Hon) University of Manitoba 1977.

1963–64   Dr. William W. Wigle
Ontario

MD CM Queen's University 1943. RCNVR 1944–45. President, Ontario Medical Association 1960–61. Member, CMA Executive Committee 1959–63. Medical director, Associated Medical Services Inc. 1961–62. President, Pharmaceutical Manufacturers Association of Canada 1965–74. Regional coroner, northwestern Ontario.

1964–65   Dr. Frank A. Turnbull
British Columbia

MD University of British Columbia 1928. RCAMC 1943–45. FRCSC 1962. Diploma, American Board of Neurosurgeons. President, British Columbia Medical Association 1955–56. Member, CMA Executive Committee 1955–57. Past president and founding member, North Pacific Society of Neurology and Psychiatry. Clinical associate professor of surgery (neurosurgery), University of British Columbia. LLD (Hon).

1965–66   Dr. Robert O. Jones
Nova Scotia

MD Dalhousie University 1937. FRCP. President Nova Scotia Medical Society 1955–56. Charter president, Canadian Psychiatric Association. Order of Canada 1981. DEng (Hon) Nova Scotia Technical College 1970. CMA Medal of Service 1982.

1966–67 Dr. R. Kenneth Thomson
Alberta

MD University of Alberta 1931. RCAMC 1939–41. RCN 1941–46. FRCPC. FACP. President, American Medical Association. Chairman, CMA General Council 1964–65. CMA Medal of Service 1978. CMA senior member 1973.

1967–68 Dr. Normand J. Belliveau
Quebec

MD Laval University 1946. RCAMC 1944–46. FRCSC. FACS. FACP. FICS (Hon). Certificate in general surgery, College of Physicians and Surgeons of Quebec. CMA honorary treasurer 1964–66. President, Quebec Medical Association 1965–66. President, Canadian Medical Protective Association. DSc (Hon) St. Anne's College 1964. LLD (Hon) Dalhousie University 1967. Surgeon to HM Queen Elizabeth II 1967. Centennial Medal 1967. Queen Elizabeth II Silver Jubilee Medal 1977. CMA senior member 1987.

1968–69 Dr. Harold D. Dalgleish
Saskatchewan

MD University of Manitoba 1936. CRCSC 1951. FRCSC 1973. President, College of Physicians and Surgeons of Saskatchewan 1968–69. Registrar, College of Physicians and Surgeons of Saskatchewan 1970–77. LLD (Hon) University of Manitoba 1969. CMA Medal of Service 1979. CMA senior member 1972.

1969–70 Dr. Ross M. Matthews
Ontario

MD University of Toronto 1933. RCAF 1940–45. President, Ontario Medical Association 1966. LLD (Hon) Trent University. CMA senior member 1975.

1970–71 Dr. Duncan L. Kippen
Manitoba

MD University of Manitoba 1942. RCAMC 1943–46. CRCPC 1950. Associate professor of medicine, University of Manitoba. President, Manitoba Medical Association 1967–68.

1971–72 **Dr. Harry D. Roberts**
Newfoundland

MD Dalhousie University 1936. President, Navy League of Canada. President, Newfoundland Medical Association 1950–51. Member, Board of Regents, Memorial University of Newfoundland. Centennial Medal 1967. CMA senior member 1978.

1972–73 **Dr. Gustave Gingras**
Quebec

MD University of Montreal 1943. RCAMC 1942–45. FRCPC. Professor of physical medicine and rehabilitation, University of Montreal 1954–76. Director, Rehabilitation Services, Prince Edward Island. President, Canadian Human Rights Foundation 1978. Chancellor, University of Prince Edward Island. Order of Canada (Member) 1967 (Companion) 1992. Pharmaceutical Manufacturers Association of Canada Medal of Honour 1973. Royal Bank Award 1972. LLD (Hon) Sir George Williams University. LLD (Hon) University of Manitoba. LLD (Hon) University of Western Ontario. DM (Hon) University of Sherbrooke. DCL (Hon) Bishops University. DSc (Hon) McMaster University. F.N.G. Starr Award 1978. CMA senior member 1982.

1973–74 **Dr. Peter J. Banks**
British Columbia

MB BS University of London 1946.
MRCS(Eng), LRCP (Eng) 1946. RAF
1948–49. MRCP (Lond) 1952. MD (Lond)
1952. FRCPC 1954. FRCP (Lond) 1973.
FRCPI (Hon) 1976. FACP 1977. DSc
(Hon) University of Hull 1974. President,
British Columbia Medical Association
1964–65. Joint-president, CMA and BMA
1973–74. Deputy speaker, CMA General
Council 1969–71. British Columbia Medical Association Silver Medal of Service
1992. CMA senior member 1988.

1974–75 **Dr. Bette Stephenson**
Ontario

MD University of Toronto 1946. Chairperson, Ontario Medical Association Board of
Directors 1968–70. President, Ontario Medical Association 1970–71. Chairperson,
CMA Board of Directors 1972–74. Minister
of labour, Province of Ontario 1975–78.
Minister of education and colleges and universities, Province of Ontario 1978–85.
Deputy premier, treasurer and minister of
economics, Province of Ontario 1985.
Centennial Medal 1967. Queen Elizabeth
II Silver Jubilee Medal 1977. CMA senior
member 1991.

1975–76 **Dr. Lloyd C. Grisdale**
Alberta

MD University of Alberta 1946. CRCSC 1950. President, Alberta Medical Association 1967. Chairman, CMA Board of Directors 1969–71. Chairman, Lancet Insurance 1973–74. Executive director, Alberta Cancer Hospital Board 1978–80. Deputy minister of hospital and medical care, Government of Alberta 1980–85. CMA Medal of Service 1983. CMA senior member 1985.

1976–77 **Mr. Barry O'Donnell**
Dublin

MB BCh. BAO (Hons) University College, Cork 1949. FRCS 1953. FRCSI 1953. MCh University College, Cork 1954. Honorary treasurer, Irish Medical Association 1966–75. Joint president, BMA, CMA and IMA 1976–77.

1976–77 Dr. Estathios W. Barootes
Saskatchewan

CMA deputy president 1976–77. MD University of Toronto 1943. RCAMC 1943–46. FRCSC 1950. FACS. Honorary treasurer, CMA 1972–75. President, Saskatchewan Medical Association 1962. President, College of Physicians and Surgeons of Saskatchewan 1964. President, Canadian Urological Association 1970. President, Medical Council of Canada 1972–73. Appointed to the Canadian Senate 1984. CMA Medal of Service 1981. CMA senior member 1987.

1977–78 Dr. Robert Gourdeau
Quebec

MD Laval University 1944. RCAMC 1944–47. FRCPC 1957. Professor of pediatrics, Laval University. President, Quebec Medical Association 1971–72. Director of Fellowship Affairs, Royal College of Physicians and Surgeons of Canada 1980–86. CMA senior member 1985.

1978–79 **Dr. Kenneth O. Wylie**
Manitoba

MD University of Manitoba 1952. CRCPC 1957. FRCPC 1976. President, Manitoba Medical Association 1973–74. President, Canadian Paediatric Society 1969–70.

1979–80 **Dr. D. Laurence Wilson**
Ontario

MD CM Queen's University, 1944. FRCPC 1951. Professor of medicine, Queen's University 1969–89. Dean, Faculty of Medicine 1982–89. President, College of Physicians and Surgeons of Ontario 1965–66. President, Ontario Medical Association 1973–74. Chairman, CMA Board of Directors 1976–78. MCFPC (Hon) 1987. CMA Medal of Service 1990. Queen Elizabeth II Silver Jubilee Medal 1977. CMA senior member 1988.

1980–81 **Dr. William D.S. Thomas**
British Columbia

MD University of British Columbia 1959. FRCSC 1964. President, British Columbia Medical Association 1974. Chairman, Board of Directors of CMA MD Investment Services Ltd.

1981–82 Dr. Léon Richard
New Brunswick

MD Laval University 1951. CRCSC 1959. President, New Brunswick Medical Society 1977–78. Member, CMA Task Force on Allocation of Health Care Resources 1983–84. Order of Canada (Member) 1984. DSc (Hon) University of Moncton 1973. LLD (Hon) Dalhousie University 1981. Chancellor, University of Moncton. CMA senior member 1990.

1982–83 Dr. Marc A. Baltzan
Saskatchewan

MD CM McGill University 1953. FRCPC 1960. FACP 1965. Diploma American Board of Internal Medicine. Founder, Saskatchewan Renal Transplant Unit 1963. Professor of medicine, University of Saskatchewan. Royal College of Physicians and Surgeons of Canada examiner in internal medicine 1970–75. President, Saskatchewan Medical Association 1968. Assistant dean of medicine 1971–73 and chairman, Department of Medicine 1974–79. President, Canadian Association of Professors of Medicine 1979. Chairman, CMA Council on Economics 1976–81. CMA Medal of Service 1986. Governor American College of Physicians 1988–92. President Saskatoon District Medical Association 1994.

1983–84 Dr. Everett Coffin
Quebec

MA University of Toronto 1950. MD University of Laval 1956. Certified Specialist in obstetrics and gynecology, College of Physicians and Surgeons of Quebec. FACOG. President, Quebec Medical Association 1980–81.

1984–85 Dr. T. Alexander McPherson
Alberta

MD University of Alberta 1962. PhD University of Melbourne 1969. FRACP 1972. Professor of medicine, University of Alberta. Director of medicine, Cross Cancer Institute, Edmonton. President, Alberta Medical Association 1981–82.

1985–86 Dr. William J. Vail
Ontario

CAOSC 1941–46. MD University of Ottawa 1952. FRCSC 1960. RCAMC Europe 1962–65. President Ontario Medical Association 1978–79. Chairman, CMA Board of Directors 1981–83. Canadian Decoration. CMA senior member 1991.

1986–87   **Dr. Jacob Dyck**
Manitoba

MD University of Manitoba 1955. FRCSC 1962. President, Manitoba Medical Association 1980–81. Member, CMA Board of Directors 1982. Member, CMA Council on Health Care 1983–85.

1987–88   **Dr. Athol L. Roberts**
Prince Edward Island

BA 1943 and BSc 1949 Acadia University. MD Dalhousie University 1954. RCAMC 1954–59. FCFPC 1978. President, Prince Edward Island Medical Society 1967–69. President, Prince Edward Island College of Family Physicians 1976–79. CMA senior member 1988.

1988–89   **Dr. John O'Brien-Bell**
British Columbia

MB BS University of London 1956. MRCS(Lond) LRCP (Eng) 1956. DRCOG. President, British Columbia Medical Association 1986–87. Member, CMA Board of Directors 1981–86. Member, CMA Executive Committee 1984–87. Founding editor, BCMA News 1971–78. Editor, Western Medical News 1978–81. Member, CMA Task Force on Allocation of Health Care Resources 1983–84.

1989–90 Dr. Marcien Fournier
Quebec

MD Laval University 1961. Province of Quebec certificate in anatomical pathology 1966. Member, Quebec Medical Association Executive Committee 1975–82. Member, CMA Board of Directors 1987–89. Member, CMA Executive Committee 1987–89. CMA honorary treasurer 1988–89.

1990–91 Dr. Lionel Lavoie
Saskatchewan

MD University of Ottawa 1964. CCFP 1971. Associate clinical professor of family medicine, University of Saskatchewan. Member, CMA Council on Health Care 1971–75. President, Saskatchewan Medical Association 1975. Director, CMA Board of Directors 1978–83. Chairman, CMA Council on Medical Education 1985–89. Commissioner, Medical Care Insurance Commission Saskatchewan 1984–88.

1991–92 **Dr. Carole Guzmán**
Ontario
MD University of Toronto 1958. MSc
McGill University 1965. FRCPC 1967. Asso-
ciate professor of medicine, University of
Ottawa 1971–92. Member, Ontario Medical
Association Board of Directors 1982–87 and
chairperson 1987–88. President, Ontario
Medical Association 1989–90. Member,
CMA Board of Directors 1988–91. CMA
associate secretary general 1992 to date.

1992–93 **Dr. Ronald F. Whelan**
Newfoundland

MD Dalhousie University 1968. FRCPC.
Clinical professor of radiology, Department
of Medicine, Memorial University of Newfoundland. Member, Newfoundland Medical Association Board 1979–83 and
chairman, 1983–87. President, Newfoundland and Labrador Medical Association
1979–80. Chairman, CMA Board of Directors 1984–87. Deputy speaker, CMA General Council 1988–89.

1993–94 Dr. Richard J. Kennedy
Alberta

MD Queen's University 1963. FRCPC. FCCP. Clinical assistant professor of medicine, University of Calgary. Member, Alberta Medical Association Board of Directors 1982–86 and president, 1986–87. Member, CMA Board of Directors 1987–89 and 1992–93.

1994–95 Dr. Bruno J. L'Heureux
Quebec

MD Laval University 1980. President, Quebec Medical Association, Montreal and Laval Districts. Member, Quebec Medical Association Board 1976–93 and chairman, 1985–91. Member, Quebec Medical Association Executive Committee 1982–84. President, Quebec Medical Association 1993–94. Member, CMA Board of Directors 1987–89 and 1992–94. Member, CMA Executive Committee 1993.

CMA CHIEF EXECUTIVE OFFICERS

1954–66 Dr. Arthur D. Kelly

MD University of Toronto 1925. Secretary, Ontario Medical Association 1937–40. RCAF Medical Branch 1940–45. Deputy general secretary, CMA 1946–54. DSc (Hon) University of British Columbia 1964. LLD (Hon) University of Western Ontario 1964. LLD (Hon) Dalhousie University 1965. Honorary member, Ontario Medical Association, Saskatchewan Medical Association, British Columbia Medical Association, Newfoundland Medical Association, 1966. Managing editor, CMA Publications 1966–69. CMA Publications (Toronto) 1969–76. Order of Canada (Member) 1973. Centennial Medal 1967. CMA Medal of Service 1967. CMA senior member 1966.

1966–70 Dr. Arthur F.W. Peart

MD CM Queen's University 1940. RCAMC 1940–46. DPh University of Toronto 1943. CRCPC 1953. FRCPC 1972. Medical Officer of Health, Swift Current 1946. Head, Division of Epidemiology, Department of National Health and Welfare, Ottawa 1948–53. CMA assistant secretary 1954–60. CMA deputy general secretary 1960–66. Medical director, Traffic Injury Research Foundation 1970–75. President, World Medical Association 1971–72. President, Medifacts Group. MBE (Military Division). Queen Elizabeth II Silver Jubilee Medal 1977. CMA senior member 1980.

1970–76 **Dr. J. Douglas Wallace**

MD University of Alberta 1940. RCAF Medical Branch 1940–45. Director Alberta Hospital Plan 1959–61. Executive director University Hospital, Edmonton 1961–66. Executive director, Toronto General Hospital 1966–70. President, Ontario Council of Administration of Teaching Hospitals 1969–70. Outstanding Achievement Award, Medical Alumni, University of Alberta 1969. Fellow, American College of Hospital Administrators 1969–76.

1976–82 **Dr. Robert G. Wilson**

Canadian Infantry Corps 1942–45. MD CM McGill University 1951. Assistant professor, Faculty of Medicine, University of British Columbia 1967–76. Executive secretary, British Columbia Medical Association 1963–69. President, Medical Services Association 1970. Chairman, CMA Board of Directors 1973–76. Queen Elizabeth II Silver Jubilee Medal 1977. CMA senior member 1993.

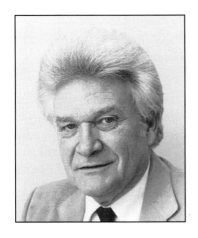

1982–86   **Mr. Bernard E. Freamo**

RCAF Europe World War II. Business administration, University of Toronto 1945–47. Administrator, Ontario Medical Association Health Plan 1947–57. Secretary, Ontario Medical Association, Department of Economics up to 1957. Secretary, CMA Department of Economics 1957–65. CMA executive secretary 1965–82. MD Management (MDM) executive vice-president 1969–86. MDM president and chief executive officer 1986–90. Executive vice-president and chief executive officer, MD Investment Services 1986–90. Chairman, MDM 1990–92. CMA Medal of Honour 1992. Honorary member CMA.

1986 to date   **Dr. Léo-Paul Landry**

MD Laval University 1967. MBA Laval University 1972. Director, Professional Services, Hôpital de l'Enfant Jésus, Montreal 1972–76, Hôpital Maisonneuve–Rosemont, Montreal 1977–81 and Montreal General Hospital 1982–86. Physician management consultant, Government of Quebec 1981–86. Medical consultant, Public Curator's Office, Province of Quebec 1979–88. Vice-president, l'Association des médecins de langue française du Canada 1977–79. Co-founder and chairman, editorial board, *L'Actualité médicale* 1980–85.

Chairmen of the General Council and Executive Committee
1952–59	Dr. Norman H. Gosse, Halifax
1959–61	Dr. Murray S. Douglas, Windsor, Ont.
1961–64	Dr. T. James Quintin, Sherbrooke, Que.
1964–66	Dr. R. Kenneth Thomson, Edmonton
1966–69	Dr. Reginald D. Atkinson, Waterloo, Ont.

In 1969 the structure of the CMA was changed. The Executive Committee became the Board of Directors and a chairman of the board was elected by the General Council. The chairman of the General Council became the speaker of that body.

Chairmen of the Board of Directors
1969–72	Dr. Lloyd C. Grisdale, Edmonton
1972–73	Dr. Bette Stephenson, Willowdale, Ont.
1973–76	Dr. Robert G. Wilson, Vancouver
1976–78	Dr. D. Laurence Wilson, Kingston, Ont.
1978–81	Dr. Edward V. Rafuse, Halifax
1981–84	Dr. William J. Vail, Newmarket, Ont.
1984–87	Dr. Ronald F. Whelan, St. John's
1987–89	Dr. Neil M. Gray, St. Albert, Alta.
1989–92	Dr. Judith C. Kazimirski, Windsor, NS
1992 to date	Dr. Colin J. McMillan, Charlottetown

Speakers of the General Council
1969–78	Dr. Reginald D. Atkinson, Waterloo, Ont.
1978–87	Dr. Christopher J. Varvis, Edmonton
1987–92	Dr. Patrick Bruce-Lockhart, Sudbury, Ont.
1992 to date	Dr. Douglas C. Perry, Edmonton

Canadian Medical Association Journal Editors
1942–55	Dr. Hugh E. MacDermot
1955–60	Dr. Stanley B. Gilder
1960–65	Dr. Donald C. Graham
1965–69	Dr. Gordon T. Dickinson
1969–75	Dr. James R. Anderson
1975–77	Dr. David A.E. Shephard
1978–80	Dr. Norman J. Wiggin
1980–82	Dr. Andrew M. Sherrington

1982–87   Dr. Peter P. Morgan
1987 to date Dr. Bruce P. Squires

CANADIAN JOURNAL OF SURGERY EDITORS

1957–64   Dr. Robert M. Janes
1964–72   Dr. Frederick G. Kergin
1972–92   Dr. Lloyd D. MacLean and Dr. C. Barber Mueller
1992 to date Dr. Roger G. Keith and Dr. Jonathan L. Meakins

RECIPIENTS OF THE F.N.G. STARR AWARD

1936   Sir Frederick Banting, Toronto
1936   Dr. James Bertram Collip, London, Ont.
1936   Dr. Charles Best, Toronto
1938   Dr. John S. McEachern, Calgary
1948   Dr. T. Clarence Routley, Toronto
1951   Dr. Alfred T. Bazin, Montreal
1953   Dr. Charles F. Martin, Montreal
1957   Dr. Duncan A. Graham, Toronto
1965   Dr. Wilder Penfield, Montreal
1967   Dr. Murray Barr, London, Ont.
1969   Dr. Bruce Chown, Winnipeg
1972   Dr. Hans Selye, Montreal
1974   Dr. Walter C. Mackenzie, Edmonton
1975   Dr. William Boyd, Toronto
1977   Dr. E. Harry Botterell, Kingston, Ont.
1978   Dr. Gustave Gingras, Monticello, PEI
1979   Dr. Armand Frappier, Valleyfield, Que.
1982   Dr Jacques Genest, Montreal
1983   Dr. Phil Gold, Montreal
1985   Dr. Gordon W. Thomas, Mabou, NS
1986   Dr. Charles G. Drake, London, Ont.
1987   Dr. Lucille Teasdale, Kampala, Uganda
1988   Dr. Robert B. McClure, Toronto
1989   Dr. David Boyes, Vancouver
1990   Dr. Fraser N. Gurd, Ottawa
1991   Dr. Henry J.M. Barnett, London, Ont.
1992   Dr. W. Gordon Bigelow, Toronto
1993   Dr. Jean Davignon, Montreal
1994   Dr. Herbert H. Jasper, Westmount, Que.

RECIPIENTS OF THE CMA MEDAL OF HONOUR

1982	Esther Robins, Calgary
1983	Dr. Harold E. Johns, Etobicoke, Ont.
1984	Dr. David T. Suzuki, Vancouver
1985	Dr. Raymond U. Lemieux, Edmonton
1986	Joan Hollobon, Toronto
1987	Rick Hansen, Vancouver
1988	Fernand Séguin, St-Charles-sur-Richelieu, Que.
1990	Hugh Clifford Chadderton, Stittsville, Ont.
1992	Bernard E. Freamo, Manotick, Ont.
1993	Douglas A. Geekie, Ottawa
1994	Michael Smith, Vancouver

RECIPIENTS OF THE CMA MEDAL OF SERVICE

1964	Dr. Joe A. McMillan, Charlottetown
1967	Dr. Arthur D. Kelly, Toronto
1969	Dr. E. Kirk Lyon, Leamington, Ont.
1970	Dr. J. Renaud Lemieux, Quebec
1971	Dr. Norman H. Gosse, Halifax
1973	Dr. Trent L. Fisher, Ottawa
1974	Dr. Glenn I. Sawyer, London, Ont.
1978	Dr. R. Kenneth Thomson, Edmonton
1979	Dr. Harold D. Dalgleish, Saskatoon
1980	Dr. Reginald D. Atkinson, Waterloo, Ont.
1981	Dr. Estathios W. Barootes, Regina
1982	Dr. Robert O. Jones, Halifax
1983	Dr. Lloyd C. Grisdale, Edmonton
1984	Dr. Chester B. Stewart, Halifax
1985	Dr. Donald I. Rice, Toronto
1986	Dr. Marc A. Baltzan, Saskatoon
1988	Dr. Dorothy C.H. Ley, Beaverton, Ont.
1989	Dr. Paul H.T. Thorlakson, Winnipeg
1990	Dr. D. Laurence Wilson, Kingston, Ont.
1991	Dr. James H. Graham, Ottawa
1992	Dr. Robert E. Beamish, Winnipeg
1993	Dr. Ernest H. Baergen, Saskatoon
1994	Dr. Augustin Roy, Montreal

Lister Orators

1924	Dr. John Stewart
1927	Sir Charles Scott Sherrington
1930	Rt. Hon. Lord Moynihan of Leeds
1933	Dr. Robert Muir
1936	Dr. Edward A. Archibald
1939	Dr. Allen O. Whipple
1945	Dr. Owen H. Wangensteen
1948	Dr. W. Edward Gallie
1951	Dr. Donald C. Balfour
1954	Sir Howard Florey
1958	Dr. Francis D. Moore
1961	Dr. Hugo Rosenquist
1964	Sir Charles Illingworth

Osler Orators

1929	Dr. Francis J. Shepherd
1932	Dr. Francis R. Packard
1935	Dr. Llewellys F. Barker
1938	Sir Humphry Rolleston
1942	Dr. Charles D. Parfitt
1948	Professor J. McMichael
1950	Dr. G.W. Thorn
1953	Dr. George S. Young
1956	Professor A. Lacassagne
1960	Sir Russell Brain
1963	Lord Cohen
1966	Dr. William B. Bean

Blackader Lecturers

1931	Dr. Edwards A. Park
1934	Dr. J. Craigie
1937	Dr. Harvey B. Cushing
1940	Dr. Alan Brown
1946	Sir Leonard G. Parsons
1949	Dr. J. Spence

1952	Dr. Richard W.B. Ellis
1955	Dr. Stanley G. Graham
1958	Dr. René J. Dubos
1962	Dr. Simon van Creveld
1965	Dr. John Lind

CMA AFFILIATED SOCIETIES

Association of Canadian Medical Colleges
Association of Canadian Pharmaceutical Physicians
Canadian Academy of Sport Medicine
Canadian Anaesthetists' Society
Canadian Association of Emergency Physicians
Canadian Association of Gastroenterology
Canadian Association of General Surgeons
Canadian Association of Internes and Residents
Canadian Association of Medical Microbiologists
Canadian Association of Nuclear Medicine
Canadian Association of Pathologists
Canadian Association of Physical Medicine and Rehabilitation
Canadian Association of Radiologists
Canadian Cardiovascular Society
Canadian Critical Care Society
Canadian Dermatology Association
Canadian Life Insurance Medical Officers Association
Canadian Medical Protective Association
Canadian Neurological Society
Canadian Neurosurgical Society
Canadian Ophthalmological Society
Canadian Orthopaedic Association
Canadian Paediatric Society
Canadian Psychiatric Association
Canadian Rheumatology Association
Canadian Society of Aerospace Medicine
Canadian Society of Clinical Neurophysiologists
Canadian Society of Internal Medicine
Canadian Society of Otolaryngology/Head & Neck Surgery
Canadian Society of Plastic Surgeons
Canadian Thoracic Society/Canadian Lung Association
Canadian Urological Association

College of Family Physicians of Canada
Federation of Medical Women of Canada
Federation of Medical Licensing Authorities of Canada
Occupational and Environmental Medicine Association of Canada
Royal College of Physicians and Surgeons of Canada
Society of Obstetricians and Gynaecologists of Canada

CMA PROVINCIAL/TERRITORIAL DIVISIONS

British Columbia Medical Association
Alberta Medical Association
Saskatchewan Medical Association
Manitoba Medical Association
Ontario Medical Association
Quebec Medical Association
New Brunswick Medical Society
Medical Society of Nova Scotia
Medical Society of Prince Edward Island
Newfoundland Medical Association
Northwest Territories Medical Association
Yukon Medical Association

ANNUAL MEETING SITES

1954	Vancouver	1955	Toronto	1956	Quebec
1957	Edmonton	1958	Halifax	1959	Toronto
1960	Banff	1961	Montreal	1962	Winnipeg
1963	Toronto	1964	Vancouver	1965	Halifax
1966	Edmonton	1967	Montreal and Quebec	1968	Regina
1969	Toronto	1970	Winnipeg	1971	Halifax
1972	Montreal	1973	Vancouver	1974	Toronto
1975	Calgary	1976	Dublin and Ottawa	1977	Quebec
1978	Winnipeg	1979	Toronto	1980	Vancouver
1981	Halifax	1982	Saskatoon	1983	Monte Carlo and Montreal
1984	Edmonton	1986	Winnipeg	1987	Charlottetown
1988	Vancouver	1989	Quebec	1990	Regina
1991	Toronto	1992	St. John's	1993	Calgary
1994	Montreal				

CMA *CODE OF ETHICS* 1954

Introductory

"As ye would that men should do to you, do ye even so to them" is a Golden Rule for all men. A Code of Ethics for physicians can only amplify or focus this and other golden rules and precepts to the special relations of practice. As a stream cannot rise above its source, so a code cannot change a low-grade man into a high-grade doctor, but it can help a good man to be a better man and a more enlightened doctor. It can quicken and inform a conscience, but not create one. Only in a few things can it decree 'thou shalt' or 'thou shalt not', but in many things it can urge 'thou shouldst' or 'thou shouldst not'.

While the highest service they can give to humanity is the only worthwhile aim for those of any profession, it is so in a special sense for physicians, since their services concern immediately and directly the health of the bodies and minds of men.

Of the Duties of Physicians to their Patients

For the honourable physician the first consideration will always be the welfare of the sick. On his conscience rest the comfort, the health and the lives of those under his care. To each he gives his utmost in science and art and human helpfulness. Their confidences are safe in his keeping, except in those rare instances when the safeguarding of society imposes a higher law. He does not multiply costs without need, nor raise needless fears, nor allay fears without full consideration. Even when he cannot cure he will alleviate, and be counsellor and friend.

It is a special duty for one who stands guard over the lives of men to keep his science and his art in good repair, to enlarge and refresh his knowledge constantly, and to give his patients treatment that is not only sympathetic, but the best possible in the circumstances. To this end he will always be willing to check and supplement his diagnosis, treatment and prognosis by consultation. No excellence in one respect can excuse slipshod, ignorant or outdated service. Every patient is entitled to adequate examination by the physician. The physician should aim to give his patient the same quality of service which he hopes, in time of need for himself or his family, to receive from another physician. If a practitioner is confining his study and practice to a special branch, he must be sure that his special knowledge and outlook are suitable and adequate to all the needs of the sick person under his care. In short, the greatest wellbeing of the sick person should be the whole study and care of the honourable physician.

> *"The greatest trust between man and man is the trust of giving counsel."*
> — *Francis Bacon*

Of the Duties of Physicians Regarding Consultations
It is the duty of the attending physician to accept the opportunity of a second opinion in any illness that is serious, obscure or difficult, or when consultation is desired by the patient or by persons authorized to act on the patient's behalf. While the physician should name the consultant he prefers, he should not refuse to meet the physician of his patient's choice though he may urge, if he so thinks, that such consultant has not the qualifications or experience that the existing situation demands.

In the following circumstances, it is particularly desirable that the attending physician, while dealing with an emergency when this exists should, whenever possible, secure consultation with a colleague:

(a) When the propriety of performing an operation or of adopting a course of treatment which may entail considerable risk to life, activities or capacities of the patient has to be considered, and particularly when the condition which it is sought to relieve by this treatment is in itself not dangerous to life.

(b) When operative measures involving the death of the foetus or of an unborn child are contemplated, particularly if labour has not begun.

(c) When the propriety of prescribing or repeating a prescription for any drug scheduled under the Opium and Narcotics Drug Act, in the case of a person seeking relief from the symptoms of addiction to that drug, is under consideration.

(d) When there are grounds for suspecting that the patient has been subjected to an illegal operation or is the victim of criminal poisoning.

Since consultation is planned wholly for the good of the sick person, there should enter into it no trace of insincerity, rivalry or envy. The attending physician and the consultant may examine the patient together or the consultant may examine the patient alone. The attending physician, should as a rule, give the consultant a brief oral or written history of the case before he examines the patient. If possible, the attending physician and the consultant should discuss the case in private, and the consultant should record his opinion either on the hospital records and/or by closed letter addressed to the attending physician. Their joint decision should be communicated to the patient and his family by the attending physician, supplemented, if necessary, by the consultant. If agreement as to diagnosis and treatment is not possible, and if either doctor is convinced that the future wellbeing of the patient is in jeopardy, a further opinion should be sought and the patient and/or the family should be informed of this by the attending physician, and the necessity for such action also explained.

If the attending physician should retire from the case, the consultant should not replace him during the present illness, except at the request of the attending physician or with his approval.

Patients Referred to Physicians or Sent to Hospitals
When a patient has been sent either for office examination or admission to a hospital under the consultant's care, it is the duty of the consultant to report findings and discuss them with the attending physician so that the latter may have all possible advantage from the consultation. It is equally the duty of the physician referring a patient to give as full information as possible to the consultant. A hospital physician should see that findings or suggestions of value concerning any patient at the time under his care in hospital are sent to the physician usually in attendance on that patient.

The Induction of Abortion
The induction or procuring of abortion involves the destruction of life. It is a violation both of the moral code and of the Criminal Code of Canada, except when there is justification for its performance. The only justification is that the continuance of pregnancy would imperil the life of the mother. It is appreciated, however, that there are certain faiths which, on religious grounds, do not recgnize this exception. Such an operation should never be undertaken unless the attending physician and consultant agree as to the necessity for such action; the consultant must be a physician in good standing and his recommendation should be put in writing. Where hospital facilities are available, the operation should be performed in a hospital, and, in such case, the superintendent or head of the institution should be notified in advance.

A Physician as Visitor
When a physician, as a personal friend, meets the patient of another physician, or calls upon him when ill, he must be careful not to be drawn into interference through suggestions or opinions. These should never be expressed except when he has been called in consultation in the authorized way.

> *"Let him be tender with the sick, honourable to men of his calling."*
> — *Ambroise Paré*

Of the Duties of the Individual Physician to the Profession At Large
The physician should be jealous for the honour of his craft, for its devotion to truth and the high quality of its service to mankind. No profession or calling

should demand higher standards of integrity or more constant devotion to the common good.

"I hold every man a debtor to his profession." — *Francis Bacon*

Of Professional Services of Physicians to Each Other

It is unwise for a physician to treat himself or members of his household in any serious illness when the services of another physician are available. Though such services are given cheerfully, and fully, and rightly so, yet if out-of-pocket expenses have been incurred, or if there has been loss through considerable absence, these should, if possible, be made good, at least in part.

If in such illnesses, whether because of friendship or to give advantages of special skill or experience, several members of the profession visit the sick physician or dependent, it must be made clear that some one designated physician has definite responsibility for the carrying on of the treatment.

Paid Advocacy

The paid advocacy of any commodity whatever its merits, cannot be reconciled with the ideals of a physician. He must be free to choose from all elements those best for his patient, and not be a merchandiser pushing one particular element for gain. It is precisely because he is a physician that his advocacy has extra market value. In thus advertising a commodity, he presumes to sell that which it is not his to sell, the common tradition and inheritance of reputation, esteem and standing of the whole profession.

Secret Commissions

The only basis on which a fee may be charged to a patient, or on which money may be received by any medical practitioner, is that of work actually done for the patient and such patient must receive a direct statement from the medical practitioner concerned. Any other arrangement between two or more medical practitioners, whereby one receives part of the fee paid to the other practitioner, is unethical and may contribute to dishonesty.

In cases where in the opinion of the attending medical practitioner, the services of one or more consultants are required, each such consultant shall render his account and submit his receipt individually.

Each practitioner should send his account to the patient individually, provided however that surgeon who has a regular assistant at operations may pay him directly. When the assistant has referred the patient to the operating surgeon, the assistant should send a statement of his fee directly to the patient.

If fees are collected by an organized clinic, medical group, medical partnership or medical practitioner employing regular assistants, each such organization is in effect regarded as a individual who acts in that capacity. The same principle applies when the clinic and hospital are combined and operate under the same ownership.

When a third person or organization enters into a financial arrangement between medical practitioner and patient, each medical practitioner should render an individual account to the third person or organization concerned; if more than one medical practitioner is carrying out professional services, a statement to the patient by the third person or organization should show the amount paid to each physician.

The receiving of secret commissions connected with the sale, by parties other than himself or his immediate professional associates, of commodities associated with the practice of medicine is entirely unethical conduct. For greater clarity, this prohibition does not imply that it is unethical for a physician or a group of physicians to dispense medicine or those commodities associated with his or their practice of medicine.

It is undesirable that medical practitioners should have a proprietary interest in preparations or appliances which it may be their duty to recommend to patients.

Standards of Fees
General rules and standards regarding fees should be adopted by the profession in each province and district. It should be deemed a point of honour among physicians to adhere to these standards with as much uniformity as varying conditions admit.

Medical Associations
A physician should associate himself with local, provincial and Canadian medical organizations to promote both his own and the general advancement in our science and art.

Group Practice and Ethics
Whatever is right and becoming in a physician is equally right for any association of physicians in clinics or other groups, and whatever is obligatory upon the individual is equally obligatory upon the group.

It is undesirable, and not in keeping with the principles of the medical profession, for medical practitioners to practise medicine in partnership with anyone not duly registered to practise medicine.

Communications to the Laity on Medical Subjects

All opinions on medical subjects which are communicated to the laity by any medium, whether it be a public meeting, the lay press, radio or television, should be presented as from some organized and recognized medical society or association and not from an individual physician. Such opinions should represent what is the generally accepted opinion of the medical profession.

When an official body of organized medicine finds it necessary to ask a medical practitioner to make a statement for the public and decides that circumstances make it necessary that his name be attached to it, the medical practitioner shall be absolved from criticism in so doing.

A physician acting in a public capacity, e.g. a Health Officer, may issue to the public warnings in notices regarding public health matters under his own name.

Radio Broadcasting

It is legitimate and even desirable that topics relating both to medical science and policy and to public health and welfare should be discussed by physicians who can speak with authority on the question at issue. In any medium of discussion, but especially in radio broadcasting because of its vast range, it is essential that the physician who takes part should avoid methods which tend to his personal professional advantage. Not only should he personally observe this rule, but he should take care that the announcer in introducing him makes no laudatory comments and no unnecessary display of the physician's medical qualifications and appointments. There is a special claim that physicians of established position and authority should observe these conditions, for their example must necessarily influence the actions of their less recognized colleagues. These remarks apply particularly to practising physicians. A physician serving in a public capacity is in a different position, but even he should see to it that it is his office, rather than himself, that is exalted.

> *"Live by the old ethics and the classical rule of honesty."*
> — *Sir Thomas Browne*

Locum Tenency

A physician who has been locum tenens should not begin practice in the same neighbourhood unless with the written consent of the practitioner for whom he has substituted, or after the lapse of a considerable time. It is suggested that misunderstanding will be avoided if a written contract is entered into by the physician and the locum tenens before the locum tenency begins.

Advertising

The word 'advertising' in relation to the medical profession must be taken in its broadest sense. It includes all those methods by which a practising physician is made known to the public either by himself or by others without his objection, in a manner which can be fairly regarded as having for its purpose the obtaining of patients or the promotion in other ways of the physician's individual professional advantage.

Excepting a plain card which conforms to local usage, any form of advertising is unprofessional for the practising physician. Practice should not be gathered by any kind of solicitation, direct or indirect. The best advertisement of a physician is a well-merited reputation for ability and probity in his profession.

Where a doctor takes over the practice of another doctor it would be correct for him to send his professional card to all other doctors in the area. It would not be unethical for the doctor whose practice is being taken over to send to his former patients a card notifying them of the takeover.

Advertising may be very insidious. A physician should not procure, sanction, be associated with or acquiesce in, notices which commend his own or any physician's skill, knowledge, services and qualifications, or which deprecate those of others.

An honourable physician will never be guilty either of boasting of cures, or of promising radical cures, or of self-praise in order to gather practice.

Differences between Physicians

> *"I prefer to attribute high motives to my friends' acts."*
>
> — *Pasteur*

Differences between physicians which cannot be adjusted after fair discussion should be referred to the Committee on Ethics of the local medical society. Complaints of unprofessional conduct should be referred in writing to the same Committee and must be signed.

Medical Witnesses

The medical witness should be actuated by a desire to assist the court in arriving at a just decision and not merely to further the interests of the party on whose behalf he has been summoned.

Of the Relations of Physicians with and in Hospitals

The modern hospital is a new element in the care of the sick and may not yet have become rightly adjusted in all its relations. Mutual understanding and cooperation between the profession and the hospitals are most essential.

Inasmuch as the positions held by members of the honourary attending staff give them unique opportunities for enlarging knowledge, such positions should be held as a trust for the general good of the community.

A physician may rightly apply for such an appointment but should not canvass for it. An appointment should never be given on account of party or favouritism, but solely on account of professional standing, industry, the spirit of cooperation and the ability and willingness to teach.

The Board of Management of a hospital has no right to dispose of the free services of physicians except as approved by the organized profession. It is the duty of hospital boards or executives to see that the free services of physicians are not asked for, or given to, or exploited for those who can and should pay, or for whom payment should be made.

While 'God's Poor' should always be cared for with charity it should be understood that the physician gives his services as an act of courtesy but not of obligation.

Nurses and Nursing

The profession of nursing has grown up to share in the care and prevention of illness, and the betterment of general health. In this large undertaking the services of the two professions, being complementary to one another, are, and must be, closely interrelated. If the spirit in both doctors and nurses is one of courtesy, understanding, appreciation, cooperation, and zeal for the welfare of the people, differences should not arise or, if they do, should be quickly adjusted.

Discoveries

No advance or discovery in any branch of medical science made by a physician should ever be capitalized or marketed by him in any way for his personal gain, or kept secret for his private advantage. Such advance or discovery should be made common for the advantage of the whole of the profession, and for the progress of science. There are well recognized methods by which physicians can place their work and discoveries before those who are fitted by education and experience to judge them. The lay press is not the proper medium for the first announcement of a physician's work or discoveries.

Emergency Calls

When a physician is called in the absence of the attending physician, or in emergency, he will, on arrival of the attending physician, hand over all care and responsibility, and retire from the case.

In a case of sudden illness or accident when several physicians are called, the first to arrive should be considered to be in charge. However, he should withdraw in favour of the regular family attendant should he arrive, or of any other physician preferred by the patient.

Forms and Certificates
In all forms where medical reports are to be filled in by physicians there should be included a declaration to be signed by the patient or a responsible relative or guardian stating that assent is given to the physician to supply the information requested. It is also strongly recommended that these forms and/or declarations be supplied in duplicate to permit the physician to retain a carbon copy.

Contract Practice
While not in itself unethical, contract practice becomes so if there is solicitation for patients, underbidding, interference with the choice of physician, or if the compensation is so low that adequate service cannot be given, or if professional services are made to yield profits to controlling lay groups.

Patent Preparations
A physician should not make use of, or recommend any remedy, the principal ingredients of which are not disclosed to the profession.

Care in Comment
When one physician succeeds another in the care of a patient he should make no adverse comment upon the treatment already given.

General Conclusion

"...the physician both individually and collectively should constantly confront his ideas and actions not only with the criticism of his own conscience but also with the sentiments of the world whose servant he is. He should never forget that his private conscience and that of the world are interwoven inseparably. Like religion in its manifold forms medicine comprises in its ethics the experience of and aspirations towards highest humanity, reflections of divine love. Hence medical ethics have contributed to the introduction of humanistic elements in our society; hence medical ethics also determine the general aspect and the conscience of culture."
— *Professor G.C. Heringa, The Netherlands*

The corollary of these words is that the complete physician is not a man apart and cannot content himself with the practice of medicine alone, but should make his contribution, as does any other good citizen, towards the well-being and betterment of the community in which he lives.

CMA *Code of Ethics* 1990

Principles of Ethical Behaviour for all physicians, including those who may not be engaged directly in clinical practice.
1. Consider first the well-being of the patient.
2. Honour your profession and its traditions.
3. Recognize your limitations and the special skills of others in the prevention and treatment of disease.
4. Protect the patient's secrets.
5. Teach and be taught.
6. Remember that integrity and professional ability should be your best advertisement.
7. Be responsible in setting a value on your services.

Guide to the Ethical Behaviour of Physicians
1. A physician should be aware of the standards established by tradition and act within the general principles which have governed professional conduct.
2. The Oath of Hippocrates represented the desire of the members of that day to establish for themselves standards of conduct in living and in the practice of their art. Since then the principles established have been retained as our basic guidelines for ethical living with the profession of medicine.
3. The International Code of Ethics and the Declaration of Geneva (1948), developed and approved by the World Medical Association, have modernized the ancient codes. They have been endorsed by each member organization, including The Canadian Medical Association, as a general guide having worldwide application.
4. The Canadian Medical Association accepts the responsibility of delineating the standard of ethical behaviour expected of Canadian physicians.

Responsibilities to the Patient

An Ethical Physician:

Standard of care
1. will practise the art and science of medicine to the best of his/her ability;
2. will continue self education to improve his/her standards of medical care;

Respect for patient
3. will practise in a fashion that is above reproach and will take neither physical, emotional nor financial advantage of the patient;

Patient's rights
4. will recognize his/her professional limitations and, when indicated, recommend to the patient that additional opinions and services be obtained;
5. will recognize that a patient has the right to accept or reject any physician and any medical care recommended. The patient having chosen a physician has the right to request of that physician opinions from other physicians of the patient's choice;
6. will keep in confidence information derived from a patient or from a colleague regarding a patient, and divulge it only with the permission of the patient except when otherwise required by law;
7. when acting on behalf of a third party will ensure that the patient understands the physician's legal responsibility to the third party before proceeding with the examination.
8. will recommend only diagnostic procedures that are believed necessary to assist in the care of the patient, and therapy that is believed necessary for the well-being of the patient. The physician will recognize a responsibility in advising the patient of the findings and recommendations and will exchange such information with the patient as is necessary for the patient to reach a decision;
9. will, upon the patient's request, supply the information that is required to enable the patient to receive any benefits to which the patient may be entitled;
10. will be considerate of the anxiety of the patient's next-of-kin and cooperate with them in the patient's interest;

Choice of patient
11. will recognize the responsibility of a physician to render medical service to any person regardless of colour, religion or political belief;
12. shall, except in an emergency, have the right to refuse to accept a patient;
13. will render all possible assistance to any patient, where an urgent need for medical care exists;
14. will, when the patient is unable to give consent and an agent of the patient is unavailable to give consent, render such therapy as the physician believes to be in the patient's interest;

Continuity of care
15. will, if absent, ensure the availability of medical care to his/her patients if possible; will, once having accepted professional responsibility for an acutely ill patient, continue to provide services until they are no longer required, or until arrangements have been made for the services of another suitable physician; may, in any other situation, withdraw from the responsibility for the care of any patient provided that the patient is given adequate notice of that intention;

Personal morality
16. will inform the patient when personal morality or religious conscience prevent the recommendation of some form of therapy;

Clinical research
17. will ensure that, before initiating clinical research involving humans, such research is appraised scientifically and ethically and approved by a responsible committee, and is sufficiently planned and supervised that the individuals are unlikely to suffer any harm. The physician will ascertain that previous research and the purpose of the experiment justify this additional method of investigation. Before proceeding, the physician will obtain the consent of all involved persons or their agents, and will proceed only after explaining the purpose of the clinical investigation and any possible health hazard that can be reasonably foreseen;

The dying patient
18. will allow death to occur with dignity and comfort when death of the body appears to be inevitable;
19. may support the body when clinical death of the brain has occurred, but need not prolong life by unusual or heroic means;

Transplantation

20. may, when death of the brain has occurred, support cellular life in the body when some parts of the body might be used to prolong the life or improve the health of others;

21. will recognize a responsibility to a donor of organs to be transplanted and will give to the donor or the donor's relatives full disclosure of the intent and purpose of the procedure; in the case of a living donor, the physician will also explain the risks of the procedure;

22. will refrain from determining the time of death of the donor patient if there is a possibility of being involved as a participant in the transplant procedure, or when his/her association with the proposed recipient might improperly influence professional judgement;

23. may treat the transplant recipient subsequent to the transplant procedure in spite of having determined the time of death of the donor;

Fees to patients

24. will consider, in determining professional fees, both the nature of the service provided and the ability of the patient to pay, and will be prepared to discuss the fee with the patient.

Responsibilities to the Profession

An Ethical Physician:

Personal conduct

25. will recognize that the profession demands integrity from each physician and dedication to its search for truth and to its service to mankind;

26. will recognize that self discipline of the profession is a privilege and that each physician has a continuing responsibility to merit the retention of this privilege;

27. will behave in a way beyond reproach and will report to the appropriate professional body any conduct by a colleague which might be generally considered as being unbecoming to the profession;

28. will behave in such a manner as to merit the respect of the public for members of the medical profession;

29. will avoid impugning the reputation of any colleague;

Contracts

30. will, when aligned in practice with other physicians, insist that the standards enunciated in this Code of Ethics and the Guide to the Ethical Behaviour of Physicians be maintained;

31. will only enter into a contract regarding professional services which allow fees derived from physicians' services to be controlled by the physician rendering the services;

32. will enter into a contract with an organization only if it will allow maintenance of professional integrity;

33. will only offer to a colleague a contract which has terms and conditions equitable to both parties;

Reporting medical research

34. will first communicate to colleagues, through recognized scientific channels, the results of any medical research, in order that those colleagues may establish an opinion of its merits before they are presented to the public;

Addressing the public

35. will recognize a responsibility to give the generally held opinions of the profession when interpreting scientific knowledge to the public; when presenting an opinion which is contrary to the generally held opinion of the profession, the physician will so indicate and will avoid any attempt to enhance his/her own personal professional reputation;

Advertising

36. will build a professional reputation based on ability and integrity, and will only advertise professional services or make professional announcements as regulated by legislation or as permitted by the provincial medical licensing authority;

37. will avoid advocacy of any product when identified as a member of the medical profession;

38. will avoid the use of secret remedies;

Consultation

39. will request the opinion of an appropriate colleague acceptable to the patient when diagnosis or treatment is difficult or obscure, or when the patient requests it. Having requested the opinion of a colleague, the physician will make available all relevant information and indicate

clearly whether the consultant is to assume the continuing care of the patient during the illness;

40. will, when consulted by a colleague, report in detail all pertinent findings and recommendations to the attending physician and may outline an opinion to the patient. The consultant will continue with the care of the patient only at the specific request of the attending physician and with the consent of the patient;

Patient care

41. will cooperate with those individuals who, in the opinion of the patient, may assist in the care of the patient;

42. will make available to another physician, upon request of the patient, a report of pertinent findings and treatment of the patient;

43. will provide medical services to a colleague and dependent family without fee, unless specifically requested to render an account;

44. will limit self-treatment or treatment of family members to minor or emergency services only; such treatments should be without fee;

Financial arrangements

45. will avoid any personal profit motive in ordering drugs, appliances or diagnostic procedures from any facility in which the physician has a financial interest;

46. will refuse to accept any commission or payment, direct or indirect, for any service rendered to a patient by other persons except direct employees and professional colleagues with whom there is a formal partnership or similar agreement.

Responsibilities to Society

Physicians who act under the principles of this Guide to the Ethical Behaviour for Physicians will find that they have fulfilled many of their responsibilities to society.

An Ethical Physician:

47. will strive to improve the standards of medical services in the community; will accept a share of the profession's responsibility to society in matters relating to the health and safety of the public, health education, and legislation affecting the health and well-being of the community;

48. will recognize the responsibility as a witness to assist the court in arriving at a just decision;
49. will, in the interest of providing good and adequate medical care, support the opportunity of other physcians to obtain hospital privileges according to individual personal and professional qualifications.

"The complete physician is not a man apart and cannot content himself with the practice of medicine alone, but should make his contribution, as does any other good citizen, towards the well-being and betterment of the community in which he lives."

INDEX

Adams, Kenneth M., 332

Advisory Committee on Benefits, Services and Membership (formerly MD Advisory Board), 158

Advisory Planning Committee on Medical Care, Sask., 69, 72-73, 74

Agnew, Harvey, 16

Aitken, D.M., 34

Alberta, 90, 108

Alberta Medical Association, 7, 16, 308, 359

Alta Vista Fund, 137, 139

American Accreditation Council for Continuing Medical Education, 168

American College of Physicians, 289

American College of Surgeons, 289

American Hospital Association, 289

American Medical Association, attends leadership conference, 302; hospital accreditation, 289-90; organization, 61; publications advice, 254, 259; role in WMA, 224, 229-30, 232; Toronto Group, 239

American Society of Law and Medicine, 222

Anderson, Jack F.C., 69, 74, 219-20, 316, 317

Anderson, James R., 34, 257, 260, 264, 354

Anderson, John, 56

Andison, Alexander W., 259, 265

Andras, A., 48

Archibald, Edward A., 357

Argue, J.F., 16-17

Arnold, Hugh A., 29, 34

Arthur Andersen and Company, 154

Association des médecins de langue française du Canada, 83, 124, 179, 290

Association of Canadian Community Colleges, 176

Association of Canadian Medical Colleges, accreditation of schools, 166; CFPC, 284; CMA affiliation, 29, 64, 358; co-publication venture, 281; continuing medical education, 167-70; internship programs, 165; medicare, 82-83, 101; physician resources, 180; primary care education, 286

Association of Canadian Pharmaceutical Physicians, 358

Association of Community Colleges of Canada, 171

Association professionnelle internationale des médecins, 224

Atkinson, Reginald D., Building Committee, 8-9, 11-13, 15, 17, 19-20; CMA Medal of Service, 356; CMA organization, 53-54, 69; General Council, 34, 36, 354

Atomic Energy of Canada Limited, 244

Australia, 77-78, 220, 221, 222, 228

Baergen, Ernest H., 356

Bahamas, 242

Baines, Cornelia J., 292

Baldwin, W.W., 30

Balfour, Donald C., 357

Baltzan, David, 73, 76

Baltzan, Marc A., 102, 200, 201, 345, 356

Banff, Alta., 70, 131, 359

Bank of Montreal, 131, 134, 137

Banks, Peter J., CMA House, 11-12, 16; president of CMA and BMA, 219, 341; role in General Council, 34, 36

Bannerman, Ronald, 137

Banting, Sir Frederick G., 293, 355

Barbados, 242, 243

Barker, Llewellys F., 357

Barnett, Henry J.M., 355

Barootes, Estathios W., Advisory Planning Committee on Medical Care, 69; Board of Directors, 34, 36; CMA House, 16; CMA Medal of Service, 356; deputy president, 321, 343; medicare, 98; physicians' savings plans, 143; Publications Committee, 263

Barr, Murray, 355

Bartlett, Lloyd, 56

Batterson, L., 299

Bazin, Alfred T., 326-27, 355

Beamish, Robert E., 356

Bean, William B., 357

Beaubrun, Matthew, 221

Bégin, Monique, 99-101, 108, 304

Bellan, Lorne, 56

Belliveau, Normand J., 10, 13, 16, 34, 338

Bennett, John S., 1971 think tank, 48; aid to developing countries, 243; CMA armorial bearings, 311; Commonwealth Medical Association, 222; medicare task force, 106; Toronto Group, 240; WMA, 237, 239

Benson, E.J., 89

Berner, Mark S., 280

Berwick, D., 304

Best, Charles H., 293, 355

Bigelow, W. Gordon, 355

Bigue, Germain, 36

Black, John H., 284

Blackader, Alexander D., 248, 330, 331

Blackader Lecture, 330-31, 357-58

Blair, Nat J., 130, 133, 135-37, 138

Board of Directors, see also Executive Commit-